Just Like an Animal

Maurice Burton

Dent

London
Melbourne and Toronto

First published 1978
© Maurice Burton 1978
All rights reserved. No part of this publication may be reproduced, stored in a retrieval system, or
transmitted, in any form or by any means, electronic, mechanical, photocopying, recording or otherwise,
without the prior permission of J. M. Dent & Sons Ltd.

Made in Great Britain by
Biddles Ltd., Guildford, Surrey

for J. M. Dent & Sons Ltd
Aldine House, Albemarle Street, London
This book is set in 11 on 12pt VIP Garamond No. 3

British Library Cataloguing in Publication Data

Burton, Maurice
  Just like an animal.
  1. Animals, Habits and behaviour of
  I. Title
  591.5   QL751

ISBN 0-460-04330-7

Contents

List
of
Plates

List
of
Figures

Introduction

Whenever I am asked why I became a zoologist, I always reply that it was the result of watching the activities of a colony of ants in the parapet of a trench on the Western Front in 1918. It was on a hot afternoon in May, when there was little war-like activity, and I was engrossed for several hours watching intently. Until then it had been my intention to study history when the war ended, but that afternoon I decided on natural history as a career, and more specifically zoology. The occasion is still clear in my memory, as is the dominating impression I carried away. This was that there was a strong similarity between ant behaviour as I had seen it and that of human beings. It came as no surprise to me therefore to learn in 1976 that the new science of sociobiology originated in the study of ants.

Admittedly on that May afternoon I was looking through the eyes of ignorance, but what I saw then continued to influence my thoughts. When, for example, thirty years later I heard a leading zoologist declare emphatically that there was no such thing as intelligence outside the human species, I failed to agree with him. Such a view seemed to me illogical. If the theory of evolution has any validity, it must follow that the behaviour of people has its roots in the non-human living world, in however crude and rudimentary a form. If people can show intelligence, it must be possible purely from an evolutionary point of view for some animals to show at least the beginnings of intelligence. There must be few who would now dispute this. And if people can show compassion or sympathy, there seems no reason why some of the higher animals should not be capable of responding in some slight measure to the sufferings of others.

Already in 1948 I had started filing what seemed at the time inconsequential items and anecdotes on animal behaviour. One file was labelled 'Compassion in Animals', though later this was changed to 'Altruism in Animals'. It is arguable that compassion may be too strong a word to use, but altruism defined simply as regard for others could be admissible. It is significant that several comparable terms have crept into the scientific literature during the last two decades. Among these are succourant behaviour, care-giving behaviour and consideration-showing behaviour. Another term that merits attention is higher-order behaviour, which embraces the other three but also includes any action that transcends the normal pattern of behaviour. Higher-order behaviour may be selfish or unselfish (i.e. altruistic) and often includes actions that the non-zoologist would regard as intelligent.

Examples of higher-order behaviour are sparsely scattered through the scientific literature and little attempt has been made to correlate them. Alleged examples, usually and often rightly regarded with scepticism by the scientific world, are more abundantly scattered through the pages of popular magazines and the world's newspapers. There is an even richer store in the unwritten repertoires of those closely associated with animals, such as farmers, breeders and pet-owners. In this book the attempt is made to bring some of these examples together and analyse them, often with surprising results. For example, in some instances it has been necessary to cast doubt on cherished beliefs. In others it has been deemed necessary, as a result of wide-ranging inquiries, to put largely unsuspected qualities in animals on a firmer basis. Together, they indicate that, whatever the motivation, some animals can be credited with altruism, often verging on compassion. Above all, it is possible to suggest that there is no hard-and-fast line between animal and human behaviour.

The anecdotes culled from magazines and newspapers vary from terse statements, usually lacking in essential details, to the sensational accounts in which exaggerated claims are made. A few have the additional value that they contain the germs of ideas that have formed the starting-point for fruitful lines of inquiry. A notable example is found in chapter 9, which deals with the ways blind animals are helped by their congeners. The terse statements can be amplified, and thereby evaluated, by reference to specialists such as veterinary surgeons, animal breeders and others, as well as experienced naturalists. The more extravagant examples can be pruned by the same methods. Both can be measured by one's personal experiences and fitted together like jig-saws. There are other examples in the form of photographs and film and they too help us in our search for the truth. The photographic evidence is inevitably scarce, but what we have is highly valuable.

This book exploits a rich source of material, as can be seen from a striking example that occurred many years ago. In 1950 my colleague at the British Museum (Natural History), the late Dr W. J. Rees, was called upon to investigate an unusual appearance of thousands of small octopuses in the English Channel. The problem defied solution until someone lent him a book of magazine and newspaper press-cuttings on the subject. This contained the complete answer to the problem. Although in the compiling of this book, countless hours have been spent combing the literature, both scientific and popular, it cannot be claimed that what is presented here is more than a sample of what could eventually be available. Even so, it suggests a form of research in the field of animal psychology that may eventually complement the more orthodox study of animal behaviour.

It remains to record my thanks to the many who have helped, by writing to me, allowing me to catechize them by telephone or in personal visits, or by expressing expert opinions on particular points. More especially, I would thank that first-class naturalist, Mrs Stéphanie Ryder, Mr and Mrs Hugh Ingram, who have never failed to respond, and Mrs Peggy Wratten, who not only had the onerous task of typing and checking the text but who has given invaluable help in a thousand ways. I would also thank my two sons, Richard and Robert, for having read the text and given helpful criticisms. Lastly, and not least, I would like to express my debtedness to the many people, too numerous to mention by name but who are named in the text, as well as the newspapers, journals and magazines from all of whom it has been possible to cull the essential and valuable information on which this text is based.

1.
Higher-Order Behaviour

Mr and Mrs Norton lived in Natal, South Africa. That was in 1954. They had a she-cat that produced litters with monotonous regularity. So Mr Norton ordained that only one out of any future litter should be kept. Several successive litters were accordingly massacred, leaving only the one kitten on each occasion. The time came when the litter produced consisted of one kitten only. 'Clever girl', exclaimed Mr Norton. Six weeks later mysterious noises were heard in the attic. Investigation disclosed five more, well-fed kittens of the same age as the one.

There can be several possible explanations. The cat may have been overtaken with a sudden, unexpected parturition in the lower part of the house. Having delivered one kitten she then made her way to the attic for the birth of the rest. Even human mothers, with all the resources of civilization at their command, are sometimes caught out, giving birth in a railway train, bus or telephone kiosk. Another possible explanation is that the cat gave birth to all six in the attic and took one of them downstairs as a decoy.

Cats, like bitches, have frequently been seen to adopt the young of other parents, even of other species, such as young rabbits or young rats. They bring them into the house and, if left undisturbed, rear these aliens with their own litter. A cow has been known to suckle a farm piglet, a mastiff bitch suckled a wild piglet. Other strange things can happen. It is not beyond the bounds of possibility that a cat, having her own litter in the attic, then chanced upon the kitten belonging to another cat, brought it home, adopted it, but kept it separate from her own litter.

Other explanations could be suggested, each more outlandish than these three. None holds water, if only because the instinct to retrieve their straying young and take them back to the nest with the rest of the litter is so strong. So we have no alternative but to accept the story, even if we do so with reserve.

Because the behaviour of the Norton she-cat is outside the range of normal behaviour for the species, and especially because it has all the appearance of cleverness (or low cunning), we can label it 'higher-order behaviour'. This is a term used by some zoologists for behaviour which is astonishing and which appears to show the animal has taken thought and has not merely acted from instinct. The mere fact that such a term can be found in the scientific literature answers the question sometimes raised by laymen, whether animals ever do things that are beyond their normal capacity. It indicates a recognition that animals, in common with us, can rise to the occasion and in emergency surpass their normal performance or perform actions not normal to them.

The story of this particular she-cat is the more easy to accept because of the many remarkable things domestic cats have been known to do. One that comes very near it is the action of a cat that had a single kitten, born in a shed a hundred yards from the house. When she wanted a night out the cat would carry the kitten in her mouth to the house, miaow at the back door, march in and deposit it on somebody's lap or on a cushion and demand to be let out again. The following morning she would return to collect the kitten and carry it back to the shed. Even so, the Norton story must be treated with reserve until such time as a dozen more witnesses have testified to having known a dozen other she-cats do something similar. Then the truth of the story, if not the interpretation, can be accepted scientifically.

The need for extreme caution in dealing with stories like that of the Norton cat, which was published in the form of a letter to a reputable magazine, can be illustrated by a personal experience. Some years ago I became interested in animals that showed an addiction to smoke. Cows in a meadow where hedge-trimmings are being burnt will converge on a bonfire and stand round it with muzzles lifted, as if inhaling the smoke. Camels have been photographed standing behind their owners and, with apparent ecstasy, inhaling the smoke from a hookah or hubble-bubble pipe. Birds have been seen on chimney pots or the smoke stacks of factories evidently enjoying a bathe in the smoke.

At the time I was first collecting smoke stories I was making trips to the Isle of Wight. This meant taking the train to Portsmouth and crossing the Solent by a steamer which tied up at the end of Ryde pier. From there a train took you the length of the pier and on to various towns on the island. In those days the trains were drawn by steam locomotives. I noticed that as the train drew out of the station its locomotive bellowed smoke. A score of gulls immediately converged on the smoke and continued in it the length of the pier. I saw this several times, so I thought there could be no doubt about it — these gulls enjoyed smoke. Accordingly, I wrote a note about it and had it published in a newspaper. A week or so later a man wrote to me. He was an engine-driver on the Ryde pier railway. He explained that he, and other drivers on that line, always started to throw bread to the gulls as soon as the train left the station and continued to do so until they reached the other end of the pier. I had been deluded by appearances.

This does not mean that the stories of animals apparently enjoying smoke had been explained away, but it was a salutary lesson in looking for another explanation. So there may still be a more prosaic answer to the story of the Norton cat. Accepting it at its face value, however, we can see the cat's behaviour as something more than the normal maternal care based on an inherited pattern of behaviour. To be able to rise above their instincts is an advantage enjoyed especially by the higher animals, the birds and mammals, although not exclusively confined to them. It is exercised at times of emergency, to a greater or lesser degree according to the demands of the emergency. In the Norton cat the motivation may have been mainly selfish. By preserving her whole litter, the she-cat would be ensuring enough hungry mouths to relieve the pressure of milk flowing into her mammary glands, if no more. Above all, and according to the latest sociobiological theory, she would be assuring the future of her genes through ensuring the survival of the maximum number of her offspring.

Higher-order behaviour need not, therefore, be in any sense altruistic, if altruism is taken to mean acting out of consideration for others at some inconvenience or loss to oneself. In other words, higher-order behaviour can be wholly selfish. What we are looking for are higher actions of this kind that go beyond the hereditary or genetic equipment of a species and which benefit other individuals. Every animal starts life with an inbuilt pattern of behaviour. It can add to this, or modify it, by learning and experience. Out of this learning and experience can arise what are commonly called intelligent actions.

For example, when a kitten is born the mother instinctively starts to lick its frail form. The licking results in the birth membranes being removed and one of the immediate benefits to the kitten is the removal of obstructions to the nostrils which would make breathing difficult. As the kitten increases in age the mother continues to lick it daily. From the moment of birth this has utilitarian results: licking of the anal region stimulates the bowel to function efficiently, licking also keeps the skin and the fur free of foreign particles, including bacteria and fungal spores. There are also more subtle side-effects, such as stimulating the circulation of the blood and the respiratory processes. Above all, it forges a bond between mother and infant. As the days pass, the repeated licking, which is basically a matter of hygiene, induces a bond of affection. At first this is unilateral, but soon the kitten begins to lick the mother's fur, feebly and desultorily at first, then gradually more strongly and frequently, as reciprocal affection emerges.

Affection may be classified as an emotion, but its basis is functional, as experiments on baby rats show. A litter is divided into two. One group is fed and given the minimum care necessary for survival, but no petting. The members of the other group are daily stroked and petted but otherwise live under precisely the same conditions as those of the first group, while receiving the same types and quantities of food. When adult, the rats of the second group prove to be livelier, more hardy, longer-lived and more intelligent.

Licking by the animal mother and stroking and petting with the human hand are comparable processes and bestow similar benefits. It is daily demonstrated in physiotherapy clinics that massage alleviates physical discomforts, improves health and imparts an immediate sense of physical and mental well-being. Significantly, it has been recorded that a fox whose mate lies injured or dead will lick the recumbent body all over in a seeming attempt at resuscitation: animal physiotherapy, in effect. By the same token, a wild female buffalo or rhinoceros in a pre-parturient condition may be helped by a companion nudging her abdomen with its snout, in what looks like crude massage.

To go back to the moment of birth, it is the common experience with dairy farmers that a cow on sniffing her newborn calf will then start to lick it. In cases where the birth has been difficult, and help has had to be given in the delivery of the calf, the mother may be recumbent and listless, and completely indifferent to the presence of the calf. With her head on the ground, the mother may show no inclination to get to her feet until the calf is placed against her nose. Then she begins to take notice. Her languor will disappear, she will sniff the calf and struggle to her feet to begin her maternal ministrations.

It may happen, in such cases, that another, unrelated cow will wander over to the newborn calf, lying on the ground neglected by the mother, will sniff the calf and begin to lick it. Should the mother have died in giving birth, it could happen that this second member of the herd will clean the calf and then suckle it, adopting it as her own. From the natural workings of her hereditary instincts she will have breached the delicate frontier between genetic altruism and true altruism. She is caring for another individual who bears no relation to her, so it is not in her selfish interests to do so. In other words, in true altruism the altruist's genes are not perpetuated by its behaviour. This frontier is difficult to fix or define, and since the word 'altruism' in its generally accepted sense is associated by tradition with selfless acts carried out by human beings, zoologists tend to look for other terms. So they speak of succourant behaviour, care-giving behaviour and consideration-showing behaviour. These may be grouped collectively as epimeletic behaviour, from the Greek meaning 'careful', and in this context it is applied to animals caring for each other. The search for the most appropriate term can be endless. Compassionate behaviour is a term that has been used, Good Samaritan behaviour is another. Both these have had only limited use because they are suggestive of the human approach and therefore are branded as anthropomorphic.

Perhaps we tend to devalue epimeletic behaviour in animals because we intuitively measure it against human achievements in the same field. For example no matter how much a cow, a cat, a buffalo or a rhinoceros may be impelled to help a companion in distress, it would be nothing compared with the services of a veterinary surgeon. Moreover, when we compare even the most striking examples of epimeletic behaviour in animals they appear insignificant beside the highly organized medical systems, philanthropic endeavours and charitable works of the most advanced human societies. Yet the two differ in quantity rather than kind.

The highly-organized 'good works' of civilized man are the result of a cultural inheritance and technological advancement stretching back over thousands of years. The emotional impulses from which they stem also owe much to education. If, however, we could compare them with the impulses actuating primitive man at a stage when he took his first steps towards tool-making and lived in family units, the comparison between animal altruism and human altruism could be remarkably close. We can make such a comparison, thanks to the American Harlan Lane, chairman of the Department of Psychology at Northeastern University. In his book *The Wild Boy of Aveyron*, he has presented us with what in some respects could be almost a model of primitive man as he first emerged from the anthropoid stock.

Victor, as the wild boy came to be named, was living alone in the forest of southern France, abandoned by his parents, at the time of the French Revolution. Around 1800 he was caught and handed over to a surgeon, Jean-Marc Itard, who from his study of Victor set in train the modern therapeutic methods of speech and hearing education of the physically and mentally handicapped and oral education of the deaf. When first captured, Victor was twelve or thirteen years of age, apparently an idiot, unable to utter or understand a single word of human speech, unclothed, unkempt and filthy. All that could be recorded of his life up to that moment, since he lacked the use of speech, was that he had lived like an animal, often ran on all-fours, climbed trees and lived mainly on nuts, especially walnuts. He climbed trees, swam in the river, and buried surplus food even after his capture. He showed no sense of property, helping himself to the food on his caretaker's plate at table and showing no resentment at food being taken from his own plate.

A favourite device of modern zoological research is to rear an animal from birth in isolation to study the emergence of natural instincts and social developments. It is a keystone of the science of ethology (animal behaviour). Victor represented a human that had grown up in isolation and showed the equipment of natural instincts together with what he had learnt entirely without the benefit of contact with fellow beings. He showed no social development. He had to be taught even the elementary habit of not depositing excrement and urine where he stood or lay. His sole occupations were to obtain food and shelter, and to try to escape, seeking freedom from restraint at any opportune moment. He showed no affection; he viewed the world around with total indifference except for seeking food or a refuge. Although his hearing was good, he took no notice of noises unconnected with feeding, for example to react sharply to the sound of a walnut being cracked behind him, yet showed no reaction whatever to the sounds of human speech, song or music.

He loved no one, was attached to no one. If he showed some preference for his caretaker it was only an expression of need, with no element of gratitude. He followed the man because the caretaker's duty was to satisfy his needs and satiate his appetite. When afraid of something, he threw himself into the arms of his caretaker and pushed him urgently towards his room. Had his caretaker at any time fallen and hurt himself, Victor would probably have done nothing to help him, because that would have been out of character. Had he, on the other hand, helped him on to his feet and assisted him to walk towards a chair, that would have gone far enough beyond his normal behaviour to merit being called care-giving, consideration-showing, succourant, epilemetic or altruistic behaviour, according to which term we choose. In other words, for the Wild Boy of Aveyron, reared in loneliness, entirely self-centred, it would have been a touch of higher-order behaviour.

If we now turn to animals, we find — and this is common knowledge — that they are capable of far higher behaviour than ever was recorded for the Wild Boy of Aveyron. Stories illustrating this are legion and have led in the past to animals being described as courageous, loyal, devoted, heroic and a range of other adjectives normally reserved for the finer actions and feelings of human beings. Organized science tends to turn away from such descriptions as anthropomorphic (the attributing of human emotions to non-human members of the animal kingdom) and also because emotions, unlike actions, cannot be observed and therefore an animal's internal feelings cannot be treated scientifi-cally. Consequently, an ethologist just deals with observable behaviour. This habit of thought and writing has led to people denying the existence of such emotions even although their non-existence is unprovable. One school of recent zoological thought goes even further and attributes all such emotions, performance of higher actions or the possession of fine emotions, even in human beings, to the impulse on the part of the individual to protect its genes. The theory can be summarized as follows. Many animals behave in such a way as to improve the chances of survival of their kin, notably in parental care. This tendency (and usually the precise behaviour patterns linked with it) is innate; that is, it is due to specific genes or groups of genes. Kin, especially offspring and siblings (children or young animals having one or both parents in common) tend to contain these same genes (i.e. for the altruism). Therefore, parental care and related forms of behaviour favour the survival of these genes, hence the evolution of this behaviour. Incidentally, the survival of accompany-ing genes is favoured, too, so effectively an animal acts to increase the survival of all its genes, in itself and its kin; that is not just those concerned with altruism.

This is not the place to enter more fully into this new aspect of zoological philosophy, conveniently labelled genetic altruism, and a simple illustration must suffice. One that has been given is that if a man sees his son in the river or sea in danger of drowning he will plunge in to his rescue. In doing so, he saves his son as well as those of his own genes which he has imparted to the son. Should the father, in his rescue attempt, lose his own life but save that of his son, there may have been a positive gain in gene material because the son's expectation of reproductive potential, purely on the grounds of age, is greater than his own. As one who has rescued a companion from drowning I am prepared to say that, except where the hazards are exceptional, there is no heroism involved anyway. One sees someone in difficulty and without taking thought one dives in and brings him ashore. The question of heroism arises when one has to weigh up the possible risks and, knowing that they are great, still goes in to attempt the rescue. It is then that true or idealistic altruism is involved. So, even when 'saving one's own genes' is involved, as when a father saves his son from drowning, heroism can enter into the action, or words have lost their meaning.

A stoat preys on rabbits. Normally the rabbit is petrified with fear in the presence of a stoat and passively submits to being killed, behaving as if it were hypnotized. A doe rabbit with a litter of babies has been seen to lash out with

Fig. 1 Mother pheasant instinctively feigns injury and, in so doing, draws a predator from her chicks. By exposing herself to risk she is showing genetic altruism, not heroism

her powerful hindfeet to kick a stoat, venturing near the nest, sixteen feet through the air. This looks like maternal devotion taken to a point of extreme courage or heroism. According to the new view, the doe rabbit is merely protecting her genes, so her action is no more than genetic altruism. (It may be worth noting that a rabbit without a litter to protect has been seen to drive a stoat off in this manner repeatedly, until the stoat admitted defeat and slunk away! Was the rabbit protecting its own genes or was it just endowed with more aggressiveness? Or can we credit it with the qualities we call courage or heroism?)

It would be too easy to be led aside in a critical appraisal of the new theory of genetic altruism. One thing at least can be said of it, that it gives us the yardstick by which we should judge the simple departures from normal behaviour we shall be examining in the following chapters. Naturally, most of them have been observed in domestic animals, and especially those living nearest to people, for the simple reason that they are the most commonly under our observation. There is, however, another reason. Man has chosen for his pets and for his animal stock, to be used as beasts of burden or for food, the warmblooded animals, the birds and, more especially, the mammals. These happen to be those with the larger, more highly-organized brains which are, as a consequence, more capable of higher-order behaviour. From our general knowledge of the Primates (apes and monkeys), the Cetacea (whales, dolphins and porpoises), elephants and the Carnivora (dogs, foxes, cats, bears), we should expect them to show this behaviour to a greater degree than the lower mammals. We should also expect some degree of it in birds, but not in reptiles, amphibians and fishes, in which the brain is even less highly organized. It would be surprising if it occurred lower in the scale than the vertebrates, in insects for example, because in them there is no brain as such, and yet our next chapter starts with insect behaviour.

Another point needs to be borne in mind. Pet animals, living so closely to people, can be expected to reveal hidden potentialities, for two reasons. The first reason can be linked with the experiments on rats already described. Pets, especially the furry ones, receive more fondling and stroking, which is calculated to increase their understanding, in other words they become more intelligent, using this word in its commonly accepted meaning. The second is that, by the nature of things, through their associations with people they can be expected to take in something of human attitudes. They are, in fact, encouraged to do so; it is part of their general education. Furthermore, they are generally longer-lived than wild animals, which gives greater scope for this education to take effect. Nevertheless, there are enough instances of unusual succourant or altruistic behaviour in wild animals, matching that observed in domestic animals, to suggest that any gulf between the two is not extensive. It probably means that as many examples could be found among wild animals if more people were able to observe them daily. As it is, wild animals shun the human presence or behave unnaturally the moment a human intruder enters their environment. Even in a zoo, and more especially in an animal laboratory, this disturbance of the environment could be still more inhibiting.

What makes the story of the Wild Boy of Aveyron so interesting is that he was a wild beast in human form, a member of the dominant species *Homo sapiens* entirely lacking in good manners. One of the clear recollections from my own boyhood days was of having impressed on me that one should cultivate good manners, and that the essence of a gentleman is to show consideration for others. Manners are the customs and habits by which we live, good manners are something more. No matter how much we may despise the conventions by which these are upheld, they are based on consideration for others. They are a compound of small kindnesses and courtesies which make life more pleasant for everybody because they make life easier. They are unnecessary in those living solitary lives, but the more the members of a species combine to live in societies, the more important do good manners become.

Manners therefore are the rules by which animals live. In an animal species they represent the normal, everyday pattern of behaviour. Good manners are those actions superimposed on this pattern while a group of animals learns to live together on terms which are socially economical. They represent the beginnings of a true altruism, and so our search for true altruism in animals must start with looking for good manners. Since the notion of what constitutes good manners varies from one human community to another, the task clearly presents difficulties, but there are certain broad principles which can claim our attention.

2.
Animal
Manners

Paradoxically, the best example of good manners in animals that I have encountered was in insects, beings that by the assessment of their nervous system should not be credited with such actions unless they are instinctive. The discovery came about by accident.

In the early summer of 1976 a wasps' nest was discovered in the garden. A cage was constructed, the wasps' nest installed in it and the cage secured on the window sill of a first-floor window. The cage was a wooden box thirteen inches long, eight inches across and eleven inches high. Its two ends were fine-meshed zinc gauze, its two long sides glazed, the glass on one side being covered with a black material. Its wooden lid was removable and on one half of it was fastened a strip of hardboard twenty-one inches long, which overlapped the top of the box at one end. At the other end of this was bored a hole about half an inch in diameter to allow the wasps to enter. Then a long rectangular tunnel was constructed of strips of glass with inner dimensions of five-eighths of an inch broad, one inch high and seventeen inches long. This left an overlap

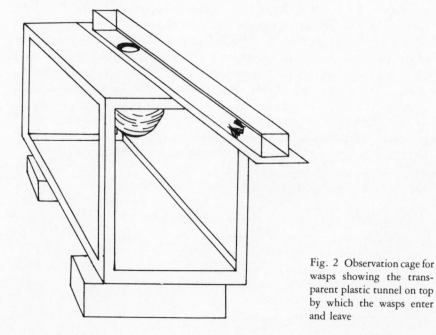

Fig. 2 Observation cage for wasps showing the transparent plastic tunnel on top by which the wasps enter and leave

of three inches of the hardboard to serve as a landing board. Wasps returning from foraging would be able to land on the landing board, run along the tunnel, go down the hole at the other end and enter the box within which the nest was to be hung.

When placed in position on the window sill, with its glazed nearside against the outside of the window pane, the box made a perfect observation chamber. One could watch the comings and goings of the foraging worker wasps and see them enlarging the nest, which was made, as usual, of paper fabricated by the wasps chewing rotten wood and mixing it with saliva. From the first morning after the move the wasps carried on their tasks as normal, apparently unaware that their home had been shifted a hundred yards into artificial surroundings in a new environment. They streamed out as the morning warmed up and soon the first to return settled on the landing board, ran the length of the tunnel, entered the hole in the roof of the observation chamber, dropped on to the top of the nest, ran down its side and disappeared into the entrance below. In no time at all, it seemed, there was a steady stream in both directions along the glass tunnel, foragers returning in one direction, others leaving after having deposited their loads, and so it continued throughout the summer. At first the returning foragers hesitated, hovering, before settling on the landing board, but this soon ceased.

It was my grandson Mark Taylor, then aged ten, who spent much time kneeling at the window watching the wasps, who first drew my attention to an important fact. He pointed out something that should have been obvious to me earlier: the wasps always kept to the left. This obviated any confusion between the incoming and outgoing wasps. Clearly, in the economy of the colony, there was no room for time to be lost. Not only must the wasps work incessantly, they must work quickly and there must be no confusion. Watching the wasps one's thoughts turned to the movements of people on the sidewalks in busy towns, where crowds jostle and are constantly taking evasive action to avoid bumping into their fellows, causing frayed tempers and loss of physical and nervous energy. Even where prominent notices are displayed, KEEP TO THE LEFT, there is always a sizeable minority that ignores them.

A further, perhaps even more important factor then emerged: the wasps had excellent manners in at least one other respect. The width of the glass tunnel had been decided by measuring the width of a wasp with closed wings, doubling this and adding a little more for comfort. What was not realized at the time was that a wasp carrying a load runs with its wings opened slightly, presumably for purposes of balance. Some returning foragers carried each a pellet of wood pulp in its jaws, others carried a carcase of a fly for feeding the grubs in the nest. In spite of our slight miscalculation, there was room for the incoming and outgoing streams to negotiate the tunnel without touching, but only just. Occasionally an incoming, loaded wasp would stray just a fraction out of the true. Invariably, when this happened, outgoing wasps, unencumbered by a load, gave way to it by walking up the vertical wall of the tunnel and so made ample room for their loaded congener to pass without let or hindrance.

There is another lesson to be emphasized. Never, in all the time we watched them, did the wasps show any sign of irritation or aggression towards each other. Their good manners were impeccable, and it is this consistent uniformity of their behaviour which suggests that the wasps, rather than having learned to keep out of each other's way, were obeying an instinctive pattern. Keeping to the left and making way for a fellow wasp carrying a load may therefore be regarded as due to an inherited pattern of behaviour, gene-controlled and best described as genetic altruism, a phrase which, for good or ill, has gained slight currency in the last year or so. The higher we go in the animal scale the less is behaviour governed by instinct. So, by contrast with the wasps, the good manners of human beings, whose conduct is less governed by inherited patterns of behaviour, are determined by training, example and the disposition of the individual, and can conveniently be described as due to idealistic altruism, or in other words a voluntary or studied consideration for others, which is learned.

Disciplined or orderly behaviour is closely linked with good manners and probably forms the basis for them. In the overcrowded communities represented by the nests of social insects orderly behaviour is essential to obviate internecine aggression. In less crowded aggregations of animals there is still need for some comparable behaviour. Among kudu, the African antelope, there is a hierarchy of dominance and subordinance, as in so many species. Should a low-ranking kudu, after a spell of activity, lie down first, a dominant individual will make it get up again until he has dropped to the ground. There may be other instances yet to be observed. The behaviour of the kudu looks uncommonly like the human practice of young men at table not seating themselves until more honoured guests, usually the more senior, have taken their places; or of standing when a woman, or a more senior man, enters the room.

In committee procedure it has become the rule, often these days more honoured in the breach than the observance, that when the chairman rises to speak, or even if he speaks while seated, other members of committee shall cease speaking until the chairman has finished, or, if standing, sit down until the chairman takes his or her seat. There seems to be a germ of this same idea in the social procedure of the hippopotamus. The Belgian zoologist, R. Verhuyen, who studied the habits of the hippopotamus in tropical Africa, found that the females and young occupied a central area of the river, while the males, each in his own territory, were ranged around the periphery. A female needing to mate wanders into the territory of her chosen male. The males normally keep outside the female domain, but a male may enter the female territory on condition that if a female rises from the recumbent position, he must lower his huge bulk into the water. Should he fail to observe this unwritten rule he is likely to be set upon by the rest of the females.

There is a biological reason for the behaviour of the hippopotamus. The male is larger and heavier than the female, giving him advantage in a fight, and he is also prone to act aggressively towards juveniles. To keep the peace and for the common good, there is this 'committee' procedure. In human committees this and other rules have been evolved for a similar reason, to prevent squabbling and disorder.

Meetings of committees occupy relatively little time in the lives of members of advanced communities, so the preponderance of good manners, certainly those that impress us most, is in the relations between the sexes. In extra-sexual behaviour the ideal is epitomized in the concept of chivalry. In modern times, until recently at least, this has been expressed in small everyday things rather than in deeds of derring-do of former times: in opening a door for a woman to pass through, allowing a woman to walk in front except where it would be a disadvantage to her to do so, and similar actions that show consideration for the female. Above all, it is exceptional for a man to show physical violence towards a woman even if he should reach the point of threatening her. Our actions may be more refined, but in essence they are no better than those of the kudu, for although their females will attack males or each other, a male will not attack a female. A young kudu male, before he is sexually mature, may sometimes threaten a female but no more. Like the generality of his human counterpart, the immature bull kudu learns to treat the female with greater respect.

It may be that the male's respect for the female is imposed by the females themselves because of their readiness to band together. On one occasion, for example, there happened to be eight ewes in a field. A ram was later let into the field and he seemed to be motivated solely towards the perpetuation of his genes. The ewes were not receptive and in a very short time all eight delivered a concerted attack on the ram and forced him to behave himself.

In all matters of animal behaviour one is compelled to generalize from the particular. It would be possible to write with even greater confidence if one could interrogate a larger number of cattle breeders, sheep farmers, dog breeders, cat breeders and the rest, as well as a greater variety of naturalists who have made intensive studies of species in the wild. Nevertheless, the impression is gained, from personal experiences and from reading, that the male animal usually, if not always, treats the female with respect, if not with courtesy. For example, E. P. Gee, in his book *The Wild Life of India*, remarks that it is safer to ride a female elephant because she is less likely to be attacked by another elephant.

Taking some of the commoner or household species the story is the same as for the kudu. There is normally no fighting between the sexes in house sparrows. Male will fight male for possession of a territory; female will fight female in defence of her nest or nestlings; and a female will savage a male, but only if he is too persistent in courtship when she is not receptive. (An outstanding exception in birds is seen in the first stage of courtship: see p. 26.) Among house mice it is the female who savages the male, never vice versa. A dog will accept punishment from a bitch without retaliating. The same is true of game fowl, domestic poultry and pheasants.

This tolerance of punishment by the female without retaliation reaches its peak in spiders and some insects. Female spiders, it is usually said, eat their mates. It does happen so, but not with the regularity we are led to believe, since the males are polygamous. After having fertilised several females the enfeebled male is then eaten. The main point is that the male shows no aggression towards the female. The same is true of the praying mantis, the female of which may eat the male and may even start to eat him during the course of copulation.

Biologically this is logical and reasonable. The female is the potential bearer of the male's offspring; the male is expendable compared with the female. The chivalry between the sexes is therefore due to a genetic altruism. Nevertheless, it can be impressive. To give an example, for 13 years we had a boxer-cross, Jason, a heavy dog that looked more like a mastiff. For ten of those years we also had two Sheltie bitches (Shetland sheep dogs) of delicate build. One of the Shelties, Poppet, was the daughter of the other and was born soon after the mother came to us.

Jason and Poppet became inseparable companions, except at feeding time, when they were given their food in separate bowls. On one occasion, Poppet was the first to finish her food and she then went to look for Jason. Just as he was about to take a favourite titbit from the mixture in his bowl, Poppet's slender snout had reached it and it was gone. Jason raised his head with an air of resignation, looked around briefly, then lowered his head to take another favoured titbit. Again Poppet got in first. This was repeated a third time, but on the fourth time Jason's patience gave out and as Poppet's long muzzle reached into the food bowl, he put his mouth to her ear and gave a short, explosive bark that sent the bitch yelping round the garden in physical distress. He showed no other physical violence; like the young kudu bulls, he had threatened but not attacked.

The two, mastiff-like dog and the delicate Sheltie bitch, played together daily. At times Jason, with his heavy paws, would inadvertently hurt Poppet and she would fly at him with every appearance of anger and bite him. He never made the slightest attempt at retaliation, although clearly she sometimes hurt him.

We had a similar experience with our foxes. The first pair were tame but were not treated as pets in the usual sense. Their pen was ample and furnished with logs and green branches, renewed from time to time, so that they had room to exercise and, as far as possible, a natural environment. The main purpose in having them — they were both hand-reared pets of which the owners had tired — was to study their natural behaviour. In general, one can say with confidence that with all their rough-and-tumbles, there was the most complete tolerance and patience shown by the dog-fox to the vixen, no matter what she did to him. In the matter of food it was a totally different story. The dog-fox was utterly selfish. Had care not been taken to feed them separately, the vixen would probably have suffered from almost permanent malnutrition. This led to what can be regarded as a most spectacular change in habits.

In the May of the second year they were with us, it was evident that the vixen was about to have a litter. A few days before the birth of the cubs she dug herself a new earth. We could not know precisely when the cubs were due and we had no wish to disturb her by prying to find out when the cubs were born. One evening, when food was placed as always in the pen, the dog-fox, instead of gulping every bit of it as fast as he could in the usual way, contrived to take all the food into his maw. This was no mean task, for when he had taken in the bulk of it he tended to drop a piece of it each time he tried to pick up another. In the end, by perseverence, he contrived to keep all of it in his mouth, went over to the nursery earth and made a low call that we had not heard before. The vixen came out and he dropped all the food on the ground in front of her. Then he stood and waited until she had eaten her fill. From the contours of the vixen's abdomen it was clear that her cubs had been born. Dog-foxes in the wild have also been seen with the mouth filled to capacity with food, and from this we may assume that wild foxes behave in the same way.

We have had foxes continuously since 1954, the year in which the first litter was born, and this has been the invariable sequence: utter selfishness on the part of the dog-fox until the moment when the cubs are born; complete unselfishness afterwards and until the cubs leave the parents. So the apparent altruism must be genetic, the result of an inherited pattern of behaviour.

In April 1961 the vixen was again large with young. All the signs pointed to imminent birth. She had dug her nursery earth and had retired to it. Late that evening, we went to make a last inspection. The dog-fox was nowhere to be seen. There was a hole in the chain-linked fence which formed their enclosure and here he had pulled the meshes of stout wire apart with his teeth. Further investigation showed that the vixen had died in the nursery earth, still with her cubs inside her, and on the ground in front of her muzzle were the contents of the food bowl. Moreover, as she lay on her side her mate had pressed close into her body the carcase of one of our bantam cockerels. It was as if the dog-fox, puzzled but realizing something more was demanded of him, had done his best to help his dead mate, and to do so had exerted all his strength to get out of the pen as well as to force his way back in to drag the bantam with him. A gallant little gentleman?

It would be possible to describe the whole episode in strictly scientific terms, without attempting an explanation of the dog-fox's motivation. Yet, although it is impossible adequately to argue the subtleties of the situation, there is the suspicion that the dog-fox had crossed the line between genetic and true altruism, just as a hunted fox will cross the frontier between a fixed behaviour pattern of flight and real intelligence, amounting almost to genius at times, in throwing hounds off the scent.

We must expect to find more convincing examples of possible breaching of the barrier between the automatic (genetic altruism) and true altruistic behaviour among mammals than among other animals, if only on account of their more highly developed brains. A rough guide to this is provided by the way the surface of the cerebral hemispheres is convoluted. This is not an absolutely reliable guide, but in general the smoother the brain the less likely is there to be a capability for departing from the thraldom of genetically fixed behaviour. Birds have smooth brains and outstandingly their behaviour tends to be ritualized (or stylized).

This comes out in the treatment of the female by the male. Sparrows have been quoted as an example of male birds being non-aggressive towards the females. Yet the general rule is that when a female bird enters the territory of a male, in the normal course of seeking a mate, his first reaction is to attack her as an intruder. It is his way of finding out whether her intentions are honourable. An intruding male when attacked shows fight. An intruding female goes into a submissive attitude thereby demonstrating that she is a female, beyond a shadow of doubt, and one intent on reproduction. When this test has been passed, courtship proceeds with the male showing her the deference due to her sex. The courtship is stereotyped, as is the nest-building, the mating, egg-laying and rearing of the young. Having observed one pair of a species from the first meeting to the departure of the fledged young, one knows what to expect in any other pair. Indeed, from species to species, in birds, the plan is fairly uniform.

Having stressed, perhaps over-emphasized, the automaton-like way of life of birds, it still has to be admitted that there are records of departure from the norm which seem to indicate that even birds are capable of true altruism. These two aspects of bird behaviour can perhaps be illustrated by two episodes on the same day in the same garden.

At one end of the lawn a starling was feeding on household scraps. A cock blackbird, the bully of the garden, tried to usurp the food but was driven off by the starling. Later, a newly-fledged song thrush edged towards the starling, which turned aggressively to the thrush and charged, as it had at the blackbird. The force of the rush pushed the young thrush on to its tail, whereupon it opened its beak wide. Gaping is the releaser signal of most young birds to which the parents automatically respond by pushing food down their throats. The starling automatically responded too. Its aggression vanished and it fed the thrush. This was genetic altruism, an automatic or instinctive response by an adult bird to the sight of a wide-open beak.

Earlier in the day, at the other end of the lawn, a group of starlings foraging at random came within sight of a heap of food put down for birds. There was a concerted advance, almost a rush, on the food, but one of the starlings had an injured leg and, hobbling, was left behind by the rest. Whether by accident or design, the group paused at the food, waited for the lame bird to reach it and eat, after which, but not until then, all jostled to grab what they could. Whether this was a real act of altruism or no, can best be judged after considering comparable episodes given in later chapters. Emphatically, it may be said that there was at the least the appearance of good manners, which are next door to altruism, if only because the unhindered birds allowed their handicapped fellow to come forward.

There was another episode on this same theme. Some people were throwing bread to two gulls, one of which had lost a foot. A dozen more gulls soon flew in and the uninjured gull of the first two, without ever itself going for a piece of bread, kept the others away while the cripple fed. This same behaviour was witnessed on two consecutive days.

I remember once watching some sparrows and chaffinches feeding in a garden on crumbs. One of the chaffinches had lost its left foot and was hopping about on the other and a stump. It reached the crumbs later than the others, but as it came near all the other birds drew back and let it feed first. It looked as if they were standing back out of compassion for the cripple and letting it have first feed. There could, of course, be another, more mundane explanation. For a bird with only one foot to survive at all it must have been able to fight for its existence. Probably this chaffinch had learned that it must bully its way through life or starve. And possibly other birds had learned it was a bully and stood back out of fear.

Greater confidence can be placed in the interpretation of such episodes when several similar stories are collected from independent sources or when the same treatment can be observed successively in the same group of individuals. There is, however, another line of argument that can be used. Showing consideration to others requires having some form of sympathy with their difficulties. Sympathy is in response to a call for sympathy.

Thus, the owner of a dog living in the United States had his address and telephone number on the dog's collar. The dog later developed the habit of wandering off for the day at the end of which it would go to the nearest house, bark, scratch at the door and hold up one leg, letting the paw hang limp, when someone opened the door. The dog would be taken in, petted, fed, warmed and its 'injured' paw examined. Then it would either be kept for the night and transported home the following morning or his owner would be telephoned. Since this usually happened between 11 p.m. and midnight the owner tended to lose patience after the twentieth occasion. After that, his response to the telephone call was to advise the caller to 'throw the rascal out' because it was quite capable of finding its way home. One irate lady who had taken pity on the dog, when it importuned at her door, threatened to report its owner to the RSPCA when he gave her this advice.

It must be commonplace with dog-owners that at some time or other their dog, about to be admonished for a misdemeanour, has held up one paw and hopped along on three legs, when in fact there was nothing at all wrong with it. It is a trick most often seen in young dogs. Older dogs have probably dropped it because they have been found out too often!

It is interesting that children, especially boys, readily find they have something wrong with them when faced with similar situations. Usually a hand or arm suddenly begins to hurt when nemesis appears to be about to overtake them. If young humans and dogs can use such ruses so readily to elicit sympathy, we can be reasonably sure that some form of communication of this kind must be more universally employed, to invite sympathy, at least in the upper reaches of the animal kingdom. If, as seems likely, we can reasonably suppose that animals, no less than humans, employ tricks to elicit sympathy, then we can expect equally reasonably that some animals at least are capable of extending sympathy. This may not be part of the syndrome of good manners, as generally understood, but it is next-door to it.

Good manners, by common consent, includes special consideration for the less fortunate members of the community and those least able to help themselves, especially babies and infants. Anything that smacks of juvenile appeal tends to call forth this response. Among animals, this deference towards early infancy and juvenility in general is especially marked in monkeys. This has been demonstrated in numerous observations in the field and in captivity. In some species of monkeys, for example, a subordinate male, needing to approach a boss male, will pick up an infant and, holding it in front of him, will succeed in inhibiting aggression on the part of the dominant male.

This same trait has been recorded for chimpanzees, although in this same record it has to be conceded that the attitude of male towards female does not follow the trend postulated here for mammals in general. The male chimpanzee will physically assault a female on occasion. But it is noticeable that he will do so only rarely when the female is carrying an infant. That this is not pure chance is demonstrated by the repeated observation that if a female is carrying an infant clinging to her front, in a situation in which the infant is hidden from view, the male may yet attack the female, but will desist as soon as he sees she is carrying an infant.

A chance observation on monkeys in captivity may possibly shed some light on the human convention by which a man holds a door open for a woman to pass through. It was seen where two parts of a pen were connected by a heavy swing door. The door would be held open for an infant to scramble through without risk to itself. It is true that the adults responsible for this care-showing behaviour were females, but not necessarily the mothers. It is intriguing to suggest that human males are responding, in their door-holding courtesy, to a practice long since forgotten, of holding open a door for a woman carrying a baby, the custom later being extended to women in general. In other words, it is symbolic of the biological care for progeny, the carriers of genes. Of course, there is always the possibility that the convention owes something to the impracticable dresses women sometimes wear.

Many more instances of the biological basis for the deference shown to females, and also to the young, will certainly come to light in the course of future research. There may be some already recorded which my search of the literature, being necessarily incomplete, may have failed to reveal. For example, Patricia Stamp has written, as recently as 1976, that among hamadryas baboons of the Ethiopian semi-desert the habitat dictates that subordinate males be sent away from the comfort and protection of the social group into exile, where many of them die. With food so scarce, the biological morality is to save resources by protecting those most necessary for the species' survival — the females and, with them, the young also. One hefty (dominant) male can protect and fertilize a whole harem of females.

3.
Cries
for
Help

The scene was a typical main street in Outer London at midday. As far as the eye could see were several hundred people all walking along minding their own business, busy with their own thoughts, regardless of the welfare of anyone or anything else. Traffic on the road was light because it was the lunch-hour. Suddenly there was a cry of pain. A stray dog trotting along had caught one of its paws between the bars of a grating in the pavement. At this agonizing yell, and as if by magic, every man and woman within earshot halted and turned towards the source of the sound. Only when someone had reached the dog, released its paw, examined it for possible injury, patted the dog's head and straightened his own back did the other passers-by resume their walking.

That one cry had caught everybody's attention and sparked off the emotion of compassion, to a varying degree no doubt, in all who heard it. In everyone there would have been aroused at least curiosity, in most a desire to help. If no person had been within earshot, only other dogs, the cry would have aroused their curiosity. It may even have sparked off an emotion of compassion. Would any one of these hypothetical dogs have made a move to help or even show sympathy?

There is no positive answer to this, largely because the vocalizations of mammals, other than bats, have been little studied. Those of birds have received more attention, but even in these the study had been empirical, or rule-of-thumb, until the invention of the sonagraph provided an instrument for systematic study. Yet this does no more than provide patterns on paper for comparative studies. The investigator still has to link the motivations behind the calls and the responses they evoke in others, and of these we are still largely ignorant, except in general terms.

One thing that has been learnt is that most species of birds and many species of mammals have wide repertoires and that, for the most part, these are different for different species. The various vocalizations in each repertoire have different meanings. It has long been recognized, however, that mammals and birds use what have been called distress vocalizations. What is needed for our present purpose is to decide whether these are the same thing as 'cries for help' in that they call forth genuine attempts at assistance or whether they may have some other function.

Not the least of the difficulties is that a particular animal may use distress signals inaudible to the human ear. Then there is the difficulty of conveying by words what the sounds are like. This can be highlighted by reference to a

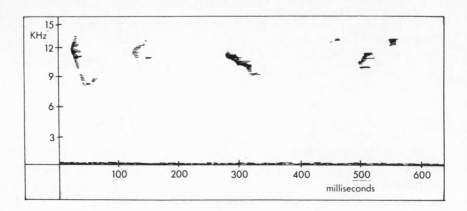

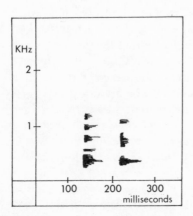

Fig. 3 Sonagrams of vocalizations made by a hedgehog; *top* the twitter, *middle* a pair of snorts, *bottom* a 'serenade' (After Gregory)

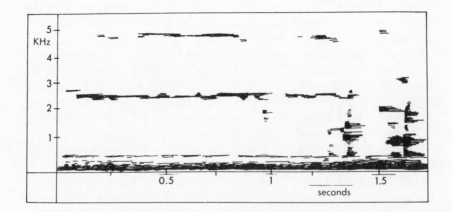

recent paper by Martin Gregory in *Mammalia* on the African hedgehog. Gregory studied and made sonagrams of the courtship sounds, screams, hisses and snorts in this species and, above all, of the vocalization he calls the twitter. The use of this word conveys little to a reader, so Gregory tries to help by describing it in words. The twitter, he explains, is a high-frequency sound usually barely audible even at a distance of twenty centimetres (eight inches), but on rare occasions it can be heard at a distance of two metres.

Audibility is relative, depending on the efficiency of the observer's own hearing. A very few people seem capable of hearing the minute scraping sounds of an earthworm's tiny bristles against the sides of the burrow. Others, not normally regarded as deaf, cannot hear the footsteps of an elephant. Presumably, by 'audible' Gregory may have meant capable of being picked up by the microphone of his sonagraph.

Sonagraph analysis of the twitter shows that over a period of 90 seconds 16 'audible' pulses are emitted. These vary in frequency from 3 to 15 KHz and each lasts 5–40 milliseconds. Even with this precise description it is difficult to imagine what the twitter of a hedgehog is like. Perhaps the most valuable result of this description is that we now know the African hedgehog can make sounds which we either cannot hear or can hear only with difficulty, and therefore can be readily overlooked. Were these to function as distress vocalizations the human observer would, in watching one hedgehog seemingly trying to help another, still be in ignorance of a vital clue to the behaviour.

Another difficulty can be illustrated by reference to elephants. For a long time it has been known that they make continuous 'tummy rumblings'. This was not surprising in view of the large quantities of vegetable matter they consume. Everybody accepted without question that they were the familiar collywobbles connected with movements of half-digested food and intestinal gases. The mystery was that an elephant seemed to be able to stop these at will, whenever anybody approached. Then, but only within recent years, it was found that these sounds have nothing to do with the digestive processes but are a kind of purring. When elephants are out of sight of each other they purr. If danger approaches one of them it stops purring. When the danger has passed the purring is resumed, and in this way the elephants are telling each other that all is well. By the use of these 'alert' and 'all clear' signals elephants can render a sort of mutual assistance.

Rodents offer another example. They have gnawing teeth in the form of two incisors in the front of the mouth, in both upper and lower jaws. The incisors grow continuously at the roots. Each incisor grows several inches in a year, so that if a tooth becomes misplaced it and the one it should have bitten against both grow rapidly in length, one curving round above the head and the other under the chin, eventually locking the jaws so that the rodent cannot feed and dies of starvation. Consequently, rodents are constantly gnawing solid objects. This keeps the incisors chisel-sharp and also keeps them of uniform length.

Only very recently has it been realized that all the time rats are not eating, or chewing hard substances as in burrowing, they are gritting their teeth. This undoubtedly counteracts the rapid growth of the incisors; it possibly also serves for communication between members of a community, like the elephants' tummy rumbling, since it seems that a rat grits its teeth only when it is relaxed and not apprehensive. Within recent years also it has become known that baby rats and mice still in the nest call the mother with ultrasonic cries when they are alarmed or disquieted. These are sounds above human hearing, possibly higher than a cat's ear is capable of detecting.

Fig. 4 A domestic hen ignores the distress of a chick she cannot hear

There may be many other vocalizations or other sounds made by animals remaining to be discovered. Some may be, in effect, cries for help or may represent other forms of communication between members of a species which are vital to our present discussion. The importance of vocalisations in distress situations is emphasized by the classic experiments with a barnyard hen and her lost chick. All chicks of this domestic species cheep all the time except when deeply asleep. When one of them is lost it makes a different cheep from the communal cheep, the one it makes when with its mother and siblings. Should one of the chicks stray and become lost among the herbage, it begins to make this special cheep. The hen responds by gathering the rest of the brood around her, all then setting off in the direction of the lost chick. When, experimentally, a chick is taken from the brood and imprisoned under a glass cover, the hen can still see it but ignores it, simply because she cannot hear it. In this instance, the distress vocalization looks very like a true call for help.

Baby jackdaws, when practising their flying, often stray and get lost. They too have a very special 'lost' cry, a very pitiful sound that makes any adult jackdaw within hearing give the 'all's well' call and guide them back. Mrs Ryder tells me of a pair she once had to rear which were adept at getting themselves blown off course or stuck in high trees. If she called them by name, they at once took off and flew back to her. If she was not about or kept silent on purpose, her blind jackdaw, Blind Jack, would call them back. If she spoke or called, Blind Jack remained silent. He seemed to know all was well when she answered. She says she often heard the 'lost' call from wild baby jackdaws and wished she could call them, but had to leave it to their own kind to do so.

An important principle is illustrated here, that certain categories of vocalizations have qualities in common that make it possible for one animal to interpret some of those of another totally distinct species, like the wild rabbit that bolts for cover on hearing a blackbird's alarm call. When a baby bird of almost any kind is caught by a cat it makes a terrific din which at once summons its parents and all small birds of any species to add their noise to the general din. This may have another value. Being very sensitive to noise, especially high notes, cats will often drop their victim if there is noise above their tolerance level. This does not seem to work for owls, who anyway squeeze their victim so viciously that the bird is unable to scream. A green parakeet, which lived free all day and returned to his aviary only in the evening to feed and roost, had a deafening alarm scream. He would give this at the sight of any wandering cat and in no time all the small birds in the garden would be out of sight.

Rooks and other members of the crow family, like the jackdaw already mentioned, seem to have a distress vocalization that is answered by all members of the species within earshot. Anyone who has rescued and hand-reared a baby rook may have had the experience of hearing it call and has then looked up to see the sky almost black with rooks flying silently round and round, down and up, in response to this one baby rook's cry.

This can be contrasted with what happened in a nesting colony of black-headed gulls which became established on a sewage farm near London Airport. The adults built their nests on areas of sludge that gave a firm foundation. As the chicks developed into fully fledged but inexperienced subadults they sometimes settled on the more fluid parts of the sludge. There they slowly sank, as in a quagmire, taking a day or more to sink below the surface to their death. To the inexperienced young gull the slow insidious descent into the morass was not recognized as a danger, and so it made no fluttering movements of the wings. Above all, it made no cries for help. Consequently, there were no rescue attempts by the adults, which could be seen standing on firm ground within a foot or so of their doomed offspring.

It is doubtful whether the adults could have effected a rescue had they been so motivated, and this takes us back to the function of distress vocalizations. Where animals live in pairs or larger groups, it is easy to see that their calls might serve to alert others of their kind to danger. They might conceivably also bring help in certain instances.

Either or both of these functions may well be served by the phenomenon of mobbing or harassing, which is especially characteristic of small songbirds. Mobbing and harassing are sometimes used as synonymous terms, but it is preferable to make a distinction between them. 'Mobbing' can be reserved for those occasions when numbers of small birds gather around, say, a perched owl, uttering their alarm notes. This is in response to the insistent alarm calling by the first bird to notice the owl. Small birds will also mob snakes, cats and squirrels when one of these is in the vicinity of a nest containing eggs or young. 'Harassing' is best reserved for those occasions when small birds gather to harass a bird-of-prey, such as a hawk or falcon. Then there is usually little use of alarm calls, other than an excited twittering, but from time to time one of the small birds will take the risk of flying at the bird-of-prey to land on its back as it flies away from the excited crowd. This embarrasses the predator, making it lose height as it seeks to shrug off its tormentor. The predator then beats a retreat.

A spectacular example of mobbing occurred after I had placed a pair of tawny owls in an aviary in the shelter of a large oak tree some years ago. The owls were in need of care and were installed in the aviary one evening at nightfall. The following morning a chaffinch noticed them, just after dawn, and started its alarm call. This was answered by other small birds who gathered progressively in the oak until there were literally hundreds in the tree making between them a terrific din, as chaffinches, greenfinches, sparrows, tits and others all joined in. Usually such a mobbing includes only scores of mobbers and it ends in a few minutes when the owl flies away. Since my owls could not fly away, the discordant chorus continued for an hour or so, gradually dying down as one by one the mobbers departed. The mobbing was repeated each morning for a week, growing less intense at each repetition until finally it died out, presumably as the birds grew used to the owls' presence.

Mobbing has been compared with the hue-and-cry method of justice in mediaeval times, when the indignation of a community boiled over and everyone joined in to pursue and, if possible, seize a malefactor, whose only hope lay in making for the nearest church for sanctuary. The comparison is not fully justified, yet the two processes have certain features in common. In both there is an element of alarm and a spontaneous coming together of outraged individuals. Both are characterized by an appearance of hysteria. It is difficult to draw further comparisons because we have no statistics for the hue-and-cry on how many criminals met their just rewards and how many escaped to sanctuary. Probably many more got away than were caught and judging from what can be seen of birds mobbing a predator the results seem to be even more unsuccessful. Certainly there are no distress vocalizations or cries for help involved and the only reason for mentioning mobbing here is to eliminate a common vocal phenomenon from the discussion as well as to compare the sounds accompanying it with the more general topic of alarm calls.

To place this last in perspective we must turn first to the distress vocalizations of solitary species. A typical species could be the European hedgehog. This is known to utter a harsh scream when caught by a leg, for example, in a gin trap. It struggles to free itself in silence at what must be the moment of greatest pain, then it pauses and screams. The two phases alternate fairly regularly and the appearance is of an animal alternately trying to free itself and then calling for help. Yet hedgehogs are well spread out and normally have little contact with each other except for a brief meeting for courtship and mating. Moreover, the situations in which the scream is heard would make rescue by other hedgehogs impossible.

The scream of a hedgehog cannot be interpreted as a juvenile trait carried into adult life, for an infant hedgehog in distress uses a call like a bird chirping. It is difficult to suggest a function of the scream unless it is a means of relieving the tension caused by pain or the frustration caused by being inexorably held captive, or an aggressive call uttered at an unseen and unrecognized enemy. Yet the scream to a human has a piteous quality, like an anguished cry for help.

The European common frog is equally solitary except when breeding. Normally it does not use its voice except at mating time, but on some occasions, such as when caught and held by a rat, a frog gives vent to loud and piteous screams. The function of this screaming is quite unknown. One can only suggest tentatively that it might serve to startle the assailant or as an alarm call alerting other frogs to possible danger. So little is known about this, however, that further speculation is idle. The European rabbit, normally silent, may sometimes make a piteous scream, as when caught by a stoat. Its normal alarm signal is to thump with the hind feet. In both the frog and the rabbit screaming is so sporadic that it is difficult to formulate a theory about its purpose. For example, a rabbit seized by a stoat may remain silent or it may scream. Usually it dies silently.

Alarm calls, recognizable as such, are more a feature of birds than of any other animal. In fact, they constitute in some species a simple form of language, one alarm call indicating the approach of a flying predator, warning all around to take cover, the other telling of the approach of a ground predator, when all fly away. In the first, the call is typically a thin sound hard to locate. In the second it is the reverse and by using it a bird draws attention to itself and thereby to the position of the lurking predator. In using it the bird lays itself open to attack, so its action is verging on the altruistic. The squawk of a captive bird, when held in the cat's mouth or the human hand, or caught in a trap, may be no more than an exaggerated form of an alarm call, distressing to our ears, but useful to other birds as an indication of danger. Whether such sounds, pitiful to us, evoke any form of desire to help in those of their kind that hear them, has yet to be fully investigated. Moreover, whether such help, if forthcoming, would be effective is doubtful.

For example, even while this chapter was being written there was a commotion here in some nearby trees where a carrion crow was robbing the nest of a mistle thrush. The persistent mobbing and the courage of the mistle thrush parents had little effect on the predator but their noisy aggressive calls were answered by three more pairs of mistle thrushes who converged on the nest and on the crow, which was unhurriedly seeking the best grip on one of the well-grown nestlings before flying off with it. The crow was equally unhurried when surrounded by a posse of eight mistle thrushes, aggressive and vociferous.

It is not easy to gain clues to the interpretation of animal distress vocalizations by comparison with those made by people. We can only say that the sounds we make are singularly like those which animals, especially mammals, make in similar situations. We moan or groan when afflicted with deep prolonged pain. We shriek or yell with sharp pains, and we whimper. Many animals use these same sounds, but human beings have the advantage that they can use words to reinforce these sounds, as well as to specify precisely how urgently the help is needed and what kind of help should be given.

The one most shared, and the one most closely approximating to a cry for help, is perhaps the whimper, found in most mammals. This could well be a juvenile trait that persists into adult life. Certainly the only sounds we can positively identify as distress vocalizations in animals are those used by infants calling to their parents. These have been noted in such diverse animals as young dolphins separated from their mothers, baby monkeys in distress and the ultrasonics of baby rats.

Vocalizations of any kind are a form of language. So too are bodily gestures, and with animals lacking the power of speech these may be more effective, especially when they express a complete change in behaviour. In that event, 'cry for help' becomes more a figure of speech. Some years ago, for instance, a story was published in the Press of a trapper in the wilds of North America who was sitting on a rock, his rifle lying at his side. As he rested he became aware of a sobbing, snuffling sound, a sort of moaning and whimpering. Along the trail came a cougar, or puma, obviously in distress. Only when it drew near did it notice the trapper. It stopped and looked at him intently, whereupon the trapper rose, looked at the animal's mouth and saw that its tongue had become impaled on one of its fangs. Forgetting everything he knew of this large wild cat, impelled only by the sight of an animal in great pain, he carefully levered the tongue up and over the fang. The cougar looked at him for a moment, then disappeared into the undergrowth.

That evening, in the trading post, he started to tell of his encounter. His friends were disbelieving. Their comments about the risks he had run were so graphic that he fainted. Only then were his listeners convinced that what he had said was true.

The striking part of this story, if true, is that both man and animal acted out of character. The man forgot to take up his rifle, approached fearlessly an animal he knew might attack him and showed compassion for a creature he was in the habit of hunting. The animal forgot its own danger in the severity of its pain and looked to its greatest enemy for help. Even when relieved it did not attack but went away without sign of aggression.

One morning a forester called at my house with a fox cub. He had found it trapped in a wire noose, doomed to a death from strangulation or starvation. He asked me to take care of it. The cub was between two and two and a half months old, well past the time when it could be expected to become tame, no matter how well it was treated. Yet as I held it cradled in my arms it was docile and appeared quite unafraid. Around its neck was a weal, a perceptible ring of swollen flesh where the wire had bruised. For the rest of that day the cub was hand-fed and for long periods it rested curled up in my lap as I stroked and petted it. It was the same throughout the next two days. The cub was hand-tame, showed no aggression or tendency to bite, and allowed me to pick it up and stroke it — in other words it behaved in an even more docile manner than one that had been hand-reared before its eyes had opened.

On the morning of the fourth day the swelling on its neck had gone down. I went into the room where the cub was being housed. For the first time since I had had it the cub retreated from me and hid behind a box. I spoke to it soothingly to no avail, so I put the dish of food down on the floor, and before I could withdraw my hand it had come out of hiding and bitten it.

> The devil was sick, the devil a saint would be.
> The devil was well and devil a saint was he.

As soon as it was well the cub's behaviour was reversed.

Perhaps even more striking was the situation with two bitterns. In two successive years a bittern had been brought to me. Both were uninjured but starving. A bittern is a medium-sized bird of the heron family, with the typical large dagger-like bill, and capable of a magnificent display of aggression. Each bird was docile, could be picked up and handled, would take food from the hand and behave in every other way as if fully tame. Within two days of being given its first meal all tameness had vanished. On the third day, now that the bird was well fed and had recovered its normal strength, not only did it refuse to be handled when I took food to it, but it spread its wings in its magnificent aggressive display and came forward to attack. It was not a matter of merely coming forward to accept the food. Even when the bowl containing it was put on the ground it ignored it and maintained its aggressive posture until I had retired well away from it.

The bittern is always described as shy and retiring and my previous experience of it had endorsed this. I therefore had the impression that this bird was docile too. I had taken the precaution of using a cautious approach so as not to alarm it, but when I was six feet from it I saw the bird drop to a crouch with wings spread and head drawn into its shoulders, and its long vicious-looking beak open. Then the bittern lunged upwards with its beak and any further thoughts of a shy, docile bird were dispelled.

Distress, whether from sickness, injury or hunger, inhibits normal behaviour and usually reverses it, at least in a human–animal context. The extent to which this happens varies with the degree and type of distress, the temperament of the animal concerned and a number of other factors. In a rabid animal, for example, the disease changes an otherwise pacific animal into a dangerous one. Docile beef cattle entering the slaughterhouse seem to sense the merciless atmosphere — or smell the blood? — and are transformed. It has been suggested that it is separation from the herd that is responsible but it can also happen with a beast that has led a solitary life.

So far we have been seeing things from the human angle in which, rabies and the slaughterhouse apart, distress calls forth our compassion and the impulse to help. It would be unsafe to assume that other animals, especially those of the same species, are impervious to the altered signals. If we take the cry of pain from the dog with its foot trapped in the grating, it is hard to believe other dogs hearing it would be wholly unresponsive, even if they did nothing active.

The only reliable guide I have in answering this question was provided by two Labradors, constant companions. They were passing through the boundary hedge of a meadow when one of them put its foot through two twisted strands of old barbed wire and could not extricate it. We had gone on ahead and the first we knew of it was when the other Labrador overtook us. It came up to the owner of the two dogs and showed clear signs of wanting to attract his attention and lead him back to the hedge. The owner followed and released the trapped paw.

So far as we could recall, the trapped dog had uttered no sound audible to us. While we were walking back, following the guidance of its companion, we could see it standing in the hedge, immobile. That, and the absence of any lacerations on the trapped leg, suggested that the dog had made no violent struggle to free itself. All the circumstances suggested that the first Labrador, finding itself a prisoner, had made no violent movements, that the second Labrador had quickly sized up the situation and come to fetch help, and that the trapped dog had had confidence in its companion and its owner that help would be quickly forthcoming. The important point is that there was no noticeable cry for help and that the second Labrador, in fetching help, seems to have been guided by its companion's behaviour.

As has been said, it could be that between members of a species what we normally think of as distress calls are danger signals alerting others and causing them to move away from the immediate danger zone. On the other hand, it may bring them nearer to investigate, if only out of curiosity. We still know too little about the functional aspects of animal vocalizations to speak with confidence on any particular set of circumstances. This can be emphasized by reference to the strandings of whales. Every year a number of whales of many species, large and small, become fatally stranded on coasts throughout the world. More spectacularly, multiple strandings of one or several hundreds, all of the same species, occur from time to time. Since whales, dolphins and porpoises are so completely adapted to a marine aquatic life the puzzle has been why these accidents should happen.

One especial feature of strandings is that those who go to great trouble to tow the cetaceans out to sea, as a rescue operation, suffer the mortification of seeing them stranded again on the next ebb tide. In the 1940s it became abundantly apparent that cetaceans, supposed before that time to be silent animals, had a rich repertoire of whistles, clicks and other sounds. Some of them are ultrasonic. Recordings of these have been made although, as with the vocalizations of other animals, we are a long way from sorting them out as to function. However, since cetaceans have been observed to go to the aid of their fellows in distress, a theory was put forward to account for stranded whales returning to the shore after being towed out to sea. It was suggested that those left on the beach were sending out distress signals in ultrasonics and their liberated fellows were returning in an unsuccessful attempt to render aid.

The false killer whale is one that several times has been known to become stranded en masse. A whole school of a hundred or more becomes stranded in what looks like a mass suicide. Here the suggestion has been made that one or a few become stranded in shallow water and, being unable to refloat, have sent out distress signals. The rest of the school then swims in to help and all are trapped.

To date, there is nothing to confirm either of these theories, although equally there is nothing to disprove them. So we are back with the original mystery. The probability is that there are no distress vocalizations, for the evidence so far seems to suggest that these are not used by most animals beyond infancy except possibly for the whimper, the moan and the groan.

This conclusion is reinforced by what we find among giraffes. Until relatively recently these animals were thought to be totally mute, in spite of the fact that they have a large voice box. Then, some thirty years ago, a giraffe calf was heard to bleat. Since then adult giraffes have been heard to snort and grunt, but only on very rare occasions. The animal's long neck carrying the head up to eighteen feet from the ground, as well as the large eyes, convert a giraffe into an animated watchtower. The animal has virtually no need of vocalizations because giraffes communicate with each other by the way they hold their necks, the position of their bodies and the posture of the tail. All these are readily visible to every giraffe in the neighbourhood. It has even been suggested that giraffes may use ultrasonics, but the more likely explanation, as implied here, is that they do not need to use the voice except on rare occasions because they convey all the messages they need by gesture and posture.

The most extensive study of vocalizations has been that made in birds. Recordings of the songs and calls of over a quarter of the nine thousand species known have been made. In the most authoritative discussions on the results of these studies it is recognized that there are songs, subsongs, alarm calls and all the rest, but little reference has been made to distress calls. The squawking of a bird caught by a cat or other predator, piteous as it may sound to the human ear, is probably to be translated as an aggressive vocalization. Most alarm calls made by birds function in alerting other members of the species in the neighbourhood to a possible danger, so that they flee. Even so, it would be unsafe to regard this as acceptable dogma until more careful attention has been directed towards the study of possible distress calls among birds. Even in fairly commonplace attempts by birds to combine against a common enemy, as happens in mobbing or harassing, either a recognizable alarm call is used or aggressive notes.

From this necessarily brief discussion it would seem that actual cries for help are few and far between, that many of the sounds which elicit our sympathy are no more than involuntary vocalizations that relieve tension in the animal itself, and that 'cries for help' is little more than a figure of speech. What we shall see, in later chapters, is that the more effective 'cries for help' lie in changes in behaviour, the vocalizations serving mainly to direct attention to these changes. Even so, there are anecdotes, still to be related, which suggest occasional definite sounds that are as much requests for help as human words can be. A single example shows this.

In 1976 M. E. Purchase reported that while walking along a country road near his home, he saw a calf that had just been born on the steep slope of a field. As he stopped to look, the new-born calf began to slide helplessly down the grassy hill. The mother cow gave a strange cry and at once six other cows ran and stood in a line on the hill and stopped the calf sliding any farther. Then they all stood around and helped the mother to lick it clean. He remarked: 'It was a wonderful thing to see.'

Had it been possible to interrogate Mr Purchase immediately after the incident, several valuable points might have emerged to help the analysis of his words. For example, he might have been able to give a vocal imitation of the cry and by tape-recording this one could have obtained the opinion of several cowmen, whether it was a vocalization with which they were experienced or familiar. It may only have been strange to Mr Purchase. A cowman might have been able to assess its significance. He might have replied that it was a call heard whenever a cow is distressed.

Mr Purchase continued: '. . . *at once* six cows *ran* and stood in line . . .' This is the most important part of the deposition. Cows do not readily run and if they did so, and at once, this suggests their appreciation that an urgent situation demanded their attention. Something more than mere curiosity was drawing them to the scene. One would have liked to know whether, when they stood in line, they stood flank to flank or head to tail. It was probably the first. In any event, it looks like a deliberate formation of a phalanx, not uncommon in hoofed animals faced with an unusual situation or even when congregating out of curiosity. It may not be possible to say whether the mother of the calf used a cry for help *per se* or a distress vocalization of a general nature. What seems more certain is that there appears to have been an element of altruism in the actions of her six herd mates.

It seems, on the evidence at present available, that definite 'cries for help' are relatively few, if they occur at all. What are usually construed as such belong mainly to the categories of alarm and aggression. The frequent use of the term 'distress vocalizations' may even be misguided, unless it is restricted to the whimper, groan and moan. More important in drawing attention to the need for help seems to be the change in behaviour, in other words, the use of visual signals — which may explain why the 'rascal' dog simulated injury to elicit sympathy!

4.
Life-Saving
Dolphins

The ancient Greeks seem to have treated dolphins with respect amounting almost to affection. They regarded them as highly intelligent. There were stories of boys being voluntarily carried on the backs of dolphins and of drowning people being rescued by dolphins. Figures of dolphins appeared abundantly on the coins and pottery of that period.

In post-classical Europe the alleged rescues of drowning people had long been treated with scepticism, as had the stories of boys riding on the backs of dolphins. Even as late as the first decades of this century, they were either wholly ignored or bracketed with the better-known Greek myths.

From Roman times came the story, recorded in detail by Pliny the Younger, of a dolphin that made friends with bathers at the ancient Carthaginian seaside resort of Hippo, now Bizerta, on the coast of Tunisia. Such was the popularity of the Hippo dolphin that visitors streamed in from far and wide. The result was that residents of Hippo grew tired of having their peace disturbed by this influx of tourists and got rid of their friendly dolphin. At best, this story was regarded as a pleasant phantasy; at worst, it was frankly ridiculed.

The only part of this history of ancient Greece and Rome to survive the centuries was the belief that dolphins and porpoises sometimes rescued drowning sailors. They were alleged to do so either by taking them on their backs or by pushing them towards the shore.

The dolphins' return to popular favour was foreshadowed by the exploits of Pelorus Jack, a Risso's dolphin, that used to swim at the bows of ships on the route between Nelson and Wellington, in Pelorus Sound, New Zealand, as if guiding the ships into harbour. Pelorus Jack became so well known and so popular that it was protected during the period 1904–1914 by an Order in Council. The real return to favour, however, of these smaller cetaceans, in both a popular and a scientific sense, can be said to have come with a rush in the late 1940s and the 1950s.

Just before the outbreak of World War II the idea had been conceived of building huge concrete tanks in Florida in which marine animals could be kept. These massive salt-water aquaria became known as marine studios. Their success soon led to others being built elsewhere in the United States, for which the name 'oceanaria' was coined. Others were built in various parts of the world and known as dolphinaria. Together, these provided amusement to large numbers of visitors as well as opportunities for scientific study, formerly undreamed of, that shed a dazzling light on the exploits and personalities of

 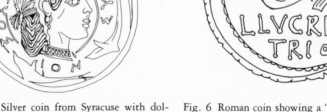

Fig. 5 Silver coin from Syracuse with dolphin motif, commemorating victory over Carthage, 479 BC

Fig. 6 Roman coin showing a 'boy' riding a dolphin

dolphins and other cetaceans, including porpoises and whales. These studies showed that dolphins very easily adjusted to captivity. They became friendly with their captors, were very playful even to inventing their own games, and they revealed a spirit of fun. It was not long before they were being generally accepted as second only to man in the animal scale.

As if to set the seal on this, in 1952 R. H. Burne published his book on the dissection of a common porpoise. Among other things, this showed the porpoise to have a convoluted brain, indicating a mental capacity at least equal to that of the apes. This added up to the revelation that the cetaceans were highly advanced animals in which man's sole interest for more than a century had, lamentably, not risen above slaughtering them for their oil and other products.

Dolphins especially, among the cetaceans, were now restored in modern times to something near the affection bestowed on them in classical times. As if to crown it, there came the much publicized report of a woman bathing off the coast of Florida in 1943 who had got into difficulties and was nudged ashore by a dolphin and so rescued. Extravagant claims began to be made in all directions, not least for the compassionate behaviour of dolphins, exceeding those that were currently being made for elephants.

As if to endorse all else that was happening during the years of mid-twentieth century, came the news in 1955 of a dolphin, at the seaside resort of Opononi, New Zealand, becoming friendly with bathers and behaving almost exactly as the dolphin had at Hippo, nearly two thousand years previously. At first, this dolphin merely followed boats inshore. Then it mingled with bathers, who began to pat it and provide it with playthings, such as beach-balls. It became especially fond of the company of children, and particularly of 13-year-old Jill Baker. In time, Jill could hold the dolphin's dorsal fin for a ride and later was permitted to sit astride.

That dolphins, and other cetaceans, are highly playful is now beyond doubt.

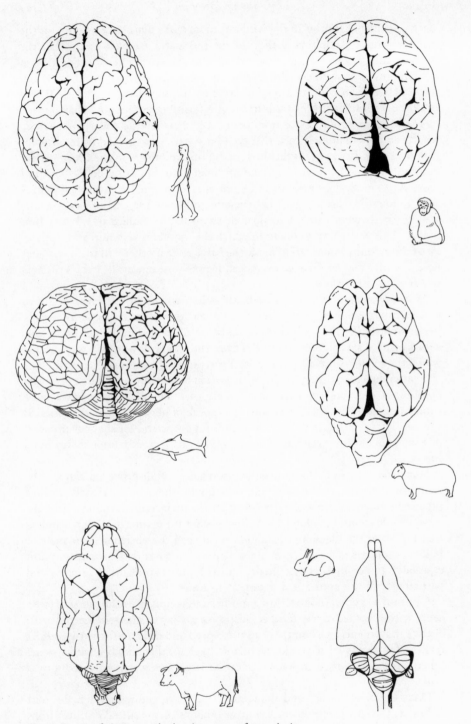

Fig. 7 Brains of six mammals showing range of convolutions

There is evidence for this in the wild but more particularly in captivity, as the many visitors to dolphinaria throughout the world are well aware. For the moment this can be set aside, though it is important to emphasize one aspect of it, dolphins' ability to coordinate their movements so that two or more can move perfectly in combination, in complete unison. This, as we shall see, could be a most valuable attribute in any form of succourant behaviour.

The next important bonus from being able to watch the daily lives of these wholly aquatic mammals, one that could not have been gained from observation in the wild, was the light shed on the first moments in the life of a baby dolphin. The actual birth may take up to an hour, the baby being born tail first. As soon as the newborn is free of the birth canal the mother swings sharply round to face it. This has the effect of snapping the umbilical cord, leaving the newborn infant to float or swim to the surface to take its first breath. This is a crucial moment in which the mother is watchful and ready to assist. Should the infant fail to make the surface the mother will lift it with her nose or with a flipper. She has even been seen to seize one of the baby's flippers to lift it to the surface.

When a female is about to give birth, other females in the school begin to take an interest in her. Swimming around her, they show a special interest in her genital region and inspect it. It can be assumed that in the wild state this detachment of several of its members from the school slows down the speed at which the school is travelling, so that a parturient female is not left behind.

In attendance, and paying special attention to watching the birth of a baby dolphin, is a second female, usually one that has all along been a close companion of the mother. It is normal to speak of her as 'auntie', although as we shall later see, 'midwife' would be more appropriate, for she may assist, if necessary, in ensuring the safe surfacing of the infant, that vital first step in its life.

Sometimes there are two aunties in attendance, while other females will be swimming around in the vicinity. No doubt these inadvertently form a protective screen against the arrival of sharks attracted by the smell of the considerable amount of blood lost by the mother at the time of labour as well as that lost from the bleeding of the umbilical cord. Furthermore, the male or bull dolphin has a tendency to show aggression towards a young dolphin, especially at the moment of birth, and the presence of other females and particularly of the auntie is a deterrent to him.

One bull was observed to follow a mother and young, with auntie, and often came within inches of the mother, clapping his jaws. The trio reacted with evasive movements, constantly changing speed and direction, the two adults making frantic efforts to shield the infant. Even so, there has been at least one other instance recorded in which a newborn calf was bitten repeatedly by a bull.

Once the baby is born and is swimming around, these same females will follow it. Given the opportunity, one or other of them will take it over from the mother, swimming around with it as if it were her own. For days and weeks on end individual dolphins, young and old, have been seen to trail a new infant and its mother and have vied with each other for the privilege of approaching it closely or of escorting it. Later, when permitted to do so, they have spared no effort to protect the infant from dangers, real or potential, perhaps even imaginary. In describing these actions Frank S. Essapian has emphasized how keenly attentive bottle-nosed dolphins, the species most commonly seen in dolphinaria, and probably all cetaceans, are to the slightest changes affecting their communal life.

Such behaviour is not the exclusive prerogative of cetaceans. It is a marked feature of the social life of many species of monkeys. Females other than the mother show a great interest in a newborn baby and endeavour to hold it and carry it around. The mother tends to be selective about it, allowing more readily those that are her companions at other times to exercise the privilege. It has been suggested that one result of this interest, and the subsequent sharing of the infant, constitutes a sort of apprenticeship in motherhood for females that have not yet given birth. It also has definite disadvantages, for there are many casualties due to their inexperience in handling infants. In one troop it was found that as many as sixty per cent of babies died at an early age from this cause alone. There is no evidence of such high casualties in baby dolphins.

Fig. 8 Female dolphin with young swimming beside her dorsal fin

In a short while the infant dolphin is able to keep up with its mother, often with the help of the auntie. The two adults swim side by side, able to coordinate their movements so that they swim as if tied together, with the baby swimming between their dorsal fins. This almost certainly assists the infant's progress through the water and reduces fatigue for it, and it protects the baby dolphin from predators.

When Opo first became friendly with Jill Baker, as we have seen, the girl was able to do no more than hold the dolphin's dorsal fin to be carried along. Later she was able to sit astride its back. Opo was a female and it has been suggested that for her a girl holding her fin or sitting astride her back was as acceptable as having her own baby swimming beside her in the region of the fin. Whether it is justifiable to make such a facile comparison is arguable. It would mean that a dolphin is unable to tell a girl from a baby dolphin. In view of the tested ability of dolphins to discriminate between small-sized objects of different shape and texture it seems unlikely. There is therefore every reason to suppose that the relationship between Jill and Opo was based on companion-ship — they were playmates. Another word for it is 'friends' and to those who ask whether it is possible for any animal to be friendly in the human sense, here is an answer.

To return to the birth process of dolphins: sometimes there is a stillbirth. It has been observed in marine studios that if a dolphin calf is stillborn, the mother not only pushes it to the surface but continues to swim up with it and hold it at the surface in the desperate attempt to resuscitate it. She may continue in this forlorn task for many hours. Normally she carries the baby up on her snout. If the baby sinks to the bottom when the mother lets go of it to take her own breath, she will retrieve it in her mouth and swim to the surface with it.

Similar behaviour has been noted in wild dolphins, especially in calm waters. (Whether it would take place amid strong wave action is an open question.) Thus, Vincent M. Mrazek and Lyle H. McDowell, district rangers, were on boat patrol in the Everglades National Park, in south Florida, when they saw two bottle-nosed dolphins, one of which was continuously bumping an object along with its snout. It was the head of a baby dolphin cut smoothly away from the body, probably bitten by a shark. It was nearly white, suggesting that the accident had occurred some days before. A year before, in 1953, Joseph Curtis Moore, also in the Everglades, had reported seeing a lone bottle-nosed dolphin supporting the body of a dolphin calf on its head. The body, three feet four inches long, was bitten nearly in two. Moore estimated it to be newborn or at most only a week or two old and to have been dead three days, the victim perhaps of a bite from a shark or barracuda. The same year, Carl Hubbs reported seeing four or five individuals of a related species in the coastal waters of California, one of which was supporting a dead baby lying across its back, against the dorsal fin. These and other comparable observations made in dolphinaria leave little doubt that these actions are purely instinctive. There is therefore nothing altruistic about them.

What we are seeing is the manifestation of the important principle that an animal in distress reverses its behaviour, and the behaviour of a congener towards it is also reversed. In a normal birth the baby dolphin swims to the surface to breathe and so long as it can do this under its own power the mother does not interfere. If it is in distress and unable to reach the surface the mother changes her normal behaviour and assists it. When the baby is stillborn, so that the change from normal behaviour is permanent, the changed behaviour of the mother is prolonged, and she will continue her resuscitation attempts until an advanced state of decay in the infant or some factor in the mother's psychology causes her to stop.

This is misplaced mother-love and it is only a short step from this to what one author has called misfiring behaviour. An instance of misfiring behaviour occurred in Marineland, California, where dolphins are kept in the usual gigantic concrete, seawater aquaria, together with other marine animals, including sharks. One of the dolphins, a female named Spray, adopted a twenty-pound carpet shark. Having fixed her mother-love on it, she seized it in her mouth, carried it to the surface and held its head out of water. It takes a lot to kill a shark, but being seized by a dolphin and having its head held out of water regularly at short intervals throughout the day began to tell on this one.

The attendants at Marineland began to view with anxiety the early loss of one of their treasured specimens, so a diver was sent into the tank to rescue the shark. Every time he went in, the dolphin went careering round the tank at great speed with the shark in her mouth. This went on for a week, with the shark showing more and more signs of wear. Eventually, the dolphin herself began to feel the strain of hunger and being presented with a tempting meal dropped the shark for a moment, whereupon the waiting diver seized it and moved it away to another tank to safety.

Since the subject of this book is animal altruism it may seem misplaced to devote so much space to what can only be called genetic altruism, or behaviour that looks altruistic but is instinctive. The point is that when, through the unique opportunities afforded by dolphinaria, it first became known that a mother or an auntie dolphin would assist a newborn calf if necessary to the surface, this was hailed as remarkable. It was just one more reason for investing cetaceans with an aura akin to that of mankind itself. To use the word that has become so popular today, there was, during the 1950s and early 1960s, an outburst of euphoria about dolphins. Another cause, similarly exaggerated, arose from the study of sounds made by dolphins. In a flush of enthusiasm it was at one time suggested that the dolphins were trying to talk to their human attendants in the dolphinaria, a claim that has since had to be abandoned, and with it some of the euphoria.

The truth seems to be that although dolphins have a good brain we have to be careful not to credit them with an altruism that does not exist. The mother dolphin assisting her calf merely comes within the ambit of normal maternal care found in other higher mammals. The same can be said of the behaviour of aunties. Even the report of dolphins rescuing drowning people must be taken with a pinch of salt. Thus, dolphins have been observed at sea nudging inanimate objects along, presumably in play or possibly even as the result of a natural curiosity aroused by any unusual objects. Articles so treated include a floating box, dead fish, live fish, turtles, a partially deflated rubber beach ball and an inflated rubber inner tube. One was seen pushing along a waterlogged mattress. It could be taken as entirely fortuitous if a drowning person were nudged towards the shore and safety. It could equally well happen that a drowning person might be pushed farther out to sea and never live to tell the tale!

On at least one occasion experiments were carried out to test the potentialities of dolphins as life-savers. The dolphins were presented with a variety of floating objects in succession, including a newly-dead baby dolphin, a plastic model of a dolphin of about equal size to a baby dolphin, a log and a length of nylon cord. The dolphins reacted to each in turn by showing curiosity mixed with apprehension. No attempt was made to touch them, let alone nudge them in any way that could be interpreted as a rescue attempt. If these experiments prove anything at all it is that to test for an animal's altruism, or even for higher-order behaviour, scientifically, that is under artificial conditions, is virtually impossible.

We can take it therefore that when a mother dolphin or an auntie shows succourant behaviour towards a new-born calf it is responding to a total situation every part of which is a natural sequence. There must be the female in labour, the emergence of a baby, the obvious distress on the part of the baby, and the rest. Dolphins, like those seen in the Everglades, pushing portions of a calf were almost certainly actuated by either a misplaced mother-love, plain curiosity or just play, and were responding to inner motivations that cannot be effectively called into order at the whim of an experimenter. You cannot, in other words, make an animal play or show concern for others if it is not in the mood to do so.

This attitude of scepticism can be justified if only because it throws into bold relief several instances, recorded during the period of euphoria, of what can be accepted as true altruism. They can be found in the pages of the *Journal of Mammalogy* for 1953 and 1956 and have received no great publicity. The first concerns a striped dolphin which stayed beside its harpooned companion, forcing its way between the dying animal and the ship, endeavouring to push it away to safety. By any counts, this had the appearance of a true act of heroism.

The second episode occurred when a ship was out collecting dolphins. A charge of dynamite was used, which stunned one of the dolphins, whereupon

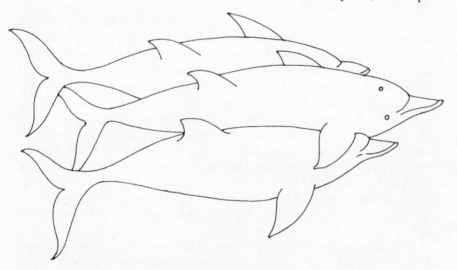

Fig. 9 Two dolphins supporting an injured companion

two others ranged themselves one on each side of it to buoy it up. That the action was deliberate is shown by the way the supporting dolphins, when they had to leave it to come up to breathe, swam in a wide arc to come back and continue to support it. (Whether it was this pair or another one that swam in to take their places, the observers could not be certain.) After several minutes the stunned dolphin had recovered and the whole school, which had remained in the vicinity, swam away at high speed making tremendous leaps, jumping in unison every 10–12 seconds, 10–12 feet out of the water, their leaps covering 25–30 feet.

That this was a deliberate rescue attempt is shown by another occasion when a similar explosion was set off but no dolphin was injured. Immediately, the whole school fled in the manner described, at high speed, with tremendous leaps. What would have been interesting to know, in the light of chapter 2, is whether on the previous occasion the stunned dolphin uttered distress calls or not. Presumably a stunned animal would not be capable of doing so, which raises the question whether dolphins keep in touch by continuous sound signals equivalent to an elephant's purring, or whether this is a good example of how keenly attentive they are to the slightest changes affecting their communal life.

The fourth observation came when a number of bottle-nosed dolphins were being caught. As each was brought aboard it was placed in a well in the ship. One struggled as it was being lifted from the sea, struck its head just behind the eye on a post and sank in seven feet of water in the well. Two of the dolphins already in the well ranged themselves on either side of it to raise it to the surface to breathe, while a third hovered near. The rescuers had to move away periodically to breathe but continued to return until their companion had recovered.

A more recent account appeared in the *National Geographic Magazine* for December 1976. It told of the captain of a ferry off Vancouver Island, British Columbia, who heard a crunch at the stern, supposed he had struck a submerged log, turned about and saw a young killer whale wallowing in the sea. An adult cow and a bull killer had lined up either side of it, so preventing the calf from turning upside-down. Occasionally the bull would lose position and the calf would heel over, showing slashes in its side from the ferry's propellor. Two weeks later, in the same waters, two whales were seen supporting a third, preventing it from turning over. It is not known whether it was the same group, but it does raise the question how long whales or dolphins can succour a companion in this way, going without food to give time for wounds to heal.

Perhaps even more remarkable is the story of a young thresher shark caught in an anchovy net and sent to the Steinhart Aquarium, in California. It was in bad shape on arrival, suffering from net burns and shock, and it lay on the floor of the tank. Sharks must keep moving to breathe, so the survival of the shark was further jeopardized. In the same tank were two white-sided dolphins. These proceeded to lift the shark to the surface, using their jaws or their dorsal fins, as they would have lifted a newborn dolphin or an injured adult. They did this repeatedly, the shark sinking again each time. The result was that the shark was kept continuously on the move. Many sharks are natural enemies of dolphins, so these two dolphins were applying the midwifery tactics which are instinctive to them in an endeavour to aid a helpless member of their natural enemies. What is so remarkable here is that the dolphins should have recognized distress in a totally different species, whereas the dolphins tested scientifically have failed so completely to attempt to give aid to a dead baby dolphin and a convincing plastic model of a dolphin.

There is yet another important contribution the dolphins have to make to our discussion. Some people hesitate to ascribe friendliness to animals, but many pets, especially domesticated animals, give every appearance of being friendly. Opo came voluntarily to the company of human beings and even allowed one of them to ride it, which no horse would do without being broken in, or at least gentled. The dolphin at Hippo did much the same, if we are to believe Pliny, and there are a number of less publicized instances of solitary dolphins and the smaller whales striking up a temporary friendship with people. A pet or domestic animal has no choice, but a dolphin living free in the sea that behaves like one of these is prompted by no such compulsion.

After the alleged rescue of a woman off Florida there was a great deal of scepticism. It was justifiably suggested that her being nudged ashore was entirely fortuitous. The dolphin may merely have treated her as a plaything, as it would have done a waterlogged mattress, and it may have been merely her good luck that the animal nudged her towards the shore instead of farther out to sea. More recently there was a comparable event off Cornwall, when a diver got into difficulty. The *Aquanaut* serves as a fishing boat and a diving boat and is owned by Bob Carswell, whose wife Hazel has recounted what happened. Apparently a diver surfaced in difficulties, whereupon a wild dolphin that had earlier disrupted a life-saving exercise in a mischievous manner, swam towards the diver and appeared to be trying to support him at the surface until Hazel reached him. As she towed the diver back to the *Aquanaut* the dolphin assisted in the operation.

Whether rescue of humans by dolphins will later be set on a more substantial foundation remains to be seen. What is already certain is that cetaceans do render help to their fellows in distress, at risk to themselves. Such truly altruistic acts are a natural outcome of an inherited or genetically altruistic behaviour. It seems also that in some of the instances recorded there was no possibility of the altruism being in response to distress vocalizations or cries of distress. The stunned dolphin, for example, was probably incapable of making such sounds.

5.
Compassionate Elephants

There is another animal species whose members have long been credited with showing concern for their fellows. This is the African elephant. To a lesser extent, so has the Indian or Asian elephant. In both of these the brain is highly convoluted and both have been regarded as highly intelligent. Their supposed compassion is based largely on their action of helping an injured congener to get on to its feet and of supporting it away from the scene of tragedy.

In 1933, David Enderby Blunt described how he was called one evening to an African village because elephants were raiding crops. He found the culprits were four bull elephants. He fired at one but missed the brain. Even so, the bull fell. Immediately, the other three closed in on him, one on each side and one behind. They 'just boosted him on to his feet' and, supporting him on either side, went off into the forest. Blunt remarked that this was the first time he had seen such a thing and was amazed by it. As it was then getting dark he could not follow them but he returned the next day and failed to find any trace of them.

As early as 1867, Emerson Tennent had recorded similar events in Ceylon (Sri Lanka) and in 1953, in a monograph, *The Elephant in East Central Africa*, published by Rowland Ward, Captain C. R. S. Pitman and G. G. Rushby quoted other examples of what has been called elephant altruism. In this monograph Pitman stated that in most cases it was cows that helped a stricken bull. In a few instances bulls helped a bull and only in one instance was there a record of a cow being helped in this way.

Judging by descriptions given since then, too much reliance should not be placed on this analysis, for in the examples now to be quoted three out of five deal with cow elephants being assisted in this way.

Authors writing on this subject are inclined to say that there are numerous such cases on record, yet B. D. Nicholson, Elephant Control Officer in what was then Tanganyika Territory (now Tanzania), commented in 1955 that he had 'only once seen elephants support and proceed to remove a wounded comrade out of the danger area'. This was in the Tunduru District. Nicholson had shot a bull and broken its shoulder. Two cows, on hearing the bull's cries of distress, turned back, ranged themselves on each side of him and half carried, half dragged him away at quite a good pace. Nicholson felt obliged to finish off the bull, so he ran alongside shouting in an attempt to drive away the cows. At this, one of the cows turned and came towards him. He had no choice but to shoot her. He then delivered a fatal shot to the bull whereupon the remaining cow began to move away. 'She went sadly on her way, every few yards stopping to listen and look back.'

Two years later, a game guard in Northern Rhodesia (now Zambia) received a report that four elephants were raiding crops. Following instructions, he set out for Chiselo Village and discovered four cows that had been settled in thick bush for three weeks. It had become the practice in such circumstances to shoot the leading elephant, so he looked for the oldest female and shot her. One of the others came aggressively towards him and pursued him for nearly half a mile. Then she returned to where the dead elephant lay. Ng'uni, the game guard, also returned to find that the remaining cows were trying to lift the carcase. It seems that the rest of the herd had now been drawn to the scene. Some were holding the head, some the tusks, some the front legs, some the hind legs and others were working on the body, all trying to lift. In the course of the lifting operations one of the dead elephant's tusks was broken off and was thrown five yards from the carcase.

Ng'uni's report is lacking, not surprisingly, in some of the finer details needed for a scientific analysis of the event. One gathers, however, that the elephants, unsuccessful in their rescue attempt, went on the rampage and spent four hours knocking down trees, 'and the place was cleared'. The herd was still there when Ng'uni left. The next morning he went back and found the dead elephant covered with Mopani branches and the herd had moved away into the Lufila Game Reserve.

In 1962 Mchilagula Kachari, a Northern Rhodesian game scout, was called to Limbani village where a herd of elephants were raiding stored grain and banana gardens. He found a herd of four cows with juveniles and shot one of the cows, after which the others came and tried unsuccessfully to lift the carcase. 'They lifted the front legs and the head, but still it was in vain.' They continued in their efforts for one and a half hours, and then the game scout went upwind, the herd got his scent and departed, leaving the carcase where it lay.

Perhaps the outstanding feature of these reports is that the attempts at rescue reported, and the degree of success achieved, differ significantly in each case. Contrasted with the failures to move the dead animal is the account given, about this same period, of a large elephant shot by hunters. The herd gathered round it and proceeded to drag it away. Curious to know the outcome, the hunters followed at a respectful distance all through the rest of the day and the following night, after which their patience presumably gave out, for the sequel is not recorded.

Alan Moorehead, writing in his book *In the Wilds of Africa* in 1957, quotes David Sheldrick, a game warden, for an account of poachers killing an elephant with poisoned arrows. The method used was the usual one, to concentrate on the elephant with the largest tusks. The wounded beast is described as crashing off into the bush with the rest of the herd. Then he falls, and as he lies thrashing about on the ground, the rest of the herd turn back and thrust their trunks under his huge body in an apparent effort to get him on to his feet again. In this they were unsuccessful and turned hopelessly away when they seemed to realize nothing useful could be done.

In the Murchison Falls National Park in Uganda in the 1950s a game warden felt compelled to shoot an elephant that was sick and in obvious pain. As soon as he had brought the animal down with a shot he watched while its companions approached and examined the carcase in great detail. He described how they felt it all over with the tips of their trunks and even tried to pull out the tusks. The identity of the Warden is not recorded, whether he was African or a white man, but the last part of his description seems to be tinctured by a long-standing piece of folklore, that elephants will pull out the tusks of a dead companion in order to prevent these being taken by ivory collectors. This can probably be explained by the fact that one or both of the tusks are pulled out, as we have seen, during attempts at rescue.

Almost certainly the most complete account of one of these elephant incidents is that given by W. H. Winter, a game warden engaged in elephant control duties in western Kenya, in September 1963. He described what he had seen as an extraordinary display of animal loyalty. The account was published in *East African Wildlife Journal* for 1964. Three elephants of a herd of thirty, comprising bulls, cows, immatures and calves, were shot in a forest clearing. Although Winter and a party of game scouts were standing in full view of the elephants, not more than sixty yards from them, they were upwind of them, and the beasts seemed to be unaware of them, so were ignorant of where the danger lay.

The confused and furious beasts milled around trumpeting and shrieking, throwing up showers of grass and stones, then with 'incredible determination and complete disregard for their own safety' tried to lift their dead companions. They pushed and butted ponderously at the inert forms, entwining their trunks with those of their dead companions as if trying to lift them and pawed at the carcases with their forefeet as if trying desperately to move them. This went on for more than half an hour. One large cow knelt beside the carcase of a female, placed her tusks under it and tried to stand, her body tensed with the effort. Suddenly there was a loud crack as her right tusk snapped and sailed through the air to land thirty feet away.

In the end the herd moved off with a tremendous commotion, smashing bamboo and small trees as they went. Then they returned trumpeting and screaming and renewed their efforts to get their dead companions to their feet and move them to safety. Indeed, they went away and returned three times, in what Winter described as their anguish at the inability of their companions to get up off the ground. Finally, the herd was led away by a large bull who was trumpeting loudly. The watchers could hear them screaming and calling from far away in the forest. There remained, however, a single cow with a large calf at foot. She stayed for several minutes before following the herd with what appeared to be extreme reluctance to abandon her dead companions. Winter and his party now approached and found the broken tusk lying in two pieces. This is of interest in relation to what will be said in a moment.

The contribution by G. G. Rushby to the Rowland Ward book on elephants, mentioned earlier, is somewhat different. Rushby was on elephant control work in the Morogoro District of Tanganyika (Tanzania). Under conservation in parks and reserves elephants tend to grow too numerous and to destroy their own habitat. The work of a control officer is to cull the surplus, thinning the ranks of the elephants, at his discretion. On this occasion, Rushby came across three full-grown cows and a half-grown bull. It was necessary to 'cull' the cows, which he did, reluctantly. He also slightly wounded the bull. Only then, to his horror, did he discover that two of the cows had been accompanied by calves, which had been hidden by the long grass. He walked towards the calves in order to drive them towards the main herd, which was a mile away. The wounded, half-grown bull became confused. Then Rushby saw the calves range themselves, on each side of the bull and help it along, just as adults have been seen to rescue one of their number.

So far, the only evidence that such rescues, or attempted rescues, actually take place is contained in depositions of eye-witnesses. There was, however, a film record of it taken in the 1920s. The title of the film is unknown to me. It was a purely 'nature' production shot by a party engaged in filming African animals in the bush. The party was charged by the leader of a herd of elephants, a huge tusker that had to be shot at very close range by the hunter in protective charge of the cameramen. The bull went down at the first shot, killed outright by a bullet in the brain, and two lesser, but still large, tuskers rushed up and, one on each side, tried with tusks and foreheads to lift the carcase. The would-be rescuers seemed soon to realize that their leader was dead and rushed off to join the stampeding herd.

It is not surprising that people writing about these incidents should refer frequently to the loyalty, affection, courage and the like shown by the elephants. What is needed now is to examine this behaviour more objectively. Certainly we should avoid the extravagant language of one writer who declared that elephants 'manifest a concern for their own aged, sick, wounded and dead which, in a primitive group of men, would be regarded as *caritas*, the essence of the higher religions'.

The mystique of elephant behaviour can lead to other fanciful ideas. One, already mentioned, is that a herd of elephants will tear the tusks out of their fallen comrades to prevent the hunters obtaining the ivory. The next elaboration is to declare that they will then shatter the tusks to pieces on rocks and boulders. No doubt such stories are based solely on the kind of incidents we have included here, of the rescuers breaking the tusks of their dead companions, or breaking their own tusks, in the course of attempted rescues.

More important for our present discussion is how far elephant rescues are the result of instinctive behaviour. In its purest form, an instinct can be defined as a pattern of behaviour performed in the same way under the same circumstances by all members of a species. Moreover, no matter how often the action is repeated there will be no significant variation in its pattern. It is a fixed pattern of behaviour, inherited in its entirety and owing little or nothing to learning or experience. An orb spider, for example, spins a cartwheel web from the first and continues to spin this same pattern throughout life. It follows from this that the same pattern of behaviour will be followed by young and old alike.

The significance of Rushby's observation, already noted, is that it was two calves, still at foot, that attempted the rescue of the young bull. This suggests that the pattern of this behaviour is basically innate. On the other hand, the differing descriptions given of the way adult elephants attempt their rescues suggest something more, as do the shrieking and trumpeting and the signs of fury. The situation may be compared with that of human beings. A baby or an infant, seeing a companion hurt, would merely cry or call for help. At the age of, say, ten it is likely to try lifting or supporting the injured one, and this tendency will increase with age. In this, and possibly in the elephant rescues also, we may be dealing with an emergent pattern of behaviour, with the impulse to help inherited and the means whereby that succour is given developing with age and, especially, experience.

Giving support to an injured companion is not the prerogative of elephants alone, although their conspicuous size makes it more evident in them and more frequently observed. It is said that wounded otters have been seen supported by two of their fellows, one on each side, although it has not been possible to find a published account of this. There are, however, well-attested accounts of rescue attempts comparable to those of elephants by African buffaloes and wildebeest.

In August 1952 the Warden of the Queen Elizabeth National Park observed an unusual sight. Of four bull buffaloes, one was elderly and obviously in pain from a broken hindleg. The Warden decided to put this bull out of its misery and dropped it with a shot behind the shoulder. Immediately, the other bulls came up and appeared to be goring the fallen bull with their horns. It soon transpired they were trying to help it get on to its feet, which it managed to do before collapsing and dying.

A longer, more detailed account of a similar incident had been given in 1935, in *The Uganda Journal*, by G. H. E. Hopkins. He reported that when on safari in western Ankole he had occasion to shoot meat for his porters. After a time three bull buffaloes were encountered and he shot one stone dead. The remaining bulls milled about for a while, then one of them endeavoured several times to raise its fallen comrade by hooking a horn under his neck. Finally, the two live bulls took up position, one on each side of the carcase, facing in opposite directions. In this position they commanded between them a view all around. Moreover, they made no attempt to move away.

Hopkins had no wish to kill again and as darkness was falling he retired discreetly from the position he had taken up to where his car was parked. Then he drove back to the spot where the buffalo lay dead; but its living companions were still on guard, one and a half hours after the shots had been fired. He tried to dazzle the buffaloes with the headlights, revved his engine, sounded both the electric and the bulb horn. Nothing would induce the buffaloes to go, even though the car and its cacophony was taken to fifteen yards from them, until after ten minutes. As Hopkins put it, when he had decided that if their nerve did not break immediately his would, they trotted slowly away.

The wildebeest seen by G. P. Visagie, nature conservation officer in the Loskop Nature Reserve, lacked the tenacity and courage of the buffalo. Visagie shot a young bull in the rump with an anaesthetic dart. As it began to droop under the anaesthetic, its two companions took up positions on either side of it and facing in the same direction. They succeeded in keeping it on its feet for a short distance. When its legs gave way under it one of the helpers inserted its horns under the bull's shoulder, trying to keep the beast upright. As it fell the other helper tried also to raise it with its horns, and as the catching party arrived on the scene the two wildebeest helpers departed.

Some of the more recent and, to some extent, more surprising observations are those made by Hans and Ute Klingel on zebras. These two authors have been able to show that the stability of the family group and the strong ties which bind it together are linked with the concern which zebra show for each other. To begin with, a group will gather and its members intermingle where there is good grazing or at a waterhole. If a foal should become separated from the group the rest of the zebra rush about braying, while the foal also runs about amongst the throng wailing in distress. The group do not abandon a sick or wounded zebra but slow down to enable it to keep up with them. On several occasions the Klingels observed the zebra coming to the aid of one of its fellows which had been immobilized with a drugged dart. On some occasions, a stallion would nip a drugged mare in an endeavour to revive her, and one went so far as to seize the neck of the mare with its teeth and drag her back to the group.

Major Pretorius, famous South African hunter, in his book *Jungle Man*, stated emphatically that he did not believe the story of elephants seeking to rescue a wounded comrade. To him it was just another tall story of the bush and in all his experience he never once witnessed it. John F. Burger, a fellow South African, who at one time or another had covered the same country as Pretorius in Central and East Africa, follows the long list of experienced and dependable witnesses in taking the contrary view. Burger observed it twice.

One of these occasions was in the then Belgian Congo (now Zaire), near the Lualabu River. Burger had followed the trail of a herd and, when fifty yards from a big bull, he fired. The bull sagged to his knees. Immediately the whole herd went on the rampage, screaming and stampeding. Burger and his trackers were forced to take refuge in the trees. For an hour they could hear the herd milling around the fallen bull, breaking off branches and pushing over trees. Suddenly there was silence and a tracker high in a tree announced that the herd was on its way heading for the river.

The party descended to the ground and made for the spot where the bull had been shot. There they found only a large pool of blood and tracks showing that several members of the herd had converged on the spot. Assuming that the bull had recovered sufficiently to move with the herd, they followed the trail for more than a mile, then they mounted a tall termite hill and saw the bull walking erect supported on either side by a cow and being virtually pushed along.

They followed the herd at a respectable distance until sunset, camped in the open and were back on the trail which they followed until midday, when they found the carcase of the bull, stiff and cold. The rest of the herd had moved on but the tracks showed that they had milled around the body for some time before deserting it.

The second sighting was near Lake Rukwa, in Tanganyika (now Tanzania), but on that occasion someone else had been responsible for the wounding. Burger was camped near a game path when he saw the procession pass. The only significant difference was that the victim was a young bull. It, too, collapsed finally and was left behind by the herd.

In Lydekker's *Harmsworth Natural History*, published in 1910, there are two photographs associated with an article on animal intelligence by Professor C. Lloyd Morgan. The caption to these pictures reads: 'The pathos of the wild: a young elephant finding the dead body of her mother and trying to rouse her.' Unfortunately, there is nothing in Morgan's text, nor in the sections on Indian and African elephants, written by F. C. Alexander and R. Lydekker respectively, giving any further details. Nevertheless, the photographs on their own are important, particularly since none of these three authors has a word to say about elephants seeking to rescue dead or injured comrades. We may therefore take it that the two photographs were included for their intrinsic interest alone.

The photographs show what the caption purports: the young elephant is pawing the recumbent corpse with its right foot in one picture, and has raised its trunk as if squealing in the other. The clues as to the total behaviour are meagre, but suggest that, like any other baby mammal beside a dead mother, the young elephant, uncomprehending the finality of the situation, is seeking to induce its mother to adopt a normal standing position. It would probably do so if she were asleep; but this situation is unlikely to arise since elephants spend so little of their sleeping time lying inert on one side.

Elephants live in family units of several mature females, the oldest of which is the herd leader, and young of both sexes. The mature bulls usually live apart, either solitarily or in herds, joining the matriarchal herds for breeding. It may be that attempts by herds to raise a fallen comrade are due to a persistence into adulthood of the kind of behaviour illustrated by these two photographs. If so, then elephants ranging themselves on either side to assist an injured comrade could be altruistic, either because it is an extension of the instinctive behaviour of a calf towards its dead mother or from purely compassionate motives.

During the 1970s, with the clampdown by African governments on the killing of elephants for their ivory, poaching has become rampant. It has recently been reported that in 1973 17,000 elephants were killed by poachers, while by 1976 the figure had risen to 70,000. Poaching is often accompanied by unspeakable cruelty in which calves are often the victims. On at least one occasion a calf has been seen to collapse to the ground from fatal injuries, and several female elephants have been observed trying in turn to lift it on to its feet. The appearance then suggests compassion rather than a purely instinctive action.

Then comes the important question of how often such rescue attempts occur. The Indian elephant has been captured, tamed and used in the service of man for at least two thousand years. Europeans have been associated with this for several centuries, yet the first recorded observation of rescue attempts came as late as 1867. Records are more common for the African elephant, yet Europeans have been killing elephants for at least a century, either in big game hunting or, more latterly, in culling excess numbers in parks and reserves. What this means in available statistics can be gauged by one record of a thousand elephants culled in one year (in the 1950s) in a single East African national park and by the figures given by E. C. Schillings, that the tusks reaching Antwerp annually, during the first year of the present century, represented 18,500 elephants.

Even if we disregard the many elephants that have been illegally killed for the ivory trade, there must still have been a large number shot by white hunters capable of recording a description, in their memoirs, or in the form of reports to scientific journals or letters to magazines. Yet the published records of elephants helping a congener are relatively few. From this we must suppose that most elephants shot or otherwise injured are not the subject of succour attempts. In that event, we can postulate that one or more elephants apparently attempting to lift a fallen comrade, impressive though this may appear, are exhibiting a form of infantile behaviour rather than adult actions based on reason or even compassion.

When a carcase of a dead elephant is dragged by the herd through the night, as described above, this is hardly a purposive action, but more to be compared with the behaviour of a female elephant that carried her small dead calf about, held under her chin, until it was in the final stages of decomposition. Female monkeys have been seen carrying the putrefying corpse of a baby monkey, and doubtless other similar examples of misplaced maternal instinct carried to excess could be cited.

Where, however, a wounded elephant is supported and helped into the bush there is the possibility that this is higher-order behaviour, with the further possibility of overtones of compassion and affection, carried out at personal risk, so that it constitutes a true altruism. In the present state of our knowledge this is about all that can be said. What the supposed rescues do reveal is the ability of elephants to work together as a team, in coordinated movements, comparable with those of dolphins. On the other hand, it should be noted that in two of the instances quoted in this chapter a man shot an elephant because it seemed to be sick or distressed. Apparently the elephant's companions had shown no concern for it, or none that was obvious, until a bullet had felled it. Then they tried to transport it to safety. This is contrary to so much of what will be said in later chapters of animals recognizing when one of their number is in distress.

In April 1931 Dr Sauvel, a veterinary surgeon in Saigon, and a friend found themselves in Cambodia tracking elephants for their tusks. One of them shot the leader of a herd of about sixty head, a large bull elephant with superb tusks. The bull lay dead on its left side, its long axis lying north to south. The rest of the herd fled in confusion. Sauvel and his companion were a long way from their base camp and to have taken the ivory then and there would have entailed a long trek through the night. They decided to bivouac about two hundred yards from the shot elephant, after having taken photographs. At twilight they heard the frightening trumpeting of the herd, then silence reigned and they fell asleep.

At one o'clock in the morning they were awakened with a start. The herd had returned. The shrill, prolonged trumpetings, the heavy resonance of trunks being banged on the ground, the breaking and snapping of the undergrowth, all told of the disturbed and angry reactions of the herd on finding themselves without the leader they had followed for so many years. The two men grabbed their rifles, retreated with the aid of an electric torch and scrambled up a tree, pelted by rain from a sudden storm and pestered by red ants and mosquitoes. Their guide talked interminably about the herd of female elephants returning to take the ivory tusks from their fallen leader, a piece of folklore found also in Africa.

Dawn came as a great relief, but when the party approached the spot where the elephant had been brought down, the corpse had vanished. For thirty yards around the spot the ground had been trampled to a morass. Their guide climbed a termite mound and located the corpse forty yards away, lying on its right side, its long axis now east to west. Presumably the herd had returned and found, as Sauvel put it, their leader unwilling to lead them or follow them, and they had tried to take him along with them.

Thanks to the rain during the night, it was possible to interpret readily the tracks and traces on the ground. Having tramped around the body of their fallen leader, wreaking destruction on the vegetation of the forest, seven or eight males (females of the Asian elephant are tuskless or nearly so) had knelt down on either side, pushed their tusks under the body and carried it fifteen yards before letting it down again on to the ground. The tracks showed this had been repeated four times at shorter intervals.

The tracks also bore witness to the prodigious efforts that had been made to transport the carcase of the bull, which Sauvel estimated to have weighed some four tons. They also showed that the dead beast had been carried erect, so that its feet dragged. The body was larded with stabs from the tusks of the elephants transporting it. This may have happened as they levered it into the upright position to transport it either resting on their tusks or held impaled on them.

Sauvel took a number of photographs both on the day the elephant was shot and on the following day. He commented that it had been his intention several months later to offer these and his story to those interested in animal psychology. The absence of irrefutable proof, however, inhibited this, although he did ultimately have enlargements made and he showed them at a *concours photographique*. He then realized that the pictures confirmed his written description as fully as could be desired.

Whether he ever published the pictures and where the negatives are now cannot be answered. Presumably this unique set of pictures must be in safe keeping somewhere, but after so great a lapse of time they may be almost impossible to locate. At all events, Sauvel seems to have been deterred from taking what can now be seen to be the most appropriate course, of giving them wide publicity, possibly from fear of incurring disbelief on the part of fellow scientists.

Apparently, although Sauvel's account is not wholly clear on this point, the 'rescue' attempt was not finally abandoned until four days after the fatal shot was fired. In any event, the whole episode suggests a remarkable solidarity within the herd which indicated a complete inability on the part of the elephants to recognize death when they saw it. They seem not to have linked the presence of human beings and the firing of a shot with the resulting immobility of their leader. That being so, we have to ask whether the violent reaction, which destroyed the undergrowth around where the dead elephant lay, was the result of fear, anger, frustration at the loss of a leader, failure to comprehend why he should lie inert when normally he would be on the move or a kind of mourning. The truth is most likely to rest with the third or fourth of these.

When we compare the rare occasions on which this behaviour has been observed with the large number of times elephants have been shot, it seems likely that this massive rescue attempt is made only when the deceased animal has been the leader of the herd. It is tempting also to compare what used to happen after a battle. The dead would be buried on the spot, while the body of a commander-in-chief would be carried away reverently for special burial.

One can only speculate, especially in view of the absence of photographic evidence. It has not been possible to trace the whereabouts of Sauvel's photographs, nor has it been possible to locate a film taken and shown commercially in the 1930s. It may be the same as the film mentioned earlier. Speaking from memory, this was part of a film sequence on African wildlife taken by a professional team (probably American). While they were filming a herd, one of the elephants charged the team and was shot by an armed guard, stationed to protect the photographers. The rest of the herd tried to raise their dead comrade with their tusks. The scene was filmed.

On 11 June 1977 a film of *King Solomon's Mines* was shown on British television. This included shots of African wildlife, one of which showed a herd of elephants. One of the herd charged the camera team, presumably, and was felled by a bullet. The rest of the herd gathered round the prostrate animal, and one of them was seen to push its tusks under the fallen animal in an effort to raise it. Others could be seen on the other side of the carcase, which obscured their actions. Then a second elephant charged, whereupon shots were fired into the air and the herd dispersed.

It is not unreasonable to suggest that, as with the succourant behaviour of cetaceans, the primary impulse in elephants to try to help a comrade on to its feet may be instinctive, but in emergencies this may be amplified into something having the appearance, at least, of an altruism. If so, then one needs to ask why such behaviour is not more general among mammals. A clue may perhaps be contained in an event reported in the Press on 4 July 1977.

Sunderkali (Beautiful Bud), a female elephant, pride of New Delhi's parades and wedding processions, stumbled and broke both bones in a front leg. We are told that, unable 'to support her four-ton weight on the three good legs, tears trickled down her face. She bleated nervously — and collapsed.' We are told also that an outraged public refused to accept the verdict that Sunderkali's condition was hopeless. Accordingly, specialists called in by Delhi Zoo and the Agricultural Ministry operated. Stainless steel pins were inserted into the bones after drilling and the leg encased in plaster. The elephant was given twenty-two quarts of sugar and salt solutions and antibiotics. She was lifted on to her feet by crane. Within twenty-four hours she was dead, allegedly from a heart attack 'caused by excitement and nerves'.

René Verhuyen, who studied hippopotamuses in Zaire, came to the conclusion that these animals, in fighting, endeavour to break an opponent's foreleg. He found that a hippo with a broken leg was doomed because it could not support its great weight on three legs. Perhaps the cause of Sunderkali's death was the broken limb and the animal's inability to support its great weight comfortably and adequately, in spite of the vets' ministrations and the steel rods. It is tempting to speculate that something like realization penetrates to an elephant's brain that the legs are their Achilles' heel. A prostrate companion would then appear to be bereft of the use of the legs, making, in the elephant philosophy, the need to lift it and transport it. Since most of these supposed rescue attempts are unsuccessful they would seem to have little survival value. Everything an animal does is supposed to have survival value at least for the genes of the animal in question, so abortive rescue attempts would be outside instinctive behaviour, the rescuers being urged on by a motivation in excess of the needs for personal survival, in a display of true altruism.

On this flimsy assumption the rescue attempts by elephants seem to verge on the altruistic.

6.
Graves
and
Graveyards

The question is sometimes asked: Where do all the dead birds go? Typically the questioner follows his inquiry with the explanatory comment that he lives in the heart of a large town, the windows of his flat look out on a sea of flat roofs, daily he sees scores of birds flying or hopping over the roofs and although dozens must die each year he never sees a carcase. The same question could be asked and the same comment added in slightly different terms by anyone living in a smaller town or in the countryside. Birds killed on the road must be exempted, for they are victims of the march of progress. Their corpses lie where they fall and are rapidly ground to dust by a never-ending procession of wheels.

One morning I noticed a hen chaffinch on the gravel path. It moved little as I passed near it. My curiosity was aroused, because it did not fly away, and as I watched it I saw it move over to where a mouse-hole opened in the side of the path. It crept in. I gently extracted it. It was listless. It remained so even in the warmth of my hands. So I put it down on the path several feet from the mouse-hole. It made at once for the hole and again crept in. Later that day it was dead. I have collected similar observations since then. So perhaps it is that animals creep into holes and corners or other sheltered places and die. Those, that is, that die of sickness, infirmity or old age, rather than by a violent death from a predator, fast-moving traffic or other accident. Do they merely seek a sheltered spot, away from unkind weather and from predators, as their metabolism wanes and their energy is lowered? Or do they actually feel the approach of death, as some humans seem to have done?

There used to be a saying in the Middle East that you never see a dead donkey. The same has been said in subsaharan Africa of elephants. There is something of a suggestion of mystery in these remarks. Yet neither is strictly true. Thus, a scientist doing field work in Africa came upon the carcase of an elephant, cause of death unknown. He diarized the sequence of events and found that in two weeks there was virtually no trace of the former mound of flesh and bones. First on the scene were the super-scavengers, the jackals, hyenas and vultures. They were followed by a variety of carrion-eaters of smaller sizes, including insects. Hyenas crunched the bones, except the skull, and rats gnawed what the hyenas left. The excrement from the scavengers and the detritus from their endless feeding fertilized the soil beneath and around the site of the carcase, and finally vegetation stimulated by the natural fertilizers grew up rank and tall, drawing a veil over any residue.

The real answer is that an animal dying in the open tends to be quickly eradicated. That would be the end of it, except that the final remains of elephants do not always disappear as rapidly or completely as this. In places their skeletons lie thick on the ground, half-a-dozen to scores within a limited area. The idea arose from such findings that these places were elephant cemeteries, that an elephant, with a potential life-span of three-score years and ten, on feeling the approach of death, goes to die on a spot favoured by generations of its forebears.

Animal cemeteries, if they exist, as well as funerals and graves, imply in the animals associated with them an ability to foretell death or at least to appreciate its approach, possibly to recognize it in their fellows. There is also a suggestion of respect, regard, even reverence for the dead. So far as elephants are concerned, this is part of a mythology that has grown up: elephants are highly intelligent, have long memories, die of a broken heart, will sit up all night practising a trick so as not to fail their owner, not to mention succouring injured comrades (See also chapter 5).

When he was in South America, Charles Darwin came across collections of skeletons of the guanaco, the wild llama. In his book *A Naturalist's Voyage*, published in 1845, he wrote:

> The guanacos appear to have favourite spots for lying down to die. On the banks of the St Cruz, in certain circumscribed places, which were generally bushy and all near the river, the ground was actually white with bones. On one such spot I counted between ten and twenty heads. I particularly examined the bones; they did not appear, as some scattered ones I had seen, gnawed or broken, as if dragged together by beasts of prey. The animals in most cases must have crawled, before dying, beneath and amongst the bushes. Mr Bynae informs me that during a former voyage he observed the same circumstances on the banks of the Rio Gallegos. I do not at all understand the reason for this, but I may observe, that the wounded guanacos at the St Cruz invariably walked towards the river.

He also recalled having seen, at Jagos on the Cape Verde Islands, 'in a ravine a retired corner covered with bones of the goat; we at the time exclaimed that it was the burial-ground of all the goats in the island'. The mention of the ravine raises suspicions that this could have been a treacherous spot where even the nimble-footed goat came to grief and, falling, added its bones to those already accumulating. The idea of special burial grounds for the guanaco was perpetuated by later naturalists, but then the truth emerged. The guanaco lives in the highlands. During severe winters it descends the slopes in search of food and takes up residence along the banks of the river where food is relatively plentiful but not sufficient for all, and so hundreds die.

The belief in guanaco burial-grounds has been forgotten long since. That of elephant cemeteries has persisted and is still a contentious topic. To begin with, the two words are not happy choices: to bury means essentially to lower something into the soil and cover it; a cemetery is a piece of ground set aside for burials. If elephants used cemeteries, in the strict sense of the word, nobody would know anything about it except by the accidental observation of an interment or through digging up the bones.

Undoubtedly, collections of elephant skeletons or parts of skeletons, especially of skulls, do occur in many places in subsaharan Africa. Several explanations have been advanced. One is that such spots mark the places where a herd of elephants has been surrounded by local hunters and slaughtered, their tusks taken and the carcases left to rot. It seems that a favourite trick used by African hunters was to set fire to the dry grass, encircling a herd within a ring of flame and then going in to kill. Another feasible explanation is that death has occurred in swamps that have since dried out exposing an accumulation of bones. An injured elephant will, where this is practicable, make for water in order to stand in it, spray itself and drink. The area might be swampy and the injured beast might be trapped, or alternatively the injuries might themselves prove fatal. In either event, wetlands stand the best chance of any terrain of accumulating skeletons.

In the *Journal of the Bombay Natural History Society* for 1946 are two photographs. One shows an elephant standing in a jungle swamp, up to its belly in water and with its left foreleg horribly swollen. The second shows the body of the same elephant lying half-submerged in water. There had been reports of much noise from elephants the day before and two were said to have been fighting. This presumably was the one that had the worst of the fight and retired to the swamp for a course of hydropathy.

Elephants need to enter water regularly to bathe and to maintain normal health. A natural impulse in all sick animals is to drink, perhaps to drink to excess and become bloated, thereby hastening their own demise. Elephants are no exception to this, which is another reason why a swamp would tend to be a repository for their skeletons, expecially one with treacherous areas of glutinous African mud causing a heavy beast like an elephant to sink with no hope of extricating itself. Rennie Bere, in his book *African Elephant*, has given instances of elephants attempting to rescue their companions from exactly this menacing situation. Not all such rescues have succeeded and it could be that one or more of the rescuers are also trapped, so adding to the number of eventual skeletons and thereby reinforcing the idea of a communal graveyard deliberately used.

It has further been suggested that mass deaths, providing materials for what appear to be communal burying grounds, may result from anthrax or some other epidemic disease. Deaths from drought should not be ruled out. Bere regards the African elephant as less skilled than the Indian species in carrying out rescues from swamps. Even so, he admits by implication that some attempts are successful while noting that frantic females sometimes push their calves farther into the mud while endeavouring to rescue them. Then he gives the remarkable escape of a near-adult bull in Kenya struggling to extricate himself from a steep-sided mud-hole. First, we are told, two young bulls arrived on the scene and examined the situation carefully. A third, older bull joined them and after much nervous trumpeting they were joined by others

1 Tree wasps' nest with two workers adding more paper to strengthen and enlarge it

2 Interior of tree wasps' nests with cells containing grubs that will later swell the ranks of the worker wasps

3 Jason, the boxer-cross, adopts as his close companion a bitch sheltie puppy

4 *Above right*: The all-purposes trunk of an African elephant allows greater opportunities for seemingly compassionate behaviour than in most animals

5 *Right*: In this posture, the potential use of trunk and tusks in lifting operations is made obvious

6 Julie and her companion, Leonardo, the Icelandic pony

7 Sheltie bitch and her puppy; even in dogs the face is the most sensitive area for showing affection

8 The water vole of Europe: one was seen carrying one of its blind offspring to water

9 Common rats have been described as diabolically clever

10 Nigerian hedgehog with spines half-raised in preliminary alert

11 12 *Right*: European hedgehog: *above* spines down in a relaxed mood; *below* spines bristling indicate disquiet

13 Sally's mournful expression never failed to elicit sympathy from passers-by

which arrived during the night. By morning the trapped bull was free. Apparently the trampling by so many elephants had resulted in the formation of a ramp and the tracks showed that, by pulling and pushing, the rescuers had dragged their unfortunate comrade free. In the absence of more details, one is tempted to wonder whether this particular rescue was not the result of good luck rather than skill, but at least it can be accepted as a bona fide attempt at rescue.

There are only two recorded examples of possible animal funeral processions and both are dealt with in my book *More Animal Legends*. The first concerns about a hundred stoats in twos following four carrying the dead body of another stoat. The story was published in the *Irish Times* and carried the comment that the legend of such 'funerals' is persistent throughout Eire. The second was contained in a letter to me from Major-General Corrie Hudson of a scene he witnessed in 1932 in India, of entellus langurs carrying a dead langur and followed by a procession of other langurs. The Major-General did not claim that this was an animal funeral, contenting himself with saying that there was the striking coincidence that this procession of monkeys was wending its way along the road towards a cemetery, and that it had almost the appearance of the kind of human procession so often seen going along that road.

David Stephens has reported seeing a vixen of the red fox retrieve the body of a cub that had been run over by a lorry and bury it, covering it lightly with earth. Since carnivores treat bodies of their own dead as carrion and eat it, and since foxes normally bury surplus carrion for later eating, this episode proves nothing.

Brian Vesey-FitzGerald has described a sow European badger burying the body of her dead mate. The sow appeared at the entrance to the set and uttered an unearthly cry. Then she went to a nearby rabbit warren and over a period of time dug a large hole. Some hours later a boar badger appeared. The sow stood still, nose lowered to the ground and back ruffling agitatedly. The boar approached her, also with snout lowered. The sow then moved her head rapidly up and down and uttered a whistling sound, at the same time moving forward with two jerky steps. When she stopped, the boar went through the same motions, after which both repeated the performance. The two badgers now disappeared down the set, to re-appear some time later dragging the body of a dead badger, the boar holding a hindleg, the sow somehow helping from behind. Thus they transported the corpse to the hole dug in the warren and covered it with soil. Then the boar departed and the sow went into the set.

It is always presumed that the normal burial of a dead badger is inside the set, the body being walled up in one of the several chambers. This is based on the frequency with which badger bones, especially skulls, are unearthed when a set is excavated. That burials may also be made outside the set is confirmed by two other observations, both in 1949, eight years after Vesey-FitzGerald published his remarkable observations. In that year Fred Dean saw a dead boar pushed out of the entrance to a set. It rolled down the slope. After this five loads of bedding were brought out by a sow and scraped over the corpse, the mound being finished with a covering of sand, earth and stones.

Equally deliberate was the action witnessed in the same year by C. T. Barlow. The body of a dead badger was this time interred under a mound when its living companion dug a circular ditch around it and threw the earth over it. The mound was finally tamped down to a smooth finish, looking like a prehistoric round barrow. Other supposed badger burials, sometimes accompanied by what appear to be ritual ceremonies, have occasionally been recorded, though it is unlikely that all dead badgers receive burial in this way.

Primitive peoples tend to garnish the graves of relatives with foliage or flowers, a practice taken to greater lengths in more sophisticated societies. Only one species of animal can be said to indulge in this and then only remotely: the African elephant. The evidence for this is scattered, anecdotal and somewhat conflicting.

John F. Burger, writing in the South African journal *Field and Tide* in 1962, remarked that one point on which every experienced elephant hunter is agreed is that elephants will often cover the dead bodies of their victims with grass or leaves. He then goes on to say that many hunters believe this is the elephant's way of showing sympathy or respect for the dead. There are also reports of elephants covering their own dead with vegetation. There seems to be a slight contradiction between the two statements. More importantly, there is the additional implication that elephants can recognize when an animal is dead. This conflicts with the known occasions when a herd has continued its rescue operations long after the companion they are trying to succour has died. It conflicts also with the first example Burger gave to illustrate his points, the case of Micky Norton.

Norton was a famous elephant hunter. On one occasion he shot what is described as a prize bull in a big herd. This time, it appears, the herd did nothing to succour their fallen leader but charged en masse and Norton was compelled to seek refuge. Nearby was a deep ravine with steep banks down which no elephant could descend with safety. Reaching the bottom, Norton ran along the ravine to hide under an overhang of rock. Eventually he was tracked down by a cow elephant and soon the whole herd was busy throwing branches and young trees into the ravine. In the end the fugitive hunter was imprisoned under many tons of timber and foliage and was forced to spend the night there. Rescue came the following morning with the arrival of his friends. No doubt Norton kept very still when he saw the first elephant approaching. He probably continued to do so as long as elephants were near his hide-out. The elephants may be forgiven if they considered he was dead and showered him with elephantine equivalents of wreaths.

Burger was taken to a place near Lake Katavi where a wounded bull had killed a mongrel dog and its African owner who had inflicted the wound. Both victims had been carefully covered with branches.

On another occasion he relates how, by the Lubudi River in Katanga, he sat high in a tree one morning watching a young bull elephant coming down a narrow path. This elephant was pulling down branches on either side of the path, for no more sufficient reason, apparently, than sheer *joi de vivre*, when suddenly he gave a loud squeal and swerved to one side. At the end of his trunk hung the uncoiled half of an enormous python. Anyone who has been near an elephant that has suddenly found a strange object looped over the end of its trunk will testify that the result is terrifying, especially when the animal is a large bull. The elephant's panic as it thrashes the air with its powerful trunk, in an endeavour to get rid of the encumbrance, is hair-raising at close quarters. We can accept Burger's word when he says the snake was dashed to the ground with great violence. The elephant then made sure of its unwitting tormentor by trampling the python to a pulp of paper thinness. But although it had been busy tearing off branches it made no attempt to cover this victim.

The third example given was of an elephant with her calf following some distance behind. A lion killed the calf, but within seconds the mother had turned, lifted the lion with her trunk and dashed him to the ground. She trampled his carcase into the ground and then rolled on it. Throughout the afternoon she stayed by the dead calf, then proceeded to tear down branches to cover what was left of the lion's carcase. She made no attempt to cover the body of her own calf.

There is an apparent contrast here with another report of a lion killing a calf and being forced by the mother to retreat, the elephant then covering the carcase of her baby with branches. This may be merely an example of a redirected response: the elephant would have covered the lion with branches had she been able to kill it. Instead she garnished her offspring's carcase.

The question of the association of elephants with portents of death has been further bemused by an account published in the *Malayan Nature Journal* in 1961, by H. M. Burkill, of the Botanic Gardens, Singapore, of an extraordinary series of events. Although these took place in 1939, Burkill had written a description of them in letters to his parents in England. Also, his final account was vouched for by his friend, Erroll Robey. Burkill had been told of a dead elephant that was a nuisance to the local people because of the stench from its putrefaction. He found the carcase, which was riddled with bullet holes, wedged in a drain four feet across and as deep, the dying elephant having evidently made its way along the ditch until it had become wedged.

He learned that the elephant was one of a small herd that had come in from the jungle to raid crops and the villagers had fired on it to drive the herd away. As the depredations were continuing Burkill replaced the wire fence, which the herd had trampled down to gain entrance, by a single strand of wire carrying inverted empty kerosene tins fitted with clappers on posts four feet high, stretched for about a hundred yards along the hillside. After a few days the herd found a way round the fence and continued to enter by this same way, which can be taken as evidence, together with other circumstances, that the same animals were paying the subsequent repeated visits that form the core of his observations.

The unenviable task of burying the carcase was duly accomplished and

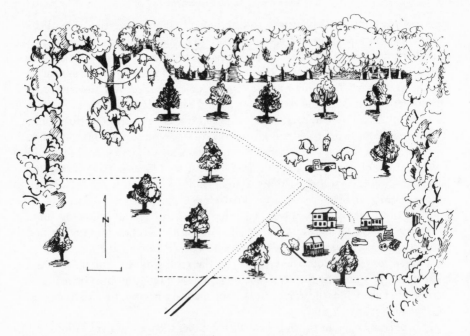

Fig. 10 Drawing based on H. M. Burkill's sketch of the incidents described by him in Malaya

Burkill took up residence in a nearby bungalow. He was therefore aware that for two months following the burial the herd visited the grave nightly. They tramped around the grave site, rubbed themselves on the trees, breaking some, knocking others down, and then departed. At the end of the two months the visits became less frequent. Finally, at intervals of a month and for a few nights each month, when the moon was full, the herd returned to repeat their macabre performance. The monthly visits went on for a year, and then the grave was exhumed to salvage the skeleton of the dead elephant which by now was cleaned of the flesh, for presentation to a museum.

There are other details in Burkill's account, but this is the main part of his story and it alone is sufficiently puzzling without complicating it further, except for one detail. When the bones had been removed, the lorry that had contained them was temporarily parked five miles from the grave site and two nights later the herd visited it, making just the one visit. It is unfortunate that this account had not been set down at the time of its occurrence, and in more complete detail. Nevertheless, Burkill's story adds one more facet to the apparent reluctance of elephants to abandon their dead. There is little more to be said about this particular series of incidents.

Spectacular though the events included in this chapter may be to those who have witnessed them, they do not provide material for precise scientific assessment. In general, however, they suggest that elephants have no premonition of death, do not always recognize death in their companions and make only clumsy attempts at rescue. Yet they give the impression of being capable of concern-showing behaviour and of something approximating to grief. Graves and graveyards seem at first sight not to be associated with altruism in any way, although among humans the burial of the dead has become a focus for sentiment of varying kinds. It can only be speculation whether very early man adopted burial for hygienic reasons, to remove the remains of a loved one from desecration by wild beasts or from a desire to show concern and respect.

So far as animals are concerned, where interment can be shown to be used hygiene would seem the most obvious motivation. On the other hand, the evidence from the badger rituals accompanying burial, as well as the scream that preceded one burial, suggests something more is involved than mere sanitation. The behaviour of Burkill's elephants takes us even further along this road. They seem to have continued their concern for the 'dear departed' for a longer period than was necessary if only hygiene was the motive. The covering of a corpse, whether of friend or enemy, with branches and foliage is too close to human customs to be wholly ignored.

At the very least, therefore, this subject should be included in a discussion on altruism if only because it leaves a sneaking suspicion in one's mind that burial may spring from a faint streak of concern-showing behaviour.

7.
Grief

One of my cousins, farming on the Isle of Wight, had an aged horse that was put out to grass. It spent much of each day standing beside a wooden post. The post itself was old and the time came when its rotted base gave way and it fell to the ground. The horse came to the spot as usual but there was no post to touch its flanks. The horse showed signs of moping. Its condition deteriorated and within a week it too was found lying on the ground beside the post, dead.

In December 1975 it was reported in the Press that Sandra, a twenty-five-year-old circus elephant, in Pisa, went on 'hunger strike' after her companion and trainer married. According to one report, on her last appearance she played the piano with her trunk and danced a little waltz, became too weak to carry on and died of a broken heart, 'in spite of intravenous injections and a jar of honey'.

The first of these two episodes speaks for itself. The second seems to be a garbled account of a similar event. Both suggest an animal dying of grief — but what is grief? Basically it is the reverse of joy, a depression of the spirits and a loss of vitality. It is a loss of hope, a feeling of emptiness of the environment, a loneliness, a loosening of the will to live, the result of something or some person importantly familiar that has gone, or appears to have gone, beyond recall.

Just as there is a diversity of definition, so grief can take many forms. Its most significant ingredient is the loss of some familiar object, for example a cuddly toy for a child, a close relative, friend or companion for an adult. This last sentence helps to set it in perspective, for a child's grief over an inanimate but treasured doll can be relatively as acute as the grief the child's mother would feel were she to lose her husband. If we can accept that a child of two is capable of grief, there is no reason to deny the same potentiality in a dog, say, of mature years. Grief, moreover, is likely to be deeper in a sociable animal, such as a person or a dog, than in a solitary animal, such as a cat. Certainly the most famous and numerous instances of 'faithfulness unto death' stem from dogs dying apparently of grief or showing seemingly protracted mourning.

Grief is a serious subject, a tragic theme, and animal grief is one that has never been the object of scientific investigation. As a result it is not possible to do other than quote instances from a variety of sources to see whether it is feasible to attribute grief to animals. They make up a heterogeneous collection.

For example, one of a pair of pigeons was killed by a passing vehicle in a

Fig. 11 A pigeon maintains vigil beside its dead companion

Birkenhead street. A passer-by, whether from compassion or a sense of tidiness, picked up the dead pigeon and placed it on a ledge above a shop window. The other pigeon 'kept watch' over it for hours each day until it had been reduced to a skeleton. Then it departed and was not seen at that spot again.

A barren nanny goat and a Flemish giant rabbit were close companions, often eating the same leaf, the rabbit sleeping between the goat's feet. A large cat killed the rabbit. The goat died a month later after showing a steady and marked deterioration in health.

In the *Countryman* for 1951, Elaine R. Bullard tells of two cows that had been brought up together from calfhood. Even the arrival of their offspring failed to separate them. One, however, reacted to the tuberculin test and was sent away. 'For several weeks the other was quite obviously heart-broken and would call at the cowshed door for her friend, tears streaming down her face.'

In 1953, a donkey in a small village near Milan ate nothing for five days following the death of its owner, Giovanni Conte, who had a great affection for the donkey and often took it into his house. It was present at his death and afterwards stubbornly refused to leave the death chamber, where it expired.

Two pet lambs and a pet pig were close companions. At night the pig slept between the lambs. One day loud screams were heard coming from the field where the sheep grazed. Investigation revealed the pig with its front feet on a dead lamb, its snout raised, giving forth the kind of squeals associated with a pig in distress. The dead lamb was not one of its companions but the pig refused to be comforted until they were brought to it and the dead lamb removed.

From Ireland, H. D. K. Money wrote of a swan (cob) that was rubbing its neck up and down a low bank and taking copious gulps of water. The cob's mate, the pen, stayed beside him. Both refused food thrown to them. For several days the neck rubbing continued, as well as the drinking, while the pen showed increasing anxiety and kept up a continuous clucking. On the sixth day the cob dragged himself up on to the bank, sank to the ground, his neck weaving round and round, and a sound came from him, 'haunting and pathetic, like the low moaning of wind'. An hour later he was dead. The pen came ashore and walked slowly round her mate, with spread wings. Then she closed her wings and stood motionless beside his corpse. Mr Money went over to drive away crows that had gathered and the pen slid into the lake. He buried the cob. For nearly a week the pen visited the spot, then she went away and did not return.

In 1961 Lt-Col. T. A. Weston wrote to me about one of his brother officers who, in Dar-es-Salaam, went out one afternoon to shoot guineafowl. He saw sitting in his path. Automatically he raised his double-barrelled, 12-bore shot gun and discharged both barrels into the lion's face. The lion lay dead. For weeks afterwards a lioness came every night to the spot where the lion was killed and 'wailed bitterly'.

Outside a village in India, twelve miles from Lucknow, two storks could be seen together in the paddy field at sundown. They had been there together for years. Then somebody shot one. The other remained there 'gradually wilting and finally dying' — of grief, it was presumed.

Aggie was a superannuated Dorking hen who had become a sort of pet wandering freely in the garden. But she was aged and almost totally blind. Nobody could pluck up courage to 'put her to sleep' and yet . . . Then it was that a bantam came to her aid by keeping constantly with her, shepherding her around, picking up food, placing it in front of her and clucking, as she would have done with a chick. The two were inseparable. They sunbathed and dustbathed together, walked around together, fed together, and at night the bantam led Aggie to her roost. Then Aggie died. The bantam would not eat, was dejected and ill-at-ease. Gradually the condition of the bantam hen deteriorated and in a week or so it too was dead.

These anecdotes amount to little more than natural history tittle-tattle. They are straws showing how the wind blows in the matter of loneliness and loss of companionship animals may suffer. The effects of these can be gauged by a series of horrible, yet scientific, experiments carried out a few years ago by Professor H. F. Harlow, S. Suomi and C. J. Domek. They selected four rhesus monkeys born within four days of each other, took them from their mothers at birth, reared them separately for fifteen days, then placed them together for ninety days in a large cage. After that they were alternately separated and placed together.

It can come as no surprise to be told that during the periods of separation from their young companions their reactions were almost identical with those resulting from the loss of their mothers! At first they showed high levels of such behaviour as locomotion, exploration of their environment and vocalization. Later, they just huddled themselves up and either rocked to and fro or remained passive. Repetition of this treatment showed that they never got used to the separation and severe loneliness. They were inconsolable. Moreover, by the time the monkeys were nine months old their social behaviour had advanced no further than that of a normal young monkey of three months of age.

In one sense these experiments were hardly necessary. One has only to read the evidence brought before the courts of cruelty to children, often by step-parents, and apply a little imagination to realize the trauma and the enduring terror engendered by isolation and loneliness and the ghastly effects absence of love and sympathy can produce, for humans and animals alike.

In 1954 a female dolphin was caught with a hook and placed in a tank in some marine studios in Florida. In her state of shock the dolphin was unable to keep afloat, so four large glass bottles were used to keep her at the surface, where she could breathe. For two days she floated helplessly, and there seemed little hope of her surviving. On the third day a healthy male of her species was introduced to the tank. In a matter of seconds the female began trying to swim. The bottles were removed and she began laboriously to swim round the tank, the male sometimes swimming under her and nudging her to the surface. The two dolphins became inseparable but two months later the female died, the male circling her at the moment of death and 'whistling constantly'. After this, he refused all food, swam ceaselessly round and round the tank, whistling most of the time, and died three days later.

A post-mortem examination revealed the presence of a perforated gastric ulcer. This may have been the cause of his death, the ulcerous condition being aggravated by his refusing to eat. Perhaps if post-mortems could have been carried out in all the other cases given here, some form of physical deterioration might have been found. The question remains, therefore, whether death from grief is more the result of existing ill-health or whether ill-health is the result of grief. It is worth noting in this connection that dolphins and whales, even those in prime good health, show a high incidence of ulcers of the digestive tract.

A general point to keep in mind is that not all species, even among the higher animals, show the same capacity for pining. Red colobus monkeys, for example, have the reputation for pining in captivity. They mope, lose condition and eventually die. So do some Black colobus, but not to the same marked degree.

The anecdotes recounted in this chapter may be tittle-tattle, but I am inclined to give them credence because of personal experiences. The first concerns a male rook and female crow, hand-reared from the fledgling stage. The rook came to us first. It had a large aviary and was later introduced to the crow. The rook courted the crow, in due course the two mated, the rook built a nest and the crow laid two eggs. Unfortunately, she sustained a prolapsed oviduct and, despite the ministrations of the vet, died in the nest. After the body was removed the rook retired to a perch in a corner of the aviary where for two days he looked the picture of misery and failed utterly to respond in his usual manner to our endeavours to raise his spirits. By the third day, he resumed normal living, as if nothing untoward had happened.

The next episode centred around a pair of magpies in an aviary overlooked from the house. I became aware that these two black-and-white figures were spending the whole of the day on the ground, in the grass at one corner of the aviary. Investigation showed that the female was dead, in a crouched position, and her body was removed. Her mate spent the next two days in that corner of the aviary, entirely lacking the vivacity characteristic of its species.

The third story is about an elderly Icelandic pony Leonardo and his equally elderly companion, a she-donkey named Julie. They had been constant companions for many years when the time came that Leonardo was so ill it was deemed kinder to have him 'put to sleep'. Julie was led out of the shed where Leonardo lay and taken across the field out of sight of the shed. Leonardo was shot, his body was carted away. Julie was released and literally ran across the field, unusual in any donkey and especially in this elderly lady. She ran into the shed and stood over the spot where Leonardo had lain when last she saw him. She appeared to be looking down. In less than thirty seconds she came out of the shed, raised her head so that her muzzle pointed to the sky and let out an anguished scream, quite unlike the usual voice of her species. The sound of her voice was eerie, agonizing, the kind of cry one does not wish to hear again.

Julie refused to eat, her condition deteriorated so that it looked as if she would die. Then someone suggested a companion, a Shetland pony. When the pony was first brought into the field Julie would have nothing to do with him. Soon, however, they became close friends and Julie is alive today, several years after Leonardo was wrenched from her.

The rook and the magpie probably recovered the more quickly because in adjacent aviaries there were other members of the crow family. Their human companions also tried to console them by paying more than usual attention to them. Julie was saved by the companionship of the pony.

A bereaved goose was revived in a quite unexpected manner. It was one of a pair of geese, and a fox took the gander. His mate followed the fox for a quarter of a mile, as the tracks showed, then became bogged down in the mud. A neighbour living near the spot heard the persistent honking, went out to investigate, at 4.30 a.m., rescued the goose and returned it to its owner.

Geese, we know, mate for life. They epitomize, in the world of birds, marital fidelity. There are known instances in which one partner of a mated pair dies and the other calls continuously for days on end. Here, then, if anywhere, we ought to expect some indication of grief at the loss of a partner. Geese also gave us our first insight into the phenomenon of imprinting. When a gosling hatches it becomes imprinted on the first thing it sees. This would normally be its parents. These it follows around, so imprinting is a natural method of keeping the young with their parents. If, however, its eyes first beheld a person, the gosling would tend to follow that person around as if tied to him by an invisible thread. A gosling has also been known to become imprinted on a wheelbarrow, the first object it saw after hatching. It rested beside it and followed it when the wheelbarrow was being used.

It so happened that the adult goose in our story, when it was returned to its owner, was placed on the ground beside a wheelbarrrow. She became imprinted. Except when grazing, she spent all her time sitting beside it. Anyone approaching the wheelbarrow was treated to an aggressive display, as the goose would have done had she had her partner with her. The goose 'talked' to the wheelbarrow before going off to graze. When someone took the wheelbarrow away, in the normal course of using it, the goose would follow honking and hissing, until the wheelbarrow was left stationary. There were occasions when the wheelbarrow had to be taken well away, out of sight of the goose. Then she would seek the company of the rear wheel of the car parked near the house.

The goose had its bereavement terminated by its inherited behaviour. The dog in our next story solved the problem for itself. It was a Labrador retriever which had lost its close companion, a terrier, by death. The two dogs had shared their food and kennel for years. When the terrier died the Labrador went off its food and refused to leave its kennel until the third day. Then, at sunset, it was seen to enter a neighbour's chicken run which, to everybody's knowledge, it had not entered before. It somehow managed to open the door and was next seen carrying a protesting pullet back to its kennel where it settled down for the night, blocking the entrance to the kennel with its own body. The next morning it took the pullet back to the run and from then on, evening and morning, it went through this set routine. The pullet took three days to settle to the routine; the dog ceased to mope.

Another dog had a remedy presented to it. Its mistress had suddenly to go to hospital. Her dog pined and refused to eat. Somebody recommended she should telephone her dog, which she did using a bedside phone. Her mother, at home, held the receiver to the dog's ear while the patient spoke to it, ending by telling him to go and eat his dinner, which he did quite happily. Each evening the dog's mistress telephoned at about the same time and with the same result. Indeed, each day he refused to touch his food until he had heard her voice. And if he reached the telephone first he would rear up on his hind legs and try to lift the receiver!

Anyone who supposes that the last piece is too much to swallow cannot have seen the BBC1 programme *That's Life* on 27 February 1977. This showed a spaniel that had developed an aversion to the telephone ringing. First it barked, then it went to the instrument, lifted the receiver and left it dangling on its cord.

While searching for possible examples of grief I came across a letter in *Animals* for 1965 from Chandrakant E. Shah, of Thike, Kenya, who wrote: 'A dwarf mongoose had entered a gutter full of mud and water, and died there, probably as a result of suffocation; some children put its body on the open ground; a few minutes later another mongoose came and stayed near its dead companion as if mourning. In spite of my approaching very close it did not move away. I think this is an example of affection in animals.'

A photograph of the incident was published with the letter. This showed two species of mongoose, one dead, lying on its back, which is almost certainly a White-tailed mongoose (*Ichneumia albicauda*), and a live Dwarf mongoose (*Helogale parvula*). The Dwarf mongoose was seen in the photograph to be resting its chin on the corpse of the White-tailed mongoose in a manner reminiscent of the dog in Landseer's painting with its chin on its master's coffin. This is an action typical of the domestic dog — usually it rests its chin on one's knee — when showing affection or expressing supplication. If Landseer and others are to be believed, it can also be associated with grief.

Chandrakant E. Shah mentions the word 'companion', which might mean that the two animals were pets and had been close companions. At all events there seemed to be too many improbabilities in the story and the picture until 1976, when Anne Rasa of the Max Planck Institut published the results of her observations in *Zeitschift für Tierpsychologie*. In this she put it beyond reasonable doubt that dwarf mongooses, which live in small packs, show consideration for the elderly and sick members of the pack. They let such a member feed first, they groom it and lick it to keep it clean, huddle to keep it warm and regulate their daily habits to give it least inconvenience. It could well be they also show grief when such a member dies, although this has not been established scientifically.

If ever a piece of what I have called natural history tittle-tattle was justified by subsequent scientific investigation it is the story from Kenya of the two mongooses.

Grief, like generosity, affection, devotion, loyalty and the other behavioural traits that make up the category labelled 'finer feelings', can be less satisfactorily assessed by scientific method than by commonsense. Insofar as it is associated with these finer feelings it deserves to be considered within the context of altruism. As to the commonsense approach, we can make a reasonable assessment on the basis of our experience with human grief. Some people, when bereaved, show a brave face to the world, so that even their close associates are not aware of the depth of their grief except as it is revealed over the subsequent years by small actions and words let slip. Others express their grief so obviously as to leave the onlooker no doubt. Some people 'go off their food', others become afflicted with ravenous appetites. There are also numerous examples of idiosyncracies arising from a deep grief.

A woman lost her favourite son out of five when he was killed in action in 1917 in the grievous First World War. Before enlisting, the young man hung his bicycle in the shed to preserve the tyres. His mother allowed no one to use the bicycle, which was still there when she died over fifty years later, in her mid-nineties. Another woman, a widow living on her own, once asked a neighbour to help her by carrying some coal to the cottage from a shed twenty feet or more from the house, at the other end of the garden. While doing so he noticed another shed near the back door. He suggested she should keep her coal in that, where it would be readily available. 'I couldn't do that,' replied the woman, 'that is my brother's toolshed.' 'I did not know you had a brother,' replied the man. 'No,' said the woman, 'he died many years ago.'

Such examples serve perhaps to emphasize that human grief is like animal grief except it is worse, because we can think back to happier times past and forward to emptier times ahead.

There was a striking sequel to the story of Julie's attachments, mentioned earlier in this chapter, which contributes significantly to our discussion. Several years after the death of Leonardo, during which Julie and the Shetland pony had been close companions, the pony needed the services of a vet. The pony was led out of the paddock and taken to a disused stable. As the vet was examining the pony he happened to look out, through the open door of the stable, and saw Julie walking quickly down the slope from the paddock. When she reached the stable and saw the pony she turned and quietly grazed until the pony was led back to the paddock, when she followed.

When Julie was first seen coming down the slope it was suspected that the gate to the paddock had been left open when the pony was led out. Investigation showed that the gate was securely shut and that there was no obvious point at which the donkey could have made an exit from the paddock. It can only be supposed that she had made a super-asinine effort and jumped the fence. It can be confidently said that this was the first time she had escaped from the paddock and the fact that she had done so shows the depth of her feelings for her companion. The whole episode suggests also that she still remembered her trauma at the loss of Leonardo. Perhaps there is more to the devotion of Greyfriars Bobby (mentioned in the next chapter), and other instances of fidelity, than has been credited here!

8.
Faithful
Dogs

In January 1977, *Komsomalskaya Pravda* printed the story of an Alsatian bitch that had been left behind by her owner at the Vnukovo airport at Moscow. For two years the dog had lived near the airport, running to meet planes as they landed. It seems that she refused to be handled. Finally, the owner was traced to Siberia and admitted to abandoning the dog because he had no veterinary certificate for her. When the story was published *Komsomalskaya Pravda* received 3470 letters from people offering a home for the dog.

About the same time film was shown on BBC television of a dog named Winston whose owner, it was said, was killed in a road accident at a crossroads in Bradford-on-Avon, in Wiltshire, England. For seven years the dog had haunted the crossroads, allegedly waiting for his master.

It would have been difficult to find out whom to write to in the Soviet Union for details of the Alsatian, but in reply to a letter I sent to the BBC they kindly supplied the name of Mrs Dorothy Power, of Bradford-on-Avon. She was good enough to reply and gave me details about Winston:

> Winston is a golden labrador who has made his home at the Bradford Leigh crossroads and has been there for about five or six years. When he first appeared there he would not allow any humans to approach him. He stayed all day and night at the crossroads, just moving his position according to the sun or seeking natural shelter in inclement weather. Eventually local people provided him with a fibre-glass kennel. Local people had been feeding him for a long time also but he would never come to take any food, no matter how tempting the morsel, the offering had to be placed on the ground and when the donor had retreated a safe distance, Winston would come and investigate. Over the years, though, Winston has mellowed and now will sometimes allow people to stroke him, particularly children, indeed local rumour has it that he has become so friendly that last year he sired a litter of pups! He makes frequent forays to the local hospital, which is near the crossroads. He receives Christmas cards and is a well-known character in his own right, since his fame spread via local and national newspapers, *Nationwide* and John Craven's *Newsround*; motorists stop in Bradford asking for directions to go and see him. Even the RSPCA came to see him and went away assured he was better cared for than many a family dog.
>
> There are two explanations as to why he stays where he does. The favourite one is that his owner was killed in an accident at the crossroads and the dog has refused to leave the crossroads ever since. The other is that he was bought as a gun-dog, when very young, by Mr Alex Moulton, CBE and disgraced himself and Mr Moulton by being gun-shy when taken out for the first time on a shoot

and then ran off and became wild. To my knowledge, neither version has been verified.

I wrote to Mr Moulton asking if he would be good enough to send me the true facts about the presence of Winston at the crossroads. He generously gave me the details in full:

> In April Mr Moulton was looking for a Labrador gun-dog. A friend told Mr Moulton about a black labrador named Bruce who belonged to a shoot in South Devon which was being closed down. It was understood that the dogs belonging to the shoot were to be put down if good homes could not be found for them.
>
> Mr Moulton travelled with Mr W. Curtis (who acts as a spare time keeper on The Hall Estate) to Devon where he met Mr Taylor, the keeper, and after seeing Bruce agreed to take him. He was also shown Winston, a golden labrador, and as the keeper confirmed that this dog was to be put down Mr Moulton agreed to take him in addition to Bruce in order to save him. The dogs were loaded into Mr Curtis' dog-carrying trailer and brought back to Bradford-on-Avon.
>
> When the trailer door was opened at The Hall Bruce stayed but Winston took off across the Estate. Mr Moulton and Mr Curtis went after him but in the end lost track of him after he had swum the River Avon. The police were informed and the search continued for several days.
>
> Eventually Winston appeared at Woolley Green Farm, where he was sleeping in the hay barn of Mr Singer, the owner. Mr Curtis went to the farm but the dog would not be handled by anyone. The police were informed of the whereabouts of the dog and the RSPCA inspector was called in. It was suggested that the dog should be put down, but Mr Singer was quite happy for Winston to stay on his farm where he was being fed and was not making a nuisance of himself.
>
> Some time later Winston started to spend a lot of his time at the crossroads where he received food and a lot of attention from passers by and eventually a great deal of publicity from the media.
>
> Winston has the choice of a secluded kennel or the hay barn, he is regularly fed by a lady dog-lover.

On the face of it, and prior to Mr Moulton's letter, it looked as if we had here two similar stories of canine devotion. In fact, they are very different stories, assuming that the details of the Moscow Alsatian, as given here, are correct. One story is of devotion and fidelity to a person, the other is of devotion and fidelity to a home or place, by a dog that has gone feral.

There must have been many instances of dogs showing spectacular devotion to a human being. Some no doubt were genuine, others may have been examples of dogs, like Winston, having gone feral and settled down in one spot. We know that dogs do return to the wild, even in over-settled England. If not disturbed by people living nearby, such dogs may establish sleeping places which they return to and continue to occupy for years. Normally their resting places are in woods or other places tolerably free of human beings. Sometimes a feral dog may be 'adopted' by local residents to the extent of their putting out food for it. The famous 'Surrey Puma' proved in the end to be one such. There must be other feral dogs, especially in built-up areas, that are collected as strays and eventually 'put to sleep'. No local legends grow up around them and their stories have no news-value, so most people hear nothing about them.

The most famous dog belonging to the other category, of alleged devotion to human beings, was Greyfriars Bobby, whose fame has spread around the world. Books and articles have been written about him and a Walt Disney film was made of his history. The details differ markedly from author to author, but the following account is correct in principle.

Bobby, as he was first named, was a Skye terrier that lived as a puppy in a farmhouse on the Pentland Hills about the middle of last century. He became attached to his owner's shepherd, John Gray, known to everybody as Auld Jock. When old enough Bobby accompanied the shepherd to his work on the hills each day, and once a week on his visit to the Edinburgh sheep market. On market days it was the shepherd's habit, as the gun on Edinburgh Castle proclaimed the hour of one o'clock, to go to the Greyfriars dining-rooms. There the terrier sat beside him and shared his dinner.

At last, Auld Jock had to retire, stricken with infirmity, and the terrier was taken back to the farmhouse on Pentland Hills. The next day he escaped and made his way to the sheep market and the dining-rooms, to find the shepherd who decided to care for him until the next market day, so he took the terrier home to his lodgings. A few days later Auld Jock died. Forty-eight hours later, neighbours found the body, with the Skye terrier standing guard over it.

When Auld Jock was laid to rest in the Greyfriars Churchyard, the terrier followed the bier, but after the burial service the dog was driven from the cemetery, as dogs were not allowed in it. As soon as it was dark, the terrier crept back into the cemetery and spent the night on his master's grave. Next day, the caretaker of the cemetery tried to drive the terrier from the churchyard, but the dog hid under a tombstone where he could still see the grave. For some weeks he hid under the tombstone by day, coming out as darkness fell to lie on the grave.

One day, to everybody's surprise, Bobby turned up at the Greyfriars dining-rooms, bedraggled and starving. The proprietor washed and fed the forlorn terrier. He would have liked to adopt the dog, but it insisted on returning to the churchyard. Every day at one o'clock, however, Bobby went to the dining-rooms to be fed. Later, the caretaker of the churchyard relented and allowed the dog to remain in the cemetery.

There came a time when the police had orders to catch all stray dogs in the city. Bobby was taken, but the Lord Provost of Edinburgh, hearing of this, paid his licence and presented him with a collar inscribed: 'Greyfriars Bobby. From the Lord Provost, 1867. Licensed.' The dog was allowed to go back to the churchyard where he spent a total of nine years.

The fame of the faithful terrier spread and among those who heard his story was the Baroness Burdett-Coutts. When Greyfriars Bobby died, in 1872, she had a statue made of him, which stands at the end of George IV Bridge, opposite the entrance to Greyfriars Churchyard.

This is a touching story, told here as briefly as possible. Yet although no one would wish to detract from the dog's fidelity, it must be conceded that the dog did not die of grief or pine away. It lived for another nine years and died at the age of fourteen, which is an advanced age for a dog. The terrier had the good sense to look for its dead master in the one place where it would find food, and the cold analysis must be that Greyfriars Bobby felt grief at the death of the old shepherd and this became sublimated to an attachment to a home or place, combining in principle the motivations of the Vnukovo airport Alsatian and Winston of Bradford-on-Avon, and many other dogs in history in many parts of the world. For example there was the tramp-dog of Quebec which, having seen his master's departure by sea, met vessels arriving at the quay for five years, refusing all offers of help or shelter and affection, and finally died of a broken heart, so it is said.

It must be wholly a matter of opinion how far grief can be regarded as altruistic. Queen Victoria mourned the early death of her beloved husband, Prince Albert. She withdrew from public life. She commanded that the Prince's room should be left exactly as it was, in every tiny detail, at the moment of his death. Except for the promptings of her ministers, this state of affairs would have continued until her own death. As it was, she was persuaded to re-emerge into public life, to fulfil her duties as Queen and Empress, and to complete one of the most memorable reigns in British history. The partnership of Victoria and Albert can be ranked as one of the great love stories of all time, to join the other great love stories of Tristan and Isolde, Romeo and Juliet and a dozen others. What is certain, since Victoria reigned for sixty years, is that she did not die of a broken heart, nor did her profound grief shorten her life.

To say this is not to detract in any way from the sublime devotion she showed to the memory of the man she loved. Nor does anything said here detract from the devotion of Greyfriars Bobby. Even the tramp dog of Quebec lived for five years after the departure of its master. If either of these retained an evergreen memory of its master, as Victoria probably did of Albert, until death overtook it, then dogs are capable of longer feats of memory than that with which they are normally credited. That is, however, another story (see chapter 21).

As we have seen in chapter 7, apparent grief in animals, with dejected posture and loss of appetite, lasts typically two to three days in birds and a few days longer in mammals, after which either the animal dies or recovers full normality to all appearances. During the period of dejection and fasting, the animal is acting to its own detriment in the cause of another entity. Since this is the accepted definition of altruism, couched in other words, grief can be accepted as a kind of altruism.

Perhaps a better example than either of those so far quoted, of devotional 'grief' in a dog, is found in the story of the Gough memorial. Helvellyn is one of the highest mountains in England, in what is now called Cumbria. There, where the Striding Edge path reaches the summit plateau, is the Gough memorial, a plaque fixed in 1890 in memory of a dog. The details of the event are totally obscured by time and other circumstances. Sir Walter Scott wrote a poem about it. Wordsworth also wrote a poem about it, eight verses of eight lines each in what must be the most atrocious piece of poetry he ever published. Several artists, including Landseer, reconstructed the scene in oils. Articles have been written about it in a number of magazines. Several people, during the hundred years that followed the event, spent much time trying to learn the truth of it. All differ in the details of what happened to the man and what followed his death. All differ in the kind of dog that accompanied the man and how it survived. All these contradictions and uncertainties are dealt with by Frank Haley in an article in the *North West Monthly* for January 1950.

So far as can be gleaned, an unfortunate young man named Charles Gough died, or fell to his death, or died while painting a canvas, in 1805 during severe wintry weather in April at a spot noted for its atrocious weather conditions at times. His body was eventually found, three months later, still being guarded by his faithful but emaciated dog, most likely a terrier. Wordsworth speaks of 'A human skeleton on the ground', suggesting that the dog may have fed on the corpse, although the 'emaciated dog' of other writers belies this. The truth will never be known.

If what is said here appears to under-rate the accounts of dogs' devotion to their owners, the balance can to some extent be restored by the story recounted by Edward Jesse in his *Gleanings in Natural History*, published in 1843. This tells of a woman lost in a snow-drift. She was not found for three days and was then frozen to death. Beside her was her mongrel dog. Only when the news had reached the village where the woman lived did people recall how on the evening of the snowstorm the dog had been in the village and 'by importunate whinings and by pulling at their clothes had in vain endeavoured to get some of the poor woman's neighbours to go with him to her assistance'. Had the snow persisted, yet another emaciated dog might well have been found eventually beside the body of its owner. It is tempting to regard this as highest-order behaviour, exceeding the higher-order behaviour of Greyfriars Bobby, the tramp-dog of Quebec and the dog of Helvellyn.

An anonymous author in the *Journal of the Bombay Natural History Society* for 1946 speculates on how far any animal can recognize death or the imminence of it. He continues: 'nevertheless I think it possible, that an animal, while in full health, may realise, in his last moments, that his dissolution is imminent. When this happens a number of animals give a peculiar cry, quite different from any cry they have made hitherto. They make it only once in their lives, immediately preceding death.' This recalls for me the legend of the Swan Song.

The writer goes on: 'I have heard this death cry most frequently uttered by boars: this is no doubt due to the fact, that when pigsticking the circumstances of death are such as to induce the cry. I can recall the death cries of stags and horses. The latter is an excruciating sound which haunts one.' (Compare the case of Julie in chapter 7.)

Then he asks the question: 'How can one explain the death cry? Are we to be satisfied with instinct as an answer? Excessive fear is ruled out by the boar's behaviour at the time.'

It may be wandering a little, but not too far, from the subject to speculate on how far the higher animals may be conscious of the imminence of death or are capable of recognizing death in others.

One of my early, but still vivid, recollections takes me back to when I was about ten years of age. I was staying with relatives in a village in the south of England. To the south of the village the fields sloped down to a valley. On the rising ground beyond was a farmhouse where lived a Mr Jacob Legge. On this morning, across the quiet countryside came the mournful howling of a dog. A voice beside me said: 'Farmer Legge must be dead.' It was my cousin, several years my senior, who spoke. She explained that Mr Legge had been ill for a week and that he must have died, since his dog was howling. True to prediction, news soon reached the village that Mr Legge was dead and that he had breathed his last at about the time I had heard his dog's mournful howling.

I have met this sort of thing many times since, usually in rural areas, where the silence is such that a dog's howl can be heard over a distance. It may be that country people, in former times at least, were more superstitious than town-dwellers; or it may be that, living close to nature as they do, they are more receptive to natural sounds and their interpretation. At all events, I have the impression that the idea of a howling dog presaging the death of a human is deeply rooted in country lore.

There was a shepherd, for example, who befriended a homeless dog. The two became much attached to each other, though the dog was never allowed inside the house, nor did it attempt to enter it, but lived in a kennel in the garden. Then the elderly shepherd fell ill and died within a few days. At more or less the exact moment of his ceasing to breathe, the dog entered the house, made its way to the foot of the stairs leading to the bedroom, sat on its haunches, raised its head and howled in a wailing voice three times. Then it left the house and went back to its kennel.

A friend of mine, when I retold this story, said that his spaniel seldom barked, but at 3 a.m. one morning it barked, which was unusual, and the bark was unusual. My friend remarked that he was puzzled; but at breakfast time that morning came the news that his father had died suddenly during the night. The dead man and the spaniel had had little to do with each other. Coincidence? There must be numerous stories to this same effect. Doubtless some of them represent coincidences, and perhaps most of them do, but the more striking of them seem to rule out mere coincidence.

The autumn issue of *The Countryman* for 1976 carried a letter on the subject. In the Spring issue for 1977 two more letters were published. One told of a man who left his spaniel in the care of his parents when he went to the war in 1914–18. The dog 'howled through the nights' before word came that his master was 'missing, believed killed'. The other told of Irish setters that slept in kennels some distance from the house and normally made no noise during the night. On the night the father of the writer died they howled continuously from 7.30 p.m., when he was taken ill, until 10.30 p.m. when he died. There followed an editorial note that several other readers had written with similar accounts.

A number of animals seem to use forms of sensory perception unusual in man. Some animal psychologists have suggested that the human race, possibly in the course of civilization, may have lost certain perceptivities which ancestral men possessed and which are still in use in animals, especially in mammals. The senses are still there but their acuteness has been blunted or their use supressed entirely. A particularly striking example is seen in homing, most familiar to us in birds, but cats, dogs, horses and hares, as well as birds, have been shown positively to perform remarkable feats of homing. Other mammals, including humans are suspected of possessing similar abilities. Thus, the pygmies of the Ituri forest, in tropical West Africa, Siberian tribes and Lapps, seem to show similar abilities, if reports are to be believed, and so have occasional individuals of industrialized nations. The ability may conceivably vary with the individual, in animals, possibly with the breed as in dogs. Even those human beings in whom this 'gift' can be demonstrated are unable to say how or by what means they can home unerringly from a distance through strange terrain. When asked how they do it they merely show surprise at the question.

Again, the difference between a dog's hearing and our own needs no stressing with anyone who has kept a dog. A telling example has been given of a Jack Russell terrier and a rhesus monkey that spent their days together in a vet's office in a building next to a busy main road. When their owner's car reached a crossroads twenty yards away the dog would bark and the monkey hoot, both having recognized the sound of his car through the roar of traffic.

Another example is given by R. H. Smythe, veterinary surgeon and author of books on animals, who acquired an overgrown garden in Cornwall which he intended to use as a boarding kennel. He imported stone from the local mines and this was cemented over to make an exercise ground. When dogs were taken to it they would stand shivering, their coats would stand on end, with every sign of acute fear. A local theory had it that the owner of the house to which the garden was attached had committed suicide and that the house had then stood for a long time unoccupied and haunted. Some years later it was realized that the stone from the mines was radio-active.

In *The Complete Dog* the story is told of how, in 1947, a man left his home in southern Scotland to fetch his mother and brother, who were coming to stay with him for the New Year. He left his wife at home with their three dogs lying asleep in front of the fire. At 4.20 p.m. all three dogs suddenly jumped up, with their hackles up. They ran to the front door barking as though somebody had come to the door. It later transpired that the car driven by their owner, with his mother and brother as passengers, had crashed at that time, the mother being killed, the two brothers seriously injured.

Another respect in which the acuteness of senses of dogs is beyond human computing is in the sense of smell. We can, however, appreciate how much it is beyond our estimating by the anecdotes just related for hearing, detection of radio-activity and the unknown sense that told of the road accident. A dog recognizes its human companions by smell. It may bark aggressively at someone it knows well but who has just appeared wearing a new suit, yet drops its aggression as it draws near that person to investigate with its nose.

Basing our deductions on these anecdotes, we may assume that some animals can be aware of events or situations, at a distance or near at hand, through the senses of smell, hearing and sight as well as through other channels or sense-organs, of which we are largely ignorant or are incapable at present of comprehending adequately. We would have to assume the existence of these things, even in the complete absence of evidence, as an explanation for what look like authentic instances of care-giving behaviour by animals.

The traditional howling or barking of dogs offers another link in the chain. Animals, and especially social animals, must be acutely aware all the time of what the other members of the group are doing or how they are behaving. We can visualize their sensory channels being continually bombarded with signals, olfactory, auditory and visual. The brain will be selecting and filtering these, just as we do not notice the ticking of a clock until suddenly it stops, because our brain is filtering environmental sounds and alerting us only for something unusual.

To answer the question why the dead shepherd's dog should have come into forbidden territory to howl, or Farmer Legge's dog should have indulged in a bout of howling, we have to understand the function of a howl. The domestic dog is almost certainly no more than a domesticated wolf. A group of wolves about to set out on a hunt will gather together, sit on their haunches, point their noses to the sky and howl in chorus. This serves the purpose of putting each member in the proper mood for the work they have in hand. A wolf that loses track of the rest will sit on its haunches, point its nose skywards and howl. The response of the others tells him where they are even though it cannot see them. This helps the lone wolf out of a difficulty or perplexity, or out of a distressing situation.

Years ago, while I was still living at my parents' home in London, our dog went temporarily missing. Search was made for him and he was found at a busy crossroads, with heavy traffic in four directions. This was before the days of traffic lights, when confusion sometimes reigned at such a crossroads. When we found the dog he was sitting on his haunches at the centre of the crossroads, with his nose directed towards the sky, howling, while cars, lorries and buses swirled around him.

This, it seems, could be the interpretation of a dog's howling when it coincides with the death of a person: the dog realizes, by one means or another, that something unusual has happened, that it is itself distressed by the change, and uses the only means it has to announce its own perturbation. It would mean also that the animal can be aware of distress, as represented by a radical change in its well-being, in another. From that could stem the first possibility of making a move to help.

Probably in no other area is the association between animals and human beings so close as in the use of guide dogs for the blind. For many centuries sightless people have had dogs as their guides and companions, but the first recorded attempt to train dogs methodically for guide work was in the eighteenth century, when a Paris hospital provided blind patients with dogs to lead them through the streets. The idea passed to Austria and Switzerland, but little was done until the First World War. In 1916 large-scale training was begun in Germany to provide guides for the many blinded in the war. Since then the movement has spread to Britain and North America and, from a purely scientific point of view, the associations dealing with guide dogs must have an accumulation of data that would be worthy of closer analysis. Meanwhile, two generalizations are possible that are helpful in this present discussion.

It has been said that the bond between guide dogs and their blind owners is so strong, while they are working together, that it is not uncommon for the physical well-being of the one to affect the health of the other. There are said to be instances of a dog becoming physically ill when its owner is sick. This seems to be based on one instance only, when the owner and the dog were afflicted with diarrhoea at the same time.

The working life of guide dogs is usually eight to ten years, so that most have a few years of active life left on being retired. Most often they settle down contentedly to a well-earned rest. Some, however, are said never to stop pining for their former companion and have to be 'put out of their misery'. Here again, it is not possible to find confirmation of the story.

According to Mr D. G. Carver, Director of Training for the Guide Dogs for the Blind Association in Great Britain, to whom I addressed my inquiry, there is general agreement that Labradors, the breed mainly used as guide dogs, show less of a link with their owners than other breeds that have been used. There are stories of guide dogs sensing fire and waking their owners, but the same is known for ordinary pet dogs and cats. One such guide dog not only did this but was credited with going into water, when called by its owner, who had lost his sense of direction while swimming, and guiding him back to the bank. There has been little scientific analysis of this extra behaviour of guide dogs, although Mr Carver expressed the opinion that he could imagine that 'with a good foundation for the relationship a dog would in its own way try to prevent a blind owner from getting into a situation whereby injury, pain or discomfort, *which I am sure the dog recognizes* [my italics], followed'.

On the whole, the manner in which guide dogs of any breed are treated on their retirement is such as to minimize ill-effects due to a change of ownership. Special care is given because the possibility of a sad development, with the dog looking unhappy, refusing to eat and losing condition, is recognized.

There is, however, another possible area to which the alleged howling of dogs presaging a human death could belong and for this I invoke two personal experiences. The first occurred in 1947, the second in 1958. Both were linked with the death of a person that was dear to me.

In 1947 I was at the theatre. The curtain was about to go up when there appeared before my eyes, on the proscenium curtain it seemed, as if on a giant television screen, a funeral party at a graveside. At that moment the auditorium lights began to dim, for which I was thankful for the tears were coursing down my cheeks uncontrollably. I knew, also, in that infinitesimal moment whose funeral it was. I had been at his bedside the day before, but there was no hint of his imminent demise. His medical specialist had pronounced that his life-expectancy was two months to two years, 'probably the latter'. His funeral took place less than a week later and the scene at the graveside was surprisingly like the picture I had seen. If this was only a hallucination, a figment of my own imagination, it is surprising there should be associated with it sufficient emotion to make me weep in public, which I had not done since I was a small boy.

In May 1958 I had a mental picture of a funeral procession drawn up at the gates of a large country house I was proposing to buy. This mental picture, which again only lasted for an infinitesimal moment, was repeated on sporadic occasions throughout the next seven months. One thing that struck me was that although it was a picture of a funeral procession, there was no hearse. The recurrence of this picture caused me no disquiet and when I confided in my brother-in-law, the only person to whom I mentioned this phenomenon, I laughingly suggested it must represent my own funeral, since I could not see the hearse. In late December my mother-in-law died, quite unexpectedly, in a nursing home nine miles away, to which she had gone merely for a rest. When the funeral took place, the mourners left what was by then my gateway in a line of cars. The hearse met us at the crematorium.

These experiences are, for me, inexplicable except as manifestations of precognition. They are, however, very real and vividly remembered to this day. If this can happen to a human, can we be so sure that something comparable may not happen to some dogs? It need not occur in all. For some dogs are known to home over long distances as can some humans: and nobody has yet given an adequate explanation for that.

9.
Helping the Blind

One of the most enduring stories about animals apparently showing compassion is that of a normal rat leading a blind rat, each holding one end of a straw or a slender twig. I call it 'compassion' because that is what it used to be called, and I have for twenty years stored records of it in a file thus labelled. These records are in the form of newspaper clippings, unsolicited letters and entries in books on the countryside. The observers in all instances have been laymen, usually farm labourers or farmers, certainly not professional zoologists. The stories therefore tend to be suspect, although one is struck by the repetition and the constancy of the reports.

Then came the time when I travelled to Bristol to take part in the BBC's *Living World* programme. Also taking part was Eric Simms, and he and I travelled back from Bristol in the same train. We had not met before and the conversation was somewhat desultory, although interesting because it was confined to the field of natural history. When we were about halfway to London, Simms electrified me by telling of an adventure he had had, with a companion, when they saw two rats walking along, one holding on to the tail of the other. His companion was carrying a shotgun which he fired, killing both rats. On examination one rat was found to be blind in both eyes.

I do not recall what led to the telling of the story, but I do recall that Simms seemed to be speaking rather on the defensive, as if he expected to be disbelieved, and he appeared to show a measure of relief when I started to catechize him. In truth, I had long hoped to meet somebody who claimed to have witnessed this event, in order to cross-examine him. This is precisely what I did, and I was given the assurance by my fellow broadcaster that he had witnessed it himself and that details were as he had stated.

I had long known of Eric Simms as a naturalist and broadcaster of repute, an ornithologist specializing in the recording of bird songs and author of several books on the subject. For me the occasion was memorable, because this was the first time I had met a professional scientist who had furnished a first-hand record for my file labelled *Compassion*. Nevertheless, I still lacked scientific proof that any rat had at any time been observed guiding a blind companion by each holding an end of a straw in its mouth. How exactly one is ever to obtain the incontrovertible proof for this phenomenon is hard to see. For one thing, the action is so contrary to the nature, disposition and known behaviour of rats as to weight the scales heavily in favour of scepticism, so heavily indeed that even a film shot of such an event is unlikely to carry conviction; there will

Fig. 12 Two rats holding a straw; one is believed to be blind

always be the accusation, direct or implied, usually the latter, that the film was faked.

Incidentally, if any non-scientist has ever recounted a natural history observation of this kind to a scientist and had his feelings hurt by being met with scepticism or total disbelief, let him take comfort. Even professional scientists have had the experience. I suspect Eric Simms has, and I know I have. For example, there is a long-standing story that a hedgehog may impale apples on its spines and carry them away. It goes back to classical times and reports of its having been seen are legion. One argument usually advanced against it is that hedgehogs do not eat fruit. This is untrue, as I have proved to my satisfaction over the last twenty-five years and, within recent years, a report published in *Acta Theriologica* 1976 Vol. 21 (30), p. 419 refers to several kinds of fruit eaten by hedgehogs. Another argument used is that it is impossible for apples to become impaled on hedgehog spines, yet I have seen it happen and my daughter Jane photographed it. Yet I am sure, from their remarks, that my professional colleagues do not believe me.

This digression is necessary to establish that science demands a high standard of evidence, and rightly so; and according to the scientific yardstick none of the stories of a rat guiding a blind rat is acceptable scientifically. Even Eric Simms' account can do no more than persuade us to keep an open mind on the subject (I am sure he will appreciate this). What we need therefore is collateral evidence, and this is available in quantity, because there are other possible explanations.

It is difficult to credit a rat with any form of compassion. Rather the reverse, for the general impression we get from everyday contact with rats is that they show no mercy even to their own fellows. That, however, may be due to prejudice. Taking a more impartial view of these stories, several explanations suggest themselves. It does sometimes happen, for example, that a rat will seize a piece of food and run off with it. Another rat then takes hold of the food and the two can be seen running in tandem. On rubbish dumps, rats will carry off small bones and it can sometimes happen that a second rat will take hold of the other end of the bone. Rats in cornfields will sometimes run off trailing a straw in the mouth. It needs only a second rat to seize the straw and the impression is given of a blind rat being assisted by one of its fellows.

In 1962 Mr G. Mostyn Lewis wrote to me about an adventure with sheep. To give the full flavour his letter is quoted in full and unaltered in any way:

> I belong to the Derby and Lancs Gliding Club and fly there at week-ends occasionally. The site is on the moors above Hathersage and has a long north-south axis and a much narrower east-west axis. We were launching on this occasion across the site into the west wind. A flock of moorland sheep which had come through a gap in the stone wall at the north end of the site began wandering down the moor towards our landing area. I started walking up the moor with a companion to drive them back. As we got near to them we clapped our hands and shouted. The flock immediately wheeled and began trotting up the moor towards the gap in the wall through which they had come. We have always found these mountain sheep very intelligent and this flock seemed to know perfectly well what was expected of them. Except for two sheep. One of these began making little nervous runs in different directions, while the other watched it and seemed uncertain what to do. We thought it was a scheme to dodge past us and we spread out slightly and continued walking towards the two animals, clapping and shouting more loudly. The rest of the flock was well up to the north by now and approaching the gap. The nervous sheep now began running in circles while its companion stood in the centre following it round with its body and keeping its eyes on it. We were too stupid to realise that this behaviour must have had some meaning, and continued our noisy approach. The circles became each time larger in diameter and began to drift across the moor at right angles to our line of approach. This brought the sheep that was running in circles gradually closer to the stone wall that marks our eastern boundary. A few moments later we were shocked to see it run full-tilt into the stone wall. Only then did we realise that it must have been blind. We retreated a little way and stood still. The sheep that had run into the wall now stood trembling and seemed somewhat dazed, but otherwise unhurt. After a few moments its companion walked quietly up to it and pushed its right shoulder against the left shoulder of the blind sheep. Contact having been established, we watched the blind sheep guided in this way by its companion right up the moor and out through the gap in the wall at the north end. We both felt very moved by this incident, and ashamed at having been so insensitive. What prompted the guide to stand its ground in the face of our approach, when at least part of its instinct must have been to follow the flock? I think they were both female, but am not quite certain.

It is of interest to compare this with a note contributed to *The Countryman* in 1971 by P. F. Downes, of New Zealand:

> Some years ago, while working on a country road, I heard a ewe calling from the other side of the hedge. Although she did not sound really distressed, there was a note of urgency and inquiry in her voice. [Was this a true cry for help?] Very conveniently, there was a ladder against a pole near by, and I climbed it to look over the hedge. There she was, close behind it, still calling and listening. The rest of the flock were some distance away, but presently one of them lifted her head, looked in the direction of the call and answered. Then she walked

slowly towards the road, answering each bleat as she came, until at last the anxious one heard her. The pleased note sounding in her next call was unmistakable, as she walked to join the friend who had come to her aid. Being completely blind, when she could no longer hear the others she was lost indeed.

In the same journal for 1966 was a brief note from E. V. Malone telling how a friend in Co. Antrim was out with his Labrador, described as a noted fighter. Suddenly, the Labrador dashed snarling across the road towards a terrier standing in a doorway. It came to a sudden halt as it drew near the terrier and ran back again without attacking the stranger. The owner of the terrier explained: 'No dog ever fights mine. It is blind.'

It might be possible to explain this on the grounds that a blind dog offers no signals to another dog. A normal dog, for example, seeing another dog approaching aggressively, would itself show signs of aggression or it would run away. In either event the aggression of the attacking dog would increase. There is a third thing it might do: drop on to its back in an attitude of submission, whereupon the attacking dog would lose interest, lower its hackles, drop its snarling grimace, turn and walk away – or so we are told. (I must accept this at its face value because I cannot recall ever having seen it happen.)

Konrad Lorenz, I think, first promulgated the theory that in adopting an attitude of submission a dog presents its most vulnerable part, its throat with its jugular vein, to its opponent. This, so far as I am aware, has not been extensively tested, although it is currently widely accepted. If the theory is sound there seems no reason why the Labrador should have halted its attack, since the terrier was not reported to have rolled on to its back in an attitude of submission.

When I came to consider more closely the stories about blind dogs, I remembered that the daughter of my friend Mrs Diana Page, living in the nearby village of Shere, had recently seen a specimen of a large stuffed dog in a London shop, had taken a fancy to it and brought it home. I telephoned Mrs Page and asked if a live dog had ever been confronted with the stuffed dog, which looked quite life-like to the human glance. She replied that it had been shown to their Alsatian, which calmly went up to it, 'sniffed it in the usual places and promptly lost interest in it'.

When I explained to Mrs Page the reason for my inquiry, she told me how a Mrs Kelly had come to live in a neighbouring house together with her dog, which was blind. As soon as he saw it, her Alsatian, which Mrs Page described as a docile and peaceable dog, ran at it, gripped it by the neck and had to be called off. She emphasized that this was surprising and unusual, since the Alsatian does not normally attack other dogs. But the blind dog, in this instance also, did not adopt the submissive attitude and did not present its jugular, nor did the Alsatian grip it in the region of the jugular but around the back of the neck.

Support for the story from Co. Antrim comes from a letter written to me in 1961 by Stephanie Stewart, of London:

There was a terrier known to be a bit of a bully who would rush up to any dog in the district to intimidate him and try to pick a fight. One day I saw him run across to another dog of about his size, who was a stranger in the street. He was bristling from head to tail in his usual belligerent manner, but when he reached the other dog who was on a lead, he stopped dead in his tracks, his growls ceased and sniffing gently round the dog's ears he walked away. The other dog was blind. The bully terrier had evidently sensed the trouble instantly.

This seeming ability on the part of a dog to recognize blindness in another is taken a step further in a letter sent by Stewart Campbell, of Warwickshire, published in *The Countryman* for 1965/66. Mr Campbell told of a neighbour's two bitches, an elderly one that was three-parts blind and very deaf, and a young one in the prime of life. One day he saw them at a junction of two roads that carried a heavy volume of traffic. The older dog started to cross but was stopped by the younger placing herself broadside on in front of her. A second or so later a car shot by. The two dogs remained still, the younger one looking to left and to right. When the coast was clear the younger bitch stepped aside, waited for her older companion to move, then escorted her across the road.

A digression is necessary here because it could be questioned whether dogs or any other animals would have the necessary road-sense for guiding another. Some dogs certainly have this. I have seen individual dogs, and wild foxes also, stop at a kerb and listen before crossing or threading their way through a column of vehicles held up on a main highway at traffic lights and then pausing to listen before crossing the other lane which was more or less clear of moving vehicles. The most striking example I have witnessed was in a moorhen, an animal that uses its eyes rather than its ears. We had this as a hatchling and put it in the care of a domestic hen. Moorhens are unusually precocious in many ways and this one was no exception. When it was subadult it took to roosting in the marsh to the north of my property, returning each morning to feed in the garden. When going to roost, it always followed the same routine. It would fly to the top of our boundary wall, beyond which is a main road. It would look left, then right, then left again and would not fly over the road unless it was clear of traffic. It was a wonderful thing to see!

In 1961 I received a letter from Miss Ruth Twinn, of Surrey, telling of her spaniel-terrier cross that injured an eye, which had to be removed. Then it lost the sight of its other eye. She continued:

> I had several cats at the time and two of them, not quite fully grown, seemed to sense the old dog's blindness and would range themselves on either side of her head just touching her ears, and would walk gently beside her as though trying to guide her about the garden. It was a wonderful and pathetic sight. Then in the evening when she lay before the fire, the cats would curl up as close as they could and the old dog seemed to appreciate their company. All this was the more remarkable because, while she had tolerated the cats, she had never been friendly with them and they would never have taken these liberties when she could see.

There is, no doubt, an endless source of stories about blind dogs if only it were possible to collect them, but this would be tediously time-consuming and we can be reasonably certain that the few given here are typical. Curiously, few have been told about blind cats. This may be because cats depend so much on sight, whereas dogs use mainly their sense of smell even when their eyes are normal. So a blind cat would presumably be doomed to an early death from accident, starvation or from a predator. It would be much the same with any wild animal, yet there are a few instances known. For example, those who study seals tell of blind seals that are apparently in good health.

One story, told in detail by R. M. Lockley, in *The Coutryman* for 1964, is titled 'Blind Lady of Little Skerry'. This was a female seal Lockley had had under observation for some time, at the pupping season. It is easy to see that a blind seal need not go without food, because seals normally feed in semi-darkness at least and use other senses than sight to catch their prey. This one, however, was able to find her way ashore, for bearing her pup and for the mating, which takes place immediately after parturition, and seemed to have no difficulty in rearing her pup. But then, communication between a cow seal and her pup is by sound and smell, and on the breeding ground the cow moves about relatively little. To reach the breeding ground she would be guided by the sounds and movements of other seals. At all events, Lockley gave no indication that fellow-seals were helping her, except possibly inadvertently.

The other observation of a blind wild animal that is outstanding is recorded in *African Wild Life* for 1952. It is one that brings us back from a general discussion about blindness in animals to our primary search, for signs of 'compassion'. A lawyer living in Windhoek, Southwest Africa, was on a car journey with his wife and a friend when his petrol tank sprung a leak. They became stranded on a dune veld south of the Kalahari. The friend volunteered to walk back to a farmhouse for help, leaving the other two to await his return. A couple of hours had passed when the lawyer and his wife became aware of a low intermittent whimper coming from a trough between the dunes. A few minutes later there came into view a solitary springbok followed by a wilde-beest, moving its head continually from side to side in an unusual way.

'It was evident', wrote E. M. Menmuir, who recorded the incident, 'that the springbok was guiding the wildebeest, for whenever it uttered its low whimper the springbok would wait for it to come up and then nose it in a reassuring manner', leading the wildebeest to a waterhole.

Examination showed that the wildebeest's head and eyes were swollen out of all proportion, possibly the result of snake venom (probably from a spitting cobra). It was clearly blinded and probably bereft of its ability to smell, at least temporarily. A mercy shot from a rifle put an end to the creature's suffering.

If there is no compassion between animals, we may well ask why their equipment includes a capacity to whimper. Natural selection involves the elimination of useless organs and useless behavioural traits, so that conversely everything an animal has or does must have a use. Whimpering may be basically something used by an infant to call forth remedial action by its parent, but since whimpering persists into adult life we should expect its usefulness to continue beyond the infant stage. Presumably, whimpering in an adult can evoke pity in neighbouring animals, sometimes real help, as in the springbok just described and the chimpanzee dealt with in chapter 14.

There are remarkably few records of blind birds. As they depend upon sight even more than cats do, their demise is probably assured even more rapidly after the onset of blindness. Julian M. Langford, writing in *British Birds* for 1962, records that when ringing linnets he found several blinded in one eye from the hooked seeds of bur-marigold on which they had fed. Other one-eyed wild birds have been recorded which seem to have adapted to the loss of one eye. There is, however, the story of Blind Jack, told in her excellent book by Stéphanie Ryder, published in 1961.

Blind Jack was a sightless jackdaw found dirty, dishevelled and emaciated in the grounds of Charterhouse School in Surrey. Mrs Ryder resuscitated the bird and kept it as a pet for several years. Since this is an instance of compassion from a human being, the story has little place here except for the possibility, carefully analysed by Mrs Ryder, that the bird may have survived the onset of blindness by several days. There is the chance that the jackdaw may have been fed by one or more of its fellows. Jackdaws are one of the few species of birds, as will be discussed in a later chapter, for which there is reliable evidence that they will share their food with each other. There is no instance that I can trace of an adult jackdaw actually observed putting food into the bill of a disabled adult, but the jackdaw does belong to the crow family, which includes jays, and there is some ground for believing, as we shall see later, that jays push food into the throat of another, as if feeding a fledgling.

The condition Blind Jack was in when rescued contrasts with that of a blacknecked heron photographed by D. C. H. Plowes. The account of it is recorded in *African Wild Life* for 1948. Mr Plowes was surprised how close the bird allowed him to approach in order to photograph it. Then he realized it was blind, or almost completely blind, its eyes crusted over, possibly as a result of an encounter with a spitting cobra. The photographs suggest that the heron had been well fed. It was not alarmed by the presence of a man but walked towards him when he made a noise. When, however, it spread its wings to take off it crashed into a bush, but picked itself up and eventually flew across the river, landing safely on the far bank.

The heron's blindness, if we assume it resulted from the venom of a spitting cobra, may have been recent and temporary. If the blindness had lasted longer, there is always the possibility that the afflicted bird was fed by other herons. Apart from some ground-living birds, including domestic fowl, birds are fed in infancy by the parents, and the parents are therefore geared to putting food into the beak of another. Later in this book we shall meet known instances of birds feeding others that are incapacitated by infancy, disability or other hampering afflictions. So the chance of a disabled bird being fed by others may be remote but not impossible. There is even the record, reinforced by photographs, of a bird that fed ornamental fish in a garden pond, the fishes swimming to the water's edge and opening their mouths to receive the food.

We are also ignorant of what goes on in the brain of an animal deprived of one or other of its senses. What we can say, on the evidence of blind persons, is that alternative senses tend to be developed to an astonishing degree. I recall an occasion in my late teens when I was in a house where a blind man was a visitor for the day. It was necessary for me to go into a room where he was sitting alone. As I looked in I saw his eyelids were drooped. Assuming he had dozed off, I entered making virtually no sound. To my surprise, he addressed me by name, although I had never met him before that day and the total of our social intercourse up to that moment did not amount to more than a few minutes.

Even more astonishing was a more recent experience. I had occasion to telephone an institution and I asked the operator, a man, to put me through to the library. 'Certainly, Dr Burton,' he replied. After I had spoken to the librarian I asked, as a matter of interest, who the telephone operator was. She asked me why I wanted to know this. 'Because', I said, 'I do not telephone your building more than once a year, on average, and it must be over a year since I last telephoned. Yet the operator knew my name without my having mentioned it.' 'The operator is blind,' replied the librarian. 'He remembers everybody by name from their voice once he has heard it' — a tremendous feat of memory!

Already it is clear that if there are any compassionate acts they are mainly among mammals, and the higher mammals at that, and there is less evidence of them among birds. Next down in the animal scale are the reptiles and amphibians, from which we would not expect compassion, and below them the fishes. It was a surprise, therefore, to come across the following letter in *The Countryman* for 1958. It was written by Mr Clifford A. Hoing, who had been out for a quiet day's fishing with three companions in southern England. After they had landed a few fish Mr Hoing went along the river bank where one of his companions was standing and calling him to come and look. In the water below them he saw swimming slowly side by side two tench, one slightly smaller and more energetic than the other, as they followed an irregular course always the same distance from the bank.

Mr Hoing commented that they kept so close together that at times they touched and when they did so the larger fish slightly altered course. Then the two men realized that the smaller tench was guiding the other one; as he put it, a push near the tail that turned it to the right and one on the head to the left. By this time all four men were watching and as the fish swam beyond them they went back to their fishing. Suddenly one of the four men shouted that the two fishes were coming back, and then the same man gave a triumphant yell as he lifted them in his landing net. The smaller fish was a male in good condition though thin, the other a female was also in good condition but blind. It is good to know that the two fishes were returned to the water.

It is difficult to believe that the smaller tench was acting out of compassion. That is something that must be beyond the capacity of such a lowly vertebrate. Ignoring the possible explanation, which is perhaps best left to the specialist in the study of fish behaviour, we can say that Mr Hoing's encounter contains a warning that a blind animal being guided by one of its fellows could be nothing more than genetic altruism. Thus some fishes, we know, tend to swim side by side. When such fishes are together in numbers this is called schooling. The two tench may have been using an incipient form of schooling, in the course of which one bumped into the other from time to time causing it to change course. It could be that the human observers read more into the incident than was justified. There are other possibilities. It is a great pity the tench could not have been kept under observation and a careful record kept of their actions.

Fortunately, we have the careful observations made by Michael Hall some ten years ago of grey mullet in the tidal estuaries and creeks of East Suffolk. After describing the behaviour of the large shoals clustering in the ponds, he also remarked that he had seen an albino specimen of about three pound weight which was apparently blind to movement and form but could distinguish between light and shade. He was, it seems, prevented from catching this pale specimen with his bare hands by an approaching boy whose shadow fell on the albino fish, causing it to swim away quickly. Later Hall saw the albino cruising in the pool with two normally coloured attendants. Every time the blind albino looked like swimming towards a bank, either or both of these attendant fishes cut close in front of it and turned it away from danger, or, at least, appeared to be doing so.

10.
Mechanics
of
Compassion

The main difficulty in assembling examples of supposed altruism in animals is that such a diversity of species is concerned. Moreover, for any given species each individual's reactions tend to be markedly different and it is hard to draw firm conclusions. When I first read the account given by E. V. Malone (chapter 9), it struck me that since domestic dogs are so numerous there must be many people possessing one that had gone blind. If therefore their experiences could be collated it might be possible to amass sufficient data from which a sound analysis could be made and meaningful conclusions reached.

My first step was to telephone Mrs Piper, of Ewhurst, who for years has been breeding bloodhounds. It turned out that she has a blind bitch bloodhound. Her comment was that the other bloodhounds treated the blind bitch with deference, as if they realized her infirmity, and were prepared to make life as easy for her as possible.

A veterinary surgeon, Mr M. D. Keeling, of the nearby city of Guildford, has a blind dog. He confirmed that other dogs show no aggression to her and also she was able to find her way about and only occasionally bumped into obstacles. This seems to be usually the case with blind dogs. For example, there is the story of a sheepdog that although blind was still able to work, provided it had a sighted companion, in rounding up sheep, only occasionally bumping into obstacles.

Another example is that given by Hugh Ingram, who had a Labrador that went blind in its later years. Before it went blind it had been taken daily for a walk through a 'rough' (a copse thinly filled with trees but with a dense undergrowth of bracken and bramble). Even when blind, the dog never experienced difficulty in finding its way through the rough. Anyone seeing it for the first time would have been surprised to learn it was blind.

In seeking further information I have made numerous inquiries of owners of blind dogs over a long period. Moreover, other people have very kindly extended inquiries on my behalf among their friends. The result of these inquiries indicates that most blind dogs are little inconvenienced by their loss of sight, mainly because their owners guard them and shelter them by confining them largely to their own houses and gardens. There the dogs know their way about in familiar surroundings. Another result of these inquiries is, for me, a growing conviction that, by and large, sighted dogs treat their blind companions with respect and deference, as indicated by Mr Malone and Mrs Piper. The truth is, however, that there are exceptions.

One of these is the blind dog belonging to Mrs Kelly (chapter 9), which Mrs Page's dog had seized by the neck. Mrs Kelly informed me that since her dog went blind it tended to be aggressive towards other dogs that came close to it. This may be why the Page's dog, with a reputation for being unusually pacific, showed aggression on first meeting it.

A clue to this may possibly lie in the behaviour of the present author and also that of a half-blind parrot at present living with him in the same house. Ten years ago I lost overnight the sight of my right eye from a haemorrhage on the retina. At first this was troublesome, but it was possible in a short while to adapt to this partial blindness in most particulars and, because the eye looks normal, nobody meeting me for the first time suspects anything is wrong. In fact, most of my acquaintances are unaware of my trouble. Externally there seems to be nothing wrong with my sight, so that even my wife forgets I have this handicap. Thus, it sometimes happens, especially when she is walking on a soft carpet or on turf, that she approaches noiselessly on my blind side. My first intimation that she is beside me comes when she speaks. It is most disconcerting suddenly to hear a voice alongside when you think you are alone. My inevitable reaction to this mild shock is to swing round with an angry remonstrance which has to be suppressed.

The half-blind parrot was first seen flying with jackdaws, obviously somebody's pet that had escaped. Mrs Ingram took to putting out food for it daily on a windowsill. The parrot became almost tame with her. Then she noticed its left eye was injured and shortly it became obvious that this eye was completely sightless, so she caught the parrot and put it in a cage, convinced it would not survive long in the wild. In due course, we took over care of it. Now, whenever anyone passes the cage or approaches it on the left side the parrot lunges vigorously with its beak, hitting the wires of the cage. It is noticeable that its aim is defective, since the beak always hits to the right of the target. In this the parrot has my sympathy; the second disadvantage of one-eyed sight is a tendency to miss the target.

The most important lesson from the one-eyed parrot, as indeed from at least one one-eyed human, is the tendency to be irascible when suddenly taken by surprise on the blind side. Perhaps this helps us to understand partly why some blind dogs tend to be on the defensive and inclined to show aggression.

How then does a sighted dog become aware that another dog is blind?

If it is true, as seems highly likely, that sighted dogs usually treat a blind dog with deference, it can only be that the blind dog, like a stuffed dog, is not giving out the normal signals. What the situation is can therefore only be a matter for speculation. We have to start with the normal encounter between two strange, male dogs. They meet, sniff noses, then move to stand flank to flank, tail to head, and each sniffs the other's anal glands. After that much will depend on circumstances, on the temperaments of the dogs, their previous experiences, on whether they are on neutral territory and on the balance between them in their social standing. At the worst it ends in a fight, in which, so far as can be seen, body odours, in the form of secretions from special glands, act as signals and so carry a greater motivating influence than visual signals.

The first principle to emerge from my inquiries is that some dogs adapt more successfully to loss of sight than do others. This almost certainly depends on the balance of the senses. Labradors, for example, are smell dogs, used to smell out explosives where urban guerillas are operating or to smell out survivors buried under the rubble of buildings destroyed by earthquakes. Other breeds rely more on sight than do Labradors, even though the olfactory sense is still the main one.

The primary senses number five: sight, smell, hearing, touch and taste. Sight must operate first in the primary encounter between two normal dogs, Thus a certain dog when emerging from the puppy stage was set upon by a sandy-coloured dog. He grew up to be a large, heavy dog, well able to defend himself yet generally pacific, except when the dog he met had a sandy-coloured coat. The adventures of this dog provide the surest indication that some dogs at least have some colour vision. They also reinforce the contention that sight is important in the opening stages of an encounter.

The next, and probably most important, sense to come into action in an encounter is that of smell. Hearing plays a small part, and usually later, in the form of premonitory growls. Taste is not involved, and touch not at all until the battle is joined. The sense of smell detects the body odours, the general body odour as well as the odours from the special glands, such as the anals and the preputial glands. How these and other scent signals could conceivably work can be best illustrated by reference to another animal, the hedgehog.

A hedgehog carries an armature of spines. In repose these lie closely to the body. At the threat of danger they start to bristle. A pet hedgehog familiar with one person will keep its spines laid against the body in the presence of that person. It is an indication of tameness. In the presence of a stranger, whom it detects by its acute sense of smell, as shown by the dripping of fluid from its nose, its spines bristle. Should that stranger, preferably using gloved hands although it can be done with bare hands, stroke the bristles from head to tail and force them gently to lie flat against the body, the hedgehog can be induced into a state of repose, or temporary tameness. When this is repeated several times by the same person, a more or less permanent tameness can be induced.

We have here a formula: danger — bristles raised; bristles artificially or forcefully lowered — sense of danger banished. It is a method of inducing a complete reversal of normal behaviour. By analogy, it can be suggested that if touch can produce such a transformation, so can the presence or absence of an odour in an animal in which the sense of smell is so highly developed. We can carry this further. When one is dispirited or dejected the corners of the mouth are pulled down. By consciously lifting the corners of the mouth to produce a smile, one's whole mood can be changed.

There is the common observation that a puppy in the presence of a male dog will lie on its back with legs in the air. A subadult or adult dog, of subordinate social rank, does much the same with a dominant dog and, as with the puppy, the dominant dog will not attack. This attitude is known as the submissive posture and the theory — too often today spoken of as a proven fact — is that the subordinate dog is presenting its jugular vein to its dominant opponent. The theory goes on to say that because the subordinate is showing no sign of aggression the dominant feels no impulse to attack (see also p. 91).

All this is plausible theory. It is possible, however, that when the submissive posture is adopted something else is happening, just as in the hedgehog its adoption is, so to speak, 'making the animal tame' because the taking up of this posture inhibits the secretions of the glands and so removes the provocative pheromones (subtle odours given out from the body, especially those from specialized glands). This also is theory but probably a more plausible one than the idea that the subordinate is exposing its jugular vein to the fangs of its opponent.

Such a theory could well explain why a blind dog is not attacked, as a rule, by the sighted dog. Its lack of sight means there is no discharge of pheromones on the approach of the other dog coming into its proximity. The sighted dog, seeing the blind dog, rushes forward aggressively but on nearing its target fails to perceive the odours (pheromones) necessary to sustain its aggression. For all the sighted dog knows to the contrary, the blind dog could be a stuffed dog.

In a blind bitch, treated with deference, a similar absence of aggressive pheromones presumably causes her to be regarded to some extent as a puppy by the other bitches and so treated with deference, even kindness.

The advantage of this theory is that it could also explain the stories of a sighted dog actually guiding a blinded dog. For such an event to take place there has to be a complete reversal of normal behaviour. Something radical must occur to produce this, and since odours are the most important means of communication between dogs, nothing is more natural than to suppose that it is change in the pheromones that produces it. Because our sense of smell is so inferior to that of a dog we are at present without adequate means of testing the theory.

For twenty years we have had foxes in captivity. Every year we have seen the same behaviour. The dog-fox has been utterly selfish over food. Unless special precautions were taken the vixen would starve, or at least suffer malnutrition. When the vixen comes into season the dog-fox courts her, but he still remains utterly selfish in regard to food. The moment the cubs are born, the dog-fox, instead of eating all the food put down for him, goes to great trouble to take every scrap of it into his mouth, goes over to the vixen, calling to her with a special low call, and drops all the food in front of her. Only when she is replete does the dog-fox attempt to eat. He continues this unselfishness until the cubs are independent and able to feed for themselves, then he reverts to his normal selfishness. This, of course, is little different from birds feeding their young, but the contrast is more marked.

From all we know of the senses of foxes there can be only one signal — unless it be some vocal signal that no one has yet detected — that indicates to the dog-fox that birth is imminent or that cubs have been born, since the vixen

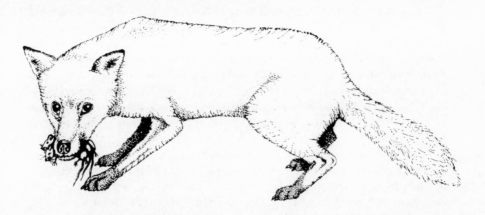

Fig. 13 Dog-fox returning to his vixen and cubs with his maw as full as possible. In so doing he is reversing his usual selfish behaviour

does not allow him into her nursery earth, and that is an odour signal (a pheromone presumably) from the vixen. Whatever it is, there is produced a complete about-turn in one aspect of his behaviour.

Further possible supporting evidence is to be seen in an episode recorded in the *Journal of Mammalogy* for 1947, in what was described as the 'peculiar' behaviour of the American red fox. The writer, William J. Comstock, wrote of seeing a fox on the opposite side of the highway, in New Jersey on 18 March as he drove along. The fox was standing by a prone object on the pavement. The fox looked up as the car went by but did no more than step off the pavement on to the shoulder of the road. So Mr Comstock turned and drove back, bringing his headlights to bear on the scene.

He reported having stepped from the car and spoken to the fox as he would have done to a dog. Then he walked to it, patted its head and scratched its ears for a while and then moved over to the prone object, to discover it was another fox that had apparently been killed by a passing car. The live fox, which proved to be a male, moved over to the corpse and began to lick its fur. Mr Comstock did not ascertain the sex of the dead animal but assumed it to be a vixen.

The corpse was still warm. Palpation revealed no sign that the supposed vixen was in whelp. Its fur was very wet over the whole body and since the dog-fox was dry it could be safely assumed the wet fur on the corpse was due to his feverish licking. Mr Comstock tried to drag the corpse by the tail from the pavement to which the dog-fox objected and tried to prevent by seizing the corpse by the neck, so that a mild tug-o'-war ensued. When the man tried to push the dog-fox away it merely whined and made no attempt to bite, nor did it show any other sign of aggression. Eventually Mr Comstock dragged the corpse off the pavement and down the embankment so that there should be no danger of the live fox being hit by any other car. There was a good deal of blood around the mouth of the vixen but the dog-fox had made no attempt to lick this. Before returning to his car Mr Comstock scratched the ears of the dog-fox and patted its flanks. The fox responded by wagging its tail a little.

There have been occasional reports of foxes eating the carcases of other foxes. It is significant that in this episode the living fox did not even lick the blood. This much indicates a complete reversal of normal behaviour in the dog-fox. Even more significant is it that an animal which normally shuns human beings like the plague, should have stood its ground and accepted the patting and ear-scratching, responding by a mild tail-wagging, the dog's way of saying 'Thank you'.

The wholesale licking is also out of character. A dog-fox will lick the head of a vixen, especially under the chin, as part of his courtship, but this extensive licking can be interpreted as an attempt to render first aid or, less likely, as an exaggerated show of affection. Taken together, the signs are of a complete reversal of normal behaviour, and this relatively trivial incident is a first-class indication that not only will a sick or injured animal show a wholesale change in behaviour, as we have seen in chapter 3, but, more importantly, it can induce in another a reciprocal radical change.

This is the core and pivot of our understanding of true altruism in animals. It is obvious that it must be so, as it is between human beings. When we meet somebody who is in normal good health and an untroubled mind, our behaviour towards that person is normal. Should this same person look ill or show signs of injury, or if by his words he conveys the impression that he is burdened with trouble, our sympathy is evoked. We have the urge to help. Our whole attitude changes and so does our behaviour. Indeed, this change of behaviour can at times verge on the monstrous. For example, I once wrote out a cheque for £300 for a relative stranger on hearing his tale of woe. It was a loan without security and, of course, he proved to be a rogue who never repaid the money. Without realizing it, all the rogues and crooks at all times are relying on the principle that a change in behaviour — simulating distress with consummate skill — will cause the victims of their wiles to behave in a way they would never dream of doing under normal circumstances. By extrapolation, we can see how in animals this could lead to their performing acts which defy analysis by the known rules of animal behaviour.

That is not the whole story, because the change in behaviour evoked by a person in distress varies with the temperament, even the mood at that moment, of the one to whom he is appealing. And so, we may be sure, it is with animals. The result is that a given situation may give rise to altruism or the reverse. In the instance quoted, another person, or even myself in another mood, might have met the request for £300 with a rebuff. The suppliant rogue might even have been rewarded by a punch on the nose. We can take the comparison to animal level by invoking the known behaviour of foxes. There are known instances of the red fox feeding on the newly-dead carcase of one of its fellows and others in which the fox has endeavoured to resuscitate it. Both represent a change in behaviour in response to the other's change in behaviour (death, in this case), one in the direction of selfishness, the other towards unselfishness.

Of all the anecdotes that can be told about animals only a very small proportion involve possible true altruism. Much the same can be said about people. There was a man who was set upon by thieves, who robbed him and left him senseless and bleeding at the side of the road. A Levite passing along the road saw him, and passed by on the other side. A Pharisee coming by also passed by on the other side. A Samaritan, of lower social status, took compassion on the victim, dressed his wounds and set him on his own ass to bear him away for hospitalization. In this parable the odds are two to one against altruistic action being taken. In the beasts of the field an altruistic response can be expected to be far less than 33 per cent of the total response to distress signals.

It would be difficult to find a better example to illustrate the difference between genetic altruism and true altruism than the reactions of sighted dogs to a blind dog. If the inquiries I made are not delusory, sighted dogs react to a blind dog by treating it with deference and respect. They show it consideration but at no loss to themselves and they do so, if my conclusions are correct, because the absence of certain signals deflects them from normal behaviour. By contrast, the sighted dog that guided a blind dog across a busy road, if this is what actually happened, was giving some of its time and incurring possible risks for the sake of one that was handicapped.

By the same token the unselfishness shown by the dog-fox at the time of cubbing is an example of genetic altruism, spectacular as it may appear to the human eye. By contrast, the dog-fox that stood by its mate on a busy road after she had been killed was showing a devotion and loyalty which carried a considerable risk from fast-moving vehicles that might at any time have mown it down. Perhaps even more striking was the case of the springbok guiding the blinded wildebeest to water. It was devoting some of its time to helping another. At the same time it was exposing itself to possible predators.

What we cannot know in all such instances is what goes on inside the benefactor. This can be illustrated by referring again to my own £300. By wordly standards this was an act of sheer stupidity, and it is how I still regard it. Yet the inner argument I used with myself, in deciding to lend the money, partakes of a simple logic. Thus, I had at that time just received a small legacy of £300 (the suppliant to whom I lent the money was not aware of this). Inwardly I argued that it would be ridiculous for me to hold on to the money, which I did not at that moment actively need, when another man's future was jeopardized (or so it was made to appear) by the lack of exactly that amount.

The normal behaviour would have been to ask for security (which the man seemingly did not possess), embody the transaction in a legal agreement, and charge a fair rate of interest. This would have been normal behaviour. It would have been business-like and it would have been wise and the equivalent of genetic altruism. Above all, and this is the point I am stressing now, no amount of scientific observation or research could have revealed what went on inside me had I not the power of speech to describe it. And man is the only species able to use words to reveal his hidden motivation.

In May 1977 a report was published in *Animal Behaviour* on studies carried out by Peter and Martha Klopfer of the Duke University, North Carolina, on the responses of a female goat to her kids. It not only tells of the way a nanny goat assists the smaller of her two kids, in the early days of its life, but also sheds light on the difficulties of investigating a behavioural process akin to altruism.

Usually it is the firstborn kid that is the larger and stronger, with a tendency to monopolize the udder, yet in a short while its smaller sibling grows faster, so this initial advantage is lost and the two can share the udder on equal terms. The reason is simple. Instead of paying more attention to the weaker of the two, the mother goat licks the stronger kid more frequently than the weaker, so knocking it off its feet and keeping it away from the udder. The weaker kid is thereby able to exploit more fully the supply of food.

The Klopfers went about testing this by weakening one kid through an injection of an anaesthetic which produced a 'profound analgesia without impairing pharyngeal-laryngeal reflexes'. That is, although the treated kid staggered about somewhat, its ability to suck was not impaired. The results were puzzling. In effect, when a strong kid was drugged it suckled more even though it was being licked more, whereas when the weaker kid was drugged it tended to suck less, became even weaker, and was neglected by the mother, to the point of death.

The next step was to ascertain by what sense the mother recognized the differences in her offspring. Immediately after the birth of the second kid she was blindfolded and her smell membranes immobilized temporarily by a spray of a local anaesthetic in the nostrils. When this was done, the mother treated both kids alike. The Klopfers could prove nothing. They had to be content with postulating that when the mother goat cannot see or smell her babies she makes no difference in her treatment of them, which is consistent with the theory put forward in this chapter that it is the change in behaviour of an animal in distress that signals their need for help and calls forth a response from a potential helper. The two investigators were content to remark that in their view 'mother-love, apparently is not blind'. If the results were inconclusive it was not the fault of the investigators, who spent three years on their task and received assistance from thirty members of the Duke Goat Watching Society, who kept watch for twenty-four hours a day.

The results, to say the least, are disappointing and amount to little more than can be gleaned by deduction from isolated observations and anecdotes. Yet there is some confirmatory evidence. Thus one begins to understand why parent birds will neglect a nestling that has weakened beyond a certain point and will throw it out of the nest or carry it out and drop it some distance from the nest. When such a nestling is still alive and is placed back in the nest, it is soon thrown out again or taken out and jettisoned. It looks as though the line between maternal solicitude and an apparent 'mercy-killing' is a very thin one. This is reinforced by a letter from C. Satkunananthan published in the *New Scientist*. He told of personal observation of a domesticated goat in Sri Lanka that often had a litter of three or four. She would choose the two stronger kids and reject the others, giving her udder to the chosen ones only. Any attempt by the rejected kids to suckle resulted in their being kicked away. (The rejected kids were successfully bottle-fed with milk taken from the mother.)

11.
Care-Giving
Birds

Up to this point we have been dealing almost exclusively with mammals, especially dolphins, elephants and dogs. As has been emphasized, these are animals that have highly developed brains. So far as dolphins and elephants are concerned the size or the complexity of the brain rivals that of the apes and therefore comes closest to the human brain. If there is any altruistic behaviour to be found at all in the animal kingdom it is among these higher mammals we should expect to find it. The question then arises of how low in the animal kingdom similar examples can be expected.

Among the examples I have collected only two concern fishes. One has already been mentioned in chapter 9, of a tench apparently guiding a blind tench. The other was told by a fisherman who had hooked a salmon in a small river in North Wales. As he brought it near the bank he could see another salmon swimming alongside and it remained alongside the other salmon for twenty minutes. In his letter to the magazine *Animals*, the fisherman remarked that three other people witnessed this but none of them could think of a possible explanation.

Two explanations spring to mind. One is that the performance was prompted by the schooling instinct. As we have seen, many species of fishes swim in schools, each individual in the school being spaced at a regular distance from its neighbours and the whole school heading in one direction. A school differs from a shoal in that it is a regular formation. In experiments aimed at determining why fishes school it was found that a single individual of a schooling species placed in an aquarium on its own would spend much of its time lengthwise beside a mirror standing in the aquarium in which the fish could see its own reflection. Unfortunately for this explanation, the salmon is not a species with a strong schooling instinct.

The other possible explanation is that the second salmon was impelled by curiosity to stay near the one that was hooked. There may be other possible explanations, but this anecdote is useful for two reasons. The first is that it shows how any such story should be examined. The second is that it is most unlikely that the free salmon was giving any sort of care-giving behaviour, which is what we should expect of fishes as a whole, in view of their low brain capacity. The same goes for amphibians and reptiles. The lowest in the scale where we should expect to find altruism is in birds.

The anecdotes discussed in this and the next three chapters all concern birds and mammals, and they are a somewhat miscellaneous collection. One way to sort them out is to think in terms of what happens when a human being is involved in an accident. Perhaps the simplest example to take is that of a person who narrowly escapes with his life from drowning. First there is the rescue, then comes first aid, such as artificial respiration, and then the ambulance work, by which either on a stretcher or in a vehicle the casualty is taken home or to a hospital. These three phases offer convenient headings under which to sort the animal episodes: rescue, first aid and ambulance work, the first being divided into two chapters, one for birds, the other for mammals.

Rescue among birds will be dealt with first and we can start with an anecdote which on the face of it seems highly improbable. It concerns house sparrows that had for some time been roosting in a garage, flying in and out through holes and cracks in the woodwork, if the doors happened to be shut. On one occasion one of the sparrows got its head stuck fast while trying to get through one of these holes. It struggled frantically but unsuccessfully to free itself, and there it was held by the neck with its body hanging down outside.

The man who told the story explained that there was no ladder readily available at the time and the owner of the garage did his best to ease the bird out of the hole with a bamboo stick. In this he failed. The bird was well and truly caught. Then suddenly another sparrow which had been perched on the garage roof took off and dived with folded wings towards the victim. As it came level with the bird that was trapped it seized its tail and hung on for a second or two before it had to let go and drop to the ground. It then flew up to the roof again and repeated the manoeuvre several times.

A second sparrow flew on to the roof and a moment or two later, as the first would-be rescuer dived again, it also took off and grabbed the tail, making three in a row. The two rescuers did this several times together and finally freed the trapped sparrow after which the three floated to the ground before taking off and going their several ways. A story of this kind stretches one's credulity to the maximum, but unless one is prepared to give this kind of report some consideration there is little point in proceeding further.

If this was not a genuine rescue attempt, the only other thing it could have been would be aggression, the free sparrow seeing an opportunity to attack, or perhaps stimulated to attack because of the trapped sparrow's struggles, and then the third sparrow joining in. Counterbalancing this is the fact that we are dealing here with a species about which there are probably more remarkable stories told of problem solving, insight behaviour and seeming altruistic behaviour than of any other species of bird. Remarkable as the story may appear, there is ground for keeping an open mind about the interpretation of it.

The next story is also about a sparrow. The writer of the account mentions that he witnessed the following event in the yard to the rear of the police station at Maidenhead, a place where we should expect accurate observation and reporting. The witness explained that the electricity supply to the recreation room was by an overhead copper wire, secured to two insulators in the usual manner, with two turns and then twisted back along itself. He was crossing the yard and heard the agitated chattering of sparrows on opposite wires at these insulators. Almost at once, one of them fluttered over the other, took a beak-grip on the back of its neck and both appeared to be trying to fly. By that time the witness was close to the sparrows and could see that one had the tip of a claw caught in the twisted part of the wire. The other appeared to be helping in an effort to pull it out.

After each struggle the birds parted, beaks open, breasts heaving. As the witness was casting about in his mind for some means to release the trapped sparrow a third sparrow arrived. A moment or two later both free birds flew over the trapped one, both took a beak-grip on the back of its neck, and all three flapped their wings in an attempt to fly away. They repeated this three times, with a rest between each attempt, always with beaks open and gasping. Then followed what had every appearance of an understanding between all three. The newcomer fluttered up, seized the back of the neck of the trapped sparrow with a beak-grip, then closed its wings and hung on so that the two were suspended below the wire, held only by the claw tip. Both were motionless. The third bird then flew over, took a beak-grip on the back of the neck of the trapped sparrow and its manner of pulling swung the other two birds back and forth, as a result of which the claw either broke or came free.

The three birds then immediately returned to the wire, chattering, fluttering their wings and hopping about. The last sparrow to arrive on the scene then flew back the way it had come and the other two after further chattering then flew off in the opposite direction. The witness concluded as follows: 'To me at the time I felt that they all three must have known just what they were going to do. When, in the first efforts, all three flapped their wings, they were getting in each other's way. In the last and successful effort, each seemed to know what the other was going to do and that it was not just by chance that each did just what it did do, to bring about the happy ending.' There was a second witness to corroborate the details of the story.

This was a rescue, if we can take it to be that, which involved higher-order behaviour, especially problem solving and insight behaviour, at which, as we have seen, house sparrows are notably adept. Four things commend the story. First, the witness was a member of the police force, used to making and recording observations. Second, the species involved is one known to be capable of higher-order behaviour. Third, I have myself observed comparable actions by house sparrows (see chapter 17). Finally, the sequence of events as set forth seems to preclude any suggestion that aggression was involved.

The song sparrow of North America is not, despite its name, a true sparrow but a bunting. E.M.L. of Illinois watched, with a friend, both using binoculars, a song sparrow struggling in the water of Lake Jacksonville. It was able to keep afloat but its struggles merely took it first in one direction, then in another, so it made no progress towards the shore. Then two more song sparrows flew off from the bushes on the shore, circled a few times above the one in the water, hovered over it, manoeuvred a short distance in front of it, then started slowly shorewards, one on the right, the other on the left of their unfortunate fellow. The swimmer grew calmer in its movements and began to propel itself slowly after them as they made for the top of a fallen tree protruding from the water. There the waterlogged sparrow struggled on to a twig and perched there before flying off.

It is difficult to fault this story, since everything in it sounds logical. All that was taking place could have happened when all three song sparrows were airborne. The important difference between what took place and normal song sparrow behaviour was that part of it which looked like a deliberate effort on the part of two birds to quiet a companion in distress.

The European moorhen, known in North America as the common gallinule, rivals the house sparrow and perhaps even exceeds it in its reputation for higher-order behaviour. In the single episode presented here, a baby moorhen was struggling through the water to reach the nest but was caught by the current in the fast-flowing river and losing ground at about two yards a minute. Then the parent moorhen appeared, swam to within six inches of the youngster and turned quickly towards the nest leaving behind a small wake in which the baby could swim easily. They had covered half the distance when the parent bird turned around, presumably to see what was happening. Her act of turning disturbed the calm water of the wake and the baby again began to be carried away. Immediately the adult bird repeated its former tactics and both reached the nest safely.

It is easy to picture this scene and everything is quite acceptable, except that it could have been sheer coincidence that the adult behaved as it did, producing the calm water in which the baby could find salvation. In view of the moorhen's reputation there is some justification for giving the benefit of the doubt and regarding this as a deliberate attempt at rescue.

A mallard duck is normally a stupid bird by comparison with a moorhen. It may lay a dozen or more eggs, all of which may hatch. It is not unusual for the whole of a brood to be lost, one duckling at a time, over the following week or two. It is also not unusual for casualties among the ducklings to be the result of the adult duck's stupidity. She may tread on one, accidentally drown a second, and so on. The mallard species therefore does not commend itself as a source of unusual care-giving behaviour. Surprisingly, there are several instances of it recorded.

One tells of a mallard duck swimming along a stream with her young family. Three ducklings were swimming level with her, two were well behind and swimming side by side 'for all they were worth', pushing a dead one along with their breasts. In a short while the family procession reached a bend in the river and was hidden from view by dense vegetation. It is therefore a matter for speculation how long the ducklings continued to push the dead one along, whether they went on until they themselves were exhausted, and whether the presence of the dead body in front of them as they swam was fortuitous. The most extraordinary part of the story is the apparent unanimity shown by the two ducklings swimming side by side when the slightest departure from their rhythm of swimming would have disturbed the corpse they were pushing along and would have allowed them to swim past it and reach the rest of the family.

More typical of the mallard is the story from Lake Coniston in northwest England. The witness was paddling a canoe near a large bed of reeds when two drakes and a duck swam out towards the centre of the lake. They passed quite close to the observer, and although this took place in the middle of the duck-shooting season, when all ducks are particularly shy, they made no attempt to fly or to put distance between themselves and the canoe.

The female bird was in the centre, the drakes on each side of her as close as they could get. Then all three birds began to flap across the surface of the lake beating their wings on the surface of the water as if each one was badly wounded. The witness drove his canoe towards them, the two drakes still keeping their formation until the prow of the canoe was almost upon them. Then the two drakes turned, one to the left and one to the right, still beating and struggling over the water. The duck dived, swam a little under the surface but came up completely exhausted. She was lifted into the canoe and found to have been shot and was so emaciated as to be little more than a framework of skin and feathers. Meanwhile the two drakes rose strongly into the air showing that there was little wrong with them and flew in circles around the canoe before they finally flew away.

William Moore was fishing on the bank of a broad river in Assam when he flushed a pair of birds, one of which was obviously crippled and dropped into the water about midstream. They were whistling teal. The second bird dived under its crippled companion and lifted it to a height of about ten feet so that it was able to spread its wings and more or less glide to the opposite bank and safety.

If two ducks can cooperate to rescue a third, it should follow logically that more than two can cooperate to the same end, which brings us to the story that received publicity in Connecticut in 1962. It had been a severe winter. Looking out from their home, Mr and Mrs Waldo Grose saw a swan frozen in the ice on the Falls River millpond. The bird was completely unable to extricate itself and its predicament was growing worse. Before the Groses could think of a practical method of rescuing the swan, they saw a flock of mallard and black duck fifty to sixty strong walk out from the weeds that came down to the shore. They were walking in a body, close to each other, and as they drew near the swan they began a lifting and dropping movement of their bodies. According to the report this broke the ice and freed the swan on one side. The ducks then moved to the other side and went through the same motions. The swan was able to reach open water. If most of this story sounds supernormal, at least its ending is true to life. Characteristically the swan, as soon as it was free, turned and drove the ducks away.

Gulls tend to live in flocks. These flocks hardly qualify for the term 'society'; nor can gulls be described as sociable. They are given to squabbling among themselves and they can, at times, be merciless killers. Herring gulls nesting on cliffs will tend their chicks with the usual parental devotion. They will kill the chicks of other herring gulls, given the opportunity. If one of their own chicks wanders prematurely from the nest, they are likely to kill it and eat it. By contrast, gulls will combine against a potential predator and anyone wandering among the nests in a gullery can expect to have a crowd of gulls flying around his head, with the birds taking it in turns to fly at his head.

Altogether, gulls are among the last birds one would expect to show consideration for the weaker members of their community. Even so, there are several instances in which gulls have, to all appearances, effected rescues of young gulls. One such was recounted to me by a friend of fifty years standing whom I know from experience to be objective in her natural history observations and meticulous in giving accurate details.

She was in Brixham, in Devon, where the houses rise in terraces from the sea-front. Looking out of the window she saw a herring gull nest in the angle between the chimney stack and the roof ridge, on the roof of the next house below where she was. A mature chick, as yet unable to fly, seemed to have fallen from the nest and slithered down the roof into the gutter. In a very short while adult gulls had flown in and settled on the gutter, either side of the youngster. Those nearest to it, on either side of it, jostled it with their breasts and the youngster was squeezed up on to the roof. Then followed what looked like concerted action as the assembled gulls crowded convergently in on the centre, so that the chick, half-scrambling was forced up the roof, at the apex of a pyramid of jostling gulls, until it was back in the nest.

The whole episode sounds unbelievable. The effort seems unnecessary since one adult gull could have achieved the same end. For example, I once watched for a long time a herring gull playing with a tennis ball on a steep rockery in a public park. The gull pushed the ball up the rockery with its bill and forehead. Arriving at the top of the rockery the bird turned around and deliberately pushed the ball over the edge so that it rolled down the slope, bouncing from rock to rock. It did this a dozen times as I watched. It was pure play and I have the suspicion that at one point in the game the gull turned to me with a faint grin on its face!

That gull could have rescued the chick on the roof single-handed. Perhaps not all herring gulls have this same propensity or skill. Or it may be that the Brixham gulls had found a new game that looked to the ignorant human eye uncommonly like a mass-attempt at rescue of a chick.

A pair of pied wagtails were going about their lawful business, catching insects, in a garden in England, when a cat appeared from out of the shrubbery and caught the hen. The cat was walking away with it when the cock wagtail ran straight at the cat and went into a broken-wing display dragging one wing along the ground as if injured, the well-known trick by which some birds seek to distract a predator from a nest containing eggs or young. The cat dropped the hen and tried to catch the cock but both flew off. This is a perfectly straightforward story; the only departure from the normal is that it concerns one adult bird using the distraction display to protect another adult. To that extent it belongs to the higher-order behaviour.

The next story is only slightly out of the normal, but again is sufficiently near-normal to be acceptable without question. A magpie was attacking a thrush when a second thrush flew down and tweaked the magpie's tail. The magpie wheeled around and the first thrush then seized its tail. This happened a number of times until the magpie flew off defeated, pursued by the two thrushes. Usually it is the magpie, in common with other members of the crow family, that does the tail tweaking, and it was a little surprising to see the thrush adopting the same tactics, more or less literally hoisting the magpie with its own petard.

Blackbirds are near relatives of the thrush but are more aggressive among themselves, the males especially fighting in spring over territory. Where three or more territories meet, there we can often see the same number of male blackbirds assembled and in violent dispute, although they seldom do each other physical harm. On one particular occasion it was not the males that were fighting but two females, readily recognized as such from their brown plumage as compared with the glossy black of the male. The two birds tumbled and rolled about the lawn, fighting most viciously until one was on its back and the other was on top of it and appeared to be trying to force its beak down the other's throat. Suddenly a male blackbird landed beside them and hurled himself on them. He seemed to tear them apart, chastised one and sent her flying, then turned on the other and did the same. After which he flew away.

It is unusual, as we have seen, for the male in any species to attack a female. It is even more uncommon for a male to interfere with two females when they are fighting — the human species not excepted! Whether we interpret this as altruistic behaviour on the part of the male blackbird or not, at least we can say that he must have run considerable risk in seeking to separate two warring females.

The story of the jackdaw from Italy comes more certainly into the realm of care-giving or altruistic behaviour. The jackdaw had been hand-reared from a nestling and on the farm where it lived it was on good terms with the cats and the other animals, but its favourite was one of four Alsatians, on whose back it was in the habit of perching.

One day a tractor turned into the farmyard. There was an improvised contraption in front of it which prevented the driver from seeing the ground immediately in front of him. He made for a gap between two buildings at an excessive pace and was bearing down on a sleeping dog, which happened to be stone deaf. The owner of the dog seeing the danger shouted at it. The dog, naturally, could not hear, and there was no time to run over to him, although people ran towards him and joined in the shouting. A stone thrown at the dog missed its mark and the dog slept on. Suddenly a black form swooped down from the roof of an outhouse. It was the jackdaw. It reached the dog, pecked its ear, the dog jumped up yapping and saw its danger just in time.

Another instance of a similar kind was recorded by a family accustomed to having tea on the lawn. They had a 'pet' robin that would come around scrounging crumbs. The lawn was surrounded by coarse herbage and a hedge, beyond which were some Rhode Island Red fowls. One afternoon a cat came through the long grass stalking the robin. The Rhode Island cockerel had also wandered on to the lawn. It stretched up its full height, so that it had a full view of the cat which was hidden from the robin. As the cat bunched for the pounce, the cockerel with half-open wings lunged itself at the robin, which flew up so that the cat just missed it.

To the best of the knowledge of those people assembled on the lawn, the cockerel had never before shown aggression towards the robin nor need one suppose that it had any aggressive intention towards it. It would be remarkable if it had. There were ample opportunities for this to happen because the two birds often foraged on the lawn at the same time. So this looks like a deliberate attempt on the part of the cockerel to warn the robin of impending danger.

This episode seems to be on a par with the action of a rook. C.L.M. who recorded the events told how, on a day when the ground was snow-covered and the sun shining, he was attracted by a persistent shriek from a bird in distress which turned out to be a starling trying frantically to escape from a sparrowhawk. At the same time the incessant cawing from a flock of rooks getting closer attracted the man's attention. He saw a rook dive from a great height to the sparrowhawk and its struggling victim. The rook attacked the sparrowhawk, forcing it to release its prey. The rook then flew off.

There is nothing new in birds attacking hawks. Groups of small birds will do so, while larger birds such as members of the crow family have been known to do so singly but more commonly in pairs. When rooks do this they tend to fly around the hawk, as if taunting it or playing with it, so that there is a kind of aerial battle which may go on for quite a long time. The rook's stooping attack and its departure as soon as the starling was free suggests supernormal behaviour, at the least, and it seems from the description to have been quite purposive.

The rook's dive must have been spectacular. Also, it was very obvious. We see less of the actions of small birds that haunt the undergrowth or the bushes, and it may be that many instances of altruistic behaviour escape our notice for this reason. There is, however, a story of a robin redbreast, seen by B.S. in England, one day in spring. He saw the bird trapped between the wiry branches of a sage bush. What caught his attention was the small cloud of dust and feathers as the robin struggled to free itself. The man went to release it and then saw another robin apparently trying to pull the twigs apart with its beak. Strikingly, it continued to do this until the man was within his arm's length of the bird. When he had freed the trapped bird it rested for a while on his open palm before flying off to join the other robin, presumably its mate, that had perched nearby.

As has been said, this is a miscellaneous collection. If it was not, one would suspect something was wrong. Each is extraordinary; but we are dealing with extraordinary behaviour. One can spend a lot of time, in a sceptical mood, pulling each story to pieces. It is a good alternative to crossword puzzles. After

Fig. 14 The earliest illustration of care-giving in a bird, from the famous legend of the pelican, said to peck her own breast to feed her chicks on her blood, in the fifteenth-century natural history book *Hortus Sanitatis*. The truth is that pelicans are poor parents. (Fourteenth-century original woodcut)

one has cross-examined a few of the tellers, and become convinced of the authenticity of their observations, one arrives at a general conclusion. This is, that if only half of the stories are correct, or even half-correct, there are grounds for suspecting that even birds can and do help each other in distress.

12.
Rescue
by
Mammals

There are many stories of unusual things done by domestic dogs, like the retriever bitch that took to stealing bottles of milk from doorsteps, removing the metal caps and drinking the milk, an event for which I can vouch personally. Although they have nothing to do with altruism or compassion they give colour to the kind of anecdote contained in the previous chapter and also to those forming the subject of this present chapter. They teach us that individual animals can depart from normal behaviour to excite our imagination.

Perhaps the simplest example of an unselfish act belonging to this same category is contained in a letter received from Australia many years ago. The writer was discoursing in the letter about one thing and another and almost incidentally recounted an observation she had made of three dogs at a railway station. She saw them jump down from one platform and cross the line. At the other side two of them jumped up on to the other platform but the third, the smallest of the trio, just could not manage it. The largest of the three dogs was seen to go to the edge of the platform, lean over and pick up this smallest dog by the scruff of its neck and lift it up on to the platform.

It was a trivial story by any standard and yet the mere fact that one dog can show concern for a companion, and have the wit to do something about it, is illuminating. It is of interest also that a similar event was actually photographed in Los Angeles. A series of three photographs showing the event was published in *Animals* for 1964. Two dogs were playing in a street when one was struck and killed by a passing car. The other, a larger dog, ran to his friend and, apparently realizing that all was not well, took hold of the harness worn by the smaller dog, dragged the body to the kerb, pulled it up out of the way of passing traffic and mounted guard over his lost friend. What is not known is how the photographer happened to be on the spot when an opportunity to take these photographs presented itself. Nevertheless it is difficult to believe from examination of these pictures that they have been faked. Assuming them to be a genuine record of an actual event, then it is very difficult to avoid the conclusion that animals do sometimes show compassion beyond what we would normally expect of them.

Both these stories are of domestic dogs performing an action in an environment far removed from the natural. The question is whether in the wild, where railway platforms and kerbs of pavements do not occur, similar rescue attempts could or would be made. Fortunately, there is an authentic observation of a pack of African hunting dogs crossing a ravine. One by one they jumped into the ravine and scrambled up the other side. All were successful except one that could not make the final jump up on to the opposite bank of the ravine. And there it was, helpless, unable to join its companions. It may have whimpered. The pack was seen to hesitate. The leader stopped and stood his ground while several of the dogs in the rear of the strung-out pack turned back and together grabbed various parts of the unfortunate one and lifted it up on to the bank. After this, the pack, as if on word of command, resumed their journey.

Reading the original, of which this is a brief summary, one becomes aware of the truth of a statement, repeated by several writers, that animals are keenly aware of all that their fellows are doing, without appearing to be so. Remarkable in this story is the unanimity of action on the part of the pack as well as the concerted action of the rescuers. On the other hand, the members of a pack of hunting dogs are related. They constitute a family, so they possess the same or similar genes. This rescue falls therefore under the heading of genetic altruism. The same cannot be said with equal confidence of the Australian dogs, each of which was a different breed. Nevertheless, both stories indicate not only a willingness to help but the same method being used. Since, by definition, the action of the Australian dogs can be interpreted justifiably as true altruism, we have in these two examples the almost perfect illustration of the fine boundary between the two forms of altruism.

The incursion into true altruism is taken a step further by Mrs Bridget Pardington, of Herefordshire, England, who trains dogs in obedience. Her father was a semi-invalid, often tied to a wheel-chair by arthritis. Despite this he took in many dogs to gentle them, train them and settle them in new homes. One of these was a savage, stray half-breed. Another was a cocker spaniel puppy that avoided the larger dog, which seemed to have taken a dislike to it. One day, when out on a walk, the puppy fell into a river in spate. The larger dog went to the bank, leaned down and took the puppy by the scruff. At that moment the bank gave way. Both dogs were now in danger of being swept away. The larger dog floundered but eventually reached a shallow where its longer legs touched bottom. For the one and only time, the puppy followed it and eventually reached the shallows and finally the bank.

This was not genetic altruism!

The theme is continued in another recorded incident, when D.W. was crossing a moor in Cumbria on a moonlit night with her collie. The dog disappeared and no amount of whistling brought him back. Then D.W. heard what she described as his 'come-and-see' bark. She finally located the collie and found him guarding a Scotch terrier with its front paw in a gin trap. The collie is described as a dog that normally would show aggression and attack any dog it met, yet when it came across one in distress it did as much as any human being could have done, short of releasing the victim: it called its owner to come and investigate.

It is gratifying to know that gin traps are now outlawed in some parts of the world, but the use of them as well as of running nooses for snares must have inflicted untold suffering over the years on a very large number of animals, wild and domestic. What happened to a few of these piteous casualties has been recorded in anecdotes about foxes being caught and doomed to an agonizing death by pain, possibly gangrene and starvation. If we are to believe these anecdotes, some foxes bit through the trapped leg and gained their freedom. (It is, however, difficult to believe that a three-legged fox would have survived for long, whether it lived in fox-hunting country or farming country. So such respite would be temporary.) There are also a few stories, not of a fox biting through its own leg but of its mate doing this for it.

The sequence can be repeated in regard to rats. There are stories of a rat caught in a trap severing its own leg with its teeth, or biting off its tail if it happened to be trapped by that member. There are also stories of another rat doing the job for the trapped one. One of the most fascinating letters on this subject I received was written by an elderly lady. She told how they were pestered by rats and had set large break-back traps. She and her sister went to inspect one of the traps and found a rat in it caught by its tail. Her sister went to find something with which to kill the rat. She herself went in the other direction for a pail of water to drown it. They both arrived simultaneously back on the scene, her sister carrying an axe and she a pail of water only to find that a second rat had arrived on the scene also and was biting through the trapped rat's tail. While the two ladies stood and watched in amazement, the now freed rat ran away followed by its companion, while the best part of the rat's tail remained secured in the spring of the trap.

The usual explanation for rat stories of this kind given by those who make a special study of them is that there cannot be any question of compassion, but that rats will so readily attack another rat, especially one that is showing abnormal behaviour, that the biting through can be regarded as an aggressive act.

There is a tendency among ethologists to use this same explanation for anecdotes about birds. The example (chapter 11) of the two sparrows allegedly trying to rescue another sparrow with its head jammed in the hole in the garage would be interpreted as one sparrow attacking another and then in turn being attacked by a third. Admittedly, this could be the correct explanation; it could also be incorrect. There is no way of testing it and ethologists are not always right.

Take the case of a person drowning. Another person dives in to the rescue and, when he reaches the spot, the drowning person clutches his arms thereby endangering the lives of both. The textbook remedy is for the lifeguard, or would-be rescuer, to push the head of the one he is trying to rescue under the water or to hit him on the jaw to stop his struggles. An intelligent being from outer space, unable to communicate with human beings and in ignorance of our ways, watching such a rescue would probably be tempted to suppose this was aggression and not compassion.

Aggression can therefore be part of compassion. When he was a game warden in Uganda, Rennie Bere at one time had an Alsatian dog and an oribi which were great friends. Caesar, the Alsatian, distinguished himself one day by saving the oribi, a medium-sized antelope, from a fully-grown cheetah, a pet of one of Bere's neighbours which was kept on a long lead when not locked up. On this occasion it had broken loose. The oribi was grazing outside as the cheetah shot past the open French windows going straight for it. The Alsatian sprang up and went straight for the cheetah, which stopped in its tracks, while the oribi escaped. Theoretically, the Alsatian should have had little chance against the cheetah. Indeed, dogs generally seem to have almost an instinctive fear of leopards and cheetahs even to the point of distrusting the dressed skin of one of these big cats. For the Alsatian to have charged the cheetah was therefore an act of great courage as well as loyalty to its friend. And courage was triumphant. Certainly it was out of character, which is roughly the equivalent of calling it higher-order behaviour.

A similar encounter on a smaller scale took place when a fox terrier was at liberty in the road. A large dog made to attack him. A cat living with the same family of people as the terrier sprang on to the neck of the big dog and diverted its attention until its owner had come up and secured it. It looked like a deliberate act of rescue, although it has to be admitted that a cat will adopt this stratagem purely in its own defence.

A retriever and a pony were firm friends. One hot day when the two were out together, the dog went into the river to swim. The pony had a drink. Then the owner of the two animals could hear the pony's hoofs clattering on the stones of the river bed. At the same time there was a furious splashing; the dog was dragged under by an otter. Without delay the pony waded in, swam strongly and swiftly to the spot, flailed with its front hoofs, striking the water again and again. At this the otter broke off the attack, the dog swam ashore and was fully recovered in a few days.

It is perhaps surprising also that an otter should attack a dog as large as a retriever, yet we have to remember that the otter was in its element and the dog was out of its element. It is more surprising that the pony should have joined in the affray, since horses do not normally encounter or attack otters, but we have the assurance of E.M.C., of Cumbria, that this did happen and presumably it is no less likely than the story I received from Ph.H., of Bruges, who, when in what is now Zaire, was driving through the Belula Country with his wife and daughter. As they were going through a village they noticed a young goat in the middle of the road trying to get away from their car. It had only the use of its front legs. Its hind quarters appeared to have been crushed by a previous vehicle and the goat was dragging itself along on the ground. Then came another goat of about the same age and size running from the village and started to push the injured one with his head to remove him from danger. Although he himself was in danger from Ph.H.'s oncoming car, he continued his gallant effort to push his companion to safety. Or was it that the second one was butting the injured goat aggressively? (Friends who keep one or more goats as pets or for their milk assure me that if they were to tell me all the things they have seen goats do I would be astonished.)

More readily acceptable, but in this instance only an example of the emergence of an inherited pattern of behaviour, was the story of the tom-cat that killed a stoat which had come into the garden. The she-cat, companion to the tom, gave a peculiar call as the stoat came towards her. The tom thereupon attacked and killed the stoat.

One wonders whether the story of Jacko the grey monkey is something more than yet another example of an instinctive behaviour. Hugh Mackay gave his small daughter, four years old, a tiny grey monkey as a pet. The two were inseparable. One day Mr and Mrs Mackay were horrified to see a cobra about to strike the child. They were helpless to intervene, but from a tree above, Jacko the monkey hurtled down, gripped the snake by its neck and buried its teeth in its body. Snake and monkey rolled over and over. Eventually Mr Mackay managed to kill the snake — but Jacko was dead from snake-bite. The snake must have struck him as he landed on it and before he had time to administer the death bite.

We know from other sources that monkeys will endeavour to succour their fellows that are in danger from snakes, but they do it usually by creating a diversion, running towards the snake and then away again, seeking to distract its attention while their comrade makes good his escape, after which all return to the trees. To that extent the story of Jacko is not typical behaviour for a monkey and seems to have constituted a deliberate intervention, taking extreme risk because the cobra was so near the young girl.

Perhaps the following story is more amusing than anything else, yet it has a contribution to make to the present discussion. Albert W. Erickson and Leo H. Miller, on 22 July 1961, were watching North American brown bears fishing for salmon in the shallow rapids of a stream, when two she-bears, each with three cubs, came down to the river. The two parties merely happened to be near each other. The two sets of cubs became mixed up and the two mothers ended by squabbling, in the course of which one cub fell into the river and was carried swiftly along. Both mothers jumped in and swam after it. The smaller she-bear reached it first and helped it to the bank. The larger she-bear made her way back to the remaining five cubs, once she had seen the other cub rescued, and was last seen leading the five away. The mother and five were again seen on 4 August still in a party or family group.

Going back to the events in the salmon river, neither of the she-bears could have known whether the one that fell into the river was hers or not and it seems not to have mattered, judging by their subsequent behaviour, whose it was. It is impossible to say therefore whether the action of the she-bears was genetically altruistic or ideally altruistic. The distinction between the two, as is already apparent from other examples given in these chapters, is frustratingly blurred. The actions of the she-bears serve to make confusion worse confounded.

How indistinct this boundary is can be shown by a recent report of a dog rescuing a baby from a possible fall to its death. This happened in Malmo, in

Sweden, in May 1977. Mr Leif Rongemo walked from the kitchen of his flat to the living room, where a few minutes earlier he had left his two-year-old daughter Anneli sitting in a chair and his Alsatian, Roy, asleep on the floor. Now, the casement window was wide open and neither child nor dog could be seen. Mr Rongemo rushed to the window, looked down to the street thirty-six feet below, then heard a scuffling noise to his left. The child must have mounted the back of a settee, undone a plastic catch on the window frame and crawled out onto a two-foot-wide ledge running around the building. She was now four feet along the ledge with the dog padding behind her and whining.

The father shouted to his wife to telephone the fire brigade, seized a bedspread, rushed downstairs, called to a neighbour to help hold out the bedspread to catch Anneli if she fell, then stood waiting, afraid to call to the child. For three minutes they waited as the child crawled farther along the ledge, the dog following, still whining. Then, suddenly, Roy reached forward, seized the child's diaper and slowly shuffled backwards dragging the child to where its mother was waiting to receive it.

Although the only source of this story was a newspaper account, it is both credible and acceptable. Moreover, it is justifiable to argue that the sequence is explainable in terms of the usual behaviour of carnivorous and other mammals, since the retrieving of young that have wandered prematurely from the nest is commonplace. In this instance, we are dealing with a domestic dog that is part of the family, that regards Mr Rongemo and his wife as pack leader and his mate and the child as in loco a puppy. The retrieving of a real puppy would normally be by the scruff, but often the most convenient part of the puppy, its leg or even its head may be taken into the mouth for purposes of transport. In this case, the diaper is the most convenient thing by which to hold it. From these considerations, it is feasible to argue that there was nothing unusual in what the Alsatian did.

There are, however, important overtones. First, it is usually the female that carries out the retrieving. Secondly, it is likely that had the child wandered from the room into the passage-way and so into another room, the dog would have made no attempt to retrieve it. To that extent we can suppose that Roy recognized a departure from the normal when the child climbed out of the window. Thirdly, the fact that the dog shuffled backwards, once it had seized the child, instead of turning to walk head-foremost, as it would in normal retrieving, suggests an appreciation of the dangers of the situation. Even a large dog like an Alsatian would be able to turn right about sure-footedly on a ledge two feet wide. With a small child held in its mouth, to turn one way would mean holding its burden over empty space and to turn the other way would be to risk rubbing the child along the harsh surface of the wall, if not worse.

Finally, and most convincing of all, the dog was described as whining, more or less throughout the operation apparently. Whining is used by a dog to draw attention to its own needs, as, for example, when it wants a door to be opened. It also whines in more distressful situations in which it itself is not in pain or discomfort, when the pain of another causes the whine to turn to a whimper. Altogether, therefore, we may have reasonable confidence that Roy, in rescuing Anneli, was using typical canine behavioural traits but not without some appreciation of the difficulties and dangers besetting its young human companion.

The great value of such an incident, in which there is a fair certainty of true altruism being shown, is that it supplies a yardstick by which other incidents, including some of those retailed in this chapter, which rest on less solid foundations, can be judged. Even so, one needs to be on the lookout for even better examples to set the matter beyond doubt. The great joy about pursuing this form of unnatural natural history is that sooner or later this further evidence is forthcoming.

We have already seen (p. 76) how a piece of solid research revealed the evidence, quite unexpectedly, that helped in the interpretation of the behaviour of a mongoose. In recent times there has been solid evidence from orthodox scientific research that trapped animals could be expected to perform auto-amputation to save themselves. This is to be found in a Russian scientific journal, *Trudy Biol. Institute* 1940, in a report by Yu. N. Klimov, entitled *Data on the biology of the ermine.*

Among other things Klimov studied the stomach contents of trapped ermine (or stoats). A translation of one sentence reads: 'In approximately 4% of the guts (that is over 50 out of a total of 1429), [portions of] the leg of the ermine itself were found, which it had chewed off after falling into the trap.' This is disappointingly laconic, yet it appears to be stating positively that some individuals were captured that lacked a leg and had fragments of ermine bone and ermine fur in their stomachs. Either that or some captives still had four legs but had ermine remains in the gut. The first of these would point to auto-amputation. The second would indicate that the individual being examined had bitten through the leg of a trapped companion to free it and then itself been caught before it could free itself or digest the remains of its companion's limb. Even amidst this welter of uncertainty there is a distinct suspicion that stories of rats, foxes and stoats seen in the act of auto-amputation or of freeing a companion by performing the operation on it, could be true. If an Alsatian can show such appreciation of the dangers attending a human baby crawling along a two-foot ledge, it should not be beyond the wit of a rat, fox or stoat to put two-and-two together and act appropriately in other situations calling for unusual rescue methods.

Now that one form of alleged rescue by stoats can be seen as having a semblance of support from organized science, another anecdote can be given greater credence. It concerns weasels, close relatives of stoats. A family of weasels, including two adults and two babies, were seen running along a river bank, the mother leading. She made several short rushes to the water's edge and then ran on again. After she had done this several times, it was seen that a third baby was in the water being swept along by the current. Then the mother climbed down a post standing in the water until she was level with the surface.

As the baby was swept towards her, she grabbed it by the scruff and held it high out of the water. When she was halfway up the post she slipped and fell into the river and had to swim with her baby to the safety of the post. Once again she fell. This time she seemed too tired to climb up the post with her burden. The father suddenly climbed down the post headfirst, took the mother by the scruff and dragged her and the baby inch by inch up the post and on to firm ground.

This method of comparing stories of animals of the same species and then equating these with what is claimed for individuals of related species, as well as with those of unrelated species, forms the best use of corroborative evidence. If we believe in what has been said of stoats (ermine) supporting the story of the weasel mother, and then recall how the weasel's method resembles that of the distantly related dog, we have a cohesive, convincing pattern and a broadening pattern.

We can do the same with sheep. It is not unusual for a ewe to be seen lying on its back with its legs in the air. She is said to be a 'cast ewe'. Apparently, a sheep eating lush grass or acorns may become distended with gases from the digestive processes. Also, cast ewes are often pregnant ewes. Whatever the cause, a cast ewe if not restored to the normal position will die in a matter of hours (up to twenty-four hours). A shepherd will assist any cast ewe he sees; a passer-by may do so. The task is not difficult. Indeed, it is not uncommon for a cast ewe, as someone approaches it, to struggle on to its feet of its own accord. It only needs that little encouragement. It is also not uncommon for another ewe to go up to it and butt it and heave it on to its feet, as if sheep were as much aware as human beings are that something is wrong and that that is the cure.

This ties in well with what we have already learned about sheep assisting a blind companion. Together, the behaviour of ewes towards a cast ewe, which is wholly credible as an almost everyday event somewhere in sheep-rearing country, and the behaviour of the guide sheep for blind ewes make the next observation more acceptable. A sheep farmer in southwest England saw one of his sheep charging a snowdrift with its head lowered. As he drew near he saw that the sheep had driven a tunnel into snow several feet deep. She also scraped at the snow with her feet, at the same time bleating. Muffled sounds, apparently in reply, were coming from deep within the drift. The farmer himself now dug into the snow, the ewe standing and watching, uttering short excited bleats. When the buried ewe was released, the two sheep 'ran to meet each other, bleating loudly'.

To balance one anecdote against another is more than merely comparing them. It is using the process of extrapolation. The true definition of extrapolation is mathematical, but the word has been used in a modified form by biologists to indicate a method of arguing or deducing from a firm and acceptable basis towards less readily acceptable phenomena or events. For instance, it is known beyond a doubt that many mammals transport or retrieve their babies holding them by the scruff with their teeth. Parents may do this even when their young are half-grown, although this is exceptional. When therefore a professional zoologist records having seen Cape hunting dogs lift one of their number out of a ravine by the same method, nobody raises an eyebrow.

By extrapolation, there is nothing remarkable in the observation of a large dog having lifted a smaller dog on to a railway platform in Australia, or of a dog lifting its dead companion on to the pavement in a street in Los Angeles. A weasel snatching her baby from the river becomes credible, as does her mate rescuing her and her baby by the same method. The rescue of a baby from a ledge overhanging the street by an Alsatian dog becomes believable. The latest in this series is the rescue of its owner by an Alsatian. Because it has been possible to investigate this one more completely than any other, it is being dealt with in greater detail than usual, in the next chapter.

13.
Heroism
Investigated

Eye-witness testimony is notoriously unreliable. It has been said that there were nineteen people present at the death-bed of King Charles II of Britain and that there are nineteen different accounts of what happened. This is not surprising. Different people notice different things in any sequence of events. As a rule nobody takes special note and remembers accurately every detail. Also, some people have better powers of observation than others. Moreover, people's memories of the same events vary because they are affected not only by the quality of individual memories but also because, as they turn the event over in their minds after it has happened, they tend to alter the emphasis, value or perspective of the various elements that make up the whole occurrence. The only way to ensure anything approaching one hundred per cent accuracy is to write down the details while they are actually occurring, and even then some things will be missed.

I am fond of quoting in this connection a personal experience. In 1949 I spent an afternoon beside a mill stream in Sussex watching eels downriver of the sluice gate trying to migrate upstream. One after another the eels swam rapidly towards the brickwork supporting the wooden sluice gate and wriggled up it. As each eel lost momentum in the climbing, it sought with its head or tail a crevice in the mortar between the bricks. From that point, the eel would then, while anchored by the head, feel with its tail for another crevice, or if the tail had been inserted into a crevice it would search with the head. By this means some of the eels managed to climb the vertical face of the brickwork and reach the seepage of water coming through the sluice gate. That briefly is what I watched time after time during the course of the afternoon. I took the precaution of taking notes at the time and when the eels had stopped I wrote the episode up in full, aided by my notes and a fresh memory, and published the account of this in the *Illustrated London News*.

I recounted this story on a number of occasions during the years that followed, always, as far as I could tell, repeating word for word my original story. Some half dozen years later it occurred to me to go back to my original published account and I was surprised to find how in the telling my story had diverged. The principle had been retained but the details had differed. Had I not committed the whole story to paper so soon after the event, but had written it up several days or weeks later, I should have been in doubt on almost every point. Had I then found myself in a witness box in court being questioned by a barrister, that same lawyer would have had little difficulty in tearing my story to pieces by dint of cross-examination, so that I would have been made to appear an unreliable witness, even a liar. Anyone who has appeared as a witness in a law case or has served on a jury and has listened to an eye-witness being cross-examined first by the opposing counsel and then by the defending counsel, will know exactly what I mean. If he has appeared, as I have done on two occasions, as an expert witness, he will be even more able to appreciate the truth of this.

If I had to leave the main discussion on alleged animal altruism at this point, I would have said enough to have nullified almost everything written in this book since, with few exceptions, it is dependent on eye-witness testimony and nothing else. It so happened that, after the text of this book had been completed, I read in the *Daily Telegraph* for 7 July 1977 an account of a dog alleged to have rescued his owner from drowning. The opportunity to investigate such a claim at firsthand was too good to miss. As it turned out, this was less easy than I would have supposed and because the circumstances are unique it seems to me essential to describe the whole course of my inquiry in full detail even at the risk of boredom. Only by doing so can anyone reading this be in possession of all the known facts, as well as the questions that arise, and therefore able to attempt his own conclusions.

First I propose to quote word for word, for completeness from the *Daily Telegraph*, the account as it appeared in that newspaper under the title 'Alsatian rescues owner':

> An Alsatian dog, which rescued its owner, Mr Michael Gibson, 24, from drowning in the River Kennet at Reading, Berks, was yesterday recommended for an RSPCA award.
>
> Mr Gibson, a builder, of Edgehill Street, Reading, was swimming in the river when he had an attack of cramp.
>
> This brought on asthma, from which Mr Gibson is a chronic sufferer.
>
> He said: 'My dog grabbed me by my T-shirt when I thought I was going under for the third time. He dragged me to the bank but it was too steep.
>
> 'I was semi-conscious and could not have got out on my own. He then swam with me about 70 yards to where the bank slopes down to the river and pulled me out of the water.'
>
> As he lay on the bank the 12-year-old dog, which Mr Gibson has had from a pup, stood guard over him, keeping away would-be helpers.
>
> The police were called and an officer persuaded the dog to let him tend Mr Gibson and send him to hospital.

I addressed a letter to Mr Gibson, the address on the envelope being given as it appeared in the newspaper report, namely Edgehill Street, Reading. I also tried to obtain from Directory Enquiries his telephone number but was told there was no subscriber of that name living in that street in Reading. This is not surprising because, as I subsequently learned, Mr Michael Gibson is a heating engineer who lives and works with his father, and their entry in the telephone directory is under the title of the father's business. I enclosed with my letter a brief questionnaire the answers to which should have given me a clearer picture of what took place. At the same time, in my covering letter, I asked Mr Gibson whether he would very kindly telephone me, or whether he would at least allow me to come to Reading to interview him.

Nearly a fortnight later my letter was returned by the Post Office marked 'Not known'. In the meantime a further note had appeared in the *Daily Telegraph* for 9 July announcing that the dog had been awarded a certificate for services to humanity by the Canine Defence League. Accordingly I telephoned the Canine Defence League who were most anxious to supply me with information, but after three telephone calls on three subsequent days they regretted that they were unable to supply Mr Gibson's full address. They were also unable to give me any details of the episode, which I found a little surprising. They did, however, recommend I should get in touch with the *Reading Chronicle*, which, they said, had also published an account of the episode.

In writing to that local newspaper I also sent a new letter and questionnaire to Mr Gibson with the request to the editor that he should very kindly address the envelope and post the letter. I also asked if I could purchase a copy of the *Reading Chronicle* in which the account had appeared. In a very short while after the despatch of this letter, Mr Gibson telephoned me and a few days later I received a copy of the *Reading Chronicle* for 8 July.

Mr Gibson's first comment when he had reached me by telephone was that the reports in the newspapers were 'slightly exaggerated'. Before going further, it may be as well to quote the report as it appeared at greater length in the *Reading Chronicle* for 8 July:

> *Life-saving medal for brave dog*
> *Alsatian hero of river drama*
> A 10-year-old alsatian will be the toast of Reading today [Friday] when he is awarded a medal for saving his master's life earlier this week.
> Mr Michael Gibson of 14, Edgehill Street, was rescued by his dog Kim, when he was close to drowning in the River Kennet on Tuesday.
> This morning the National Canine Defence League will present Kim with their top award in the offices of the *Chronicle*.
> A spokesman for the league said they only made such awards to animals on very rare occasions.
> 'But this sounds such a marvellous story about a very brave dog that we will certainly have to make an award,' said the spokesman.
> Kim's owner, Michael, was delighted when he heard the news.
> 'The dog does certainly deserve the honour, after all he saved my life — normally he would never go into that stretch of river as it is much too fast-flowing for him. I just don't know how he managed to do it and there is no way I could ever reward him enough,' he said.
> Mr Gibson was swimming in the Kennet near Courage's Brewery when he had cramp and suffered an asthmatic attack.
> 'I just could not breathe and I managed to grab hold of a piece of metal above me,' explained Mr Gibson.
> 'I could not move and must have held on to the metal bar for about an hour. I knew I was going under and became unconscious.'

Seeing his master on the verge of drowning, the dog, Kim, jumped into the fast flowing river and dragged him ashore.

'I was out cold. The next thing I knew was when I regained consciousness and found myself lying on the towpath. Kim must somehow have dragged me out by his teeth.'

'If he had not been there I would definitely have gone. The water was about seven or eight feet deep.'

Kim was reluctant to let the matter rest there and when a policeman arrived on the scene the dog ferociously defended his unconscious master from the intruder. Eventually, however, P.C. Ian Bateman was able to reach Mr Gibson and get him taken to Battle Hospital.

There are clearly important points of difference between the two newspaper reports, and both differ from Mr Gibson's own account. This was, that he was swimming in the River Kennet and got into difficulties with cramp. The dog was also swimming with him, so there was no question of the dog having entered the water to give assistance. Mr Gibson explained to me that he managed to struggle to the bank and although he was able to grasp a support he was unable to pull himself out of the water owing to the steepness and the height of the bank. Then he felt himself losing consciousness and came to seventy yards downstream where the bank was low and the dog had been able to haul him out of the water, after having dragged him by his shirt to that point. Then, as the two newspaper reports claimed, the dog had stood over his owner and defied anyone to go near, until a policeman was able to persuade the dog to move. The spot where this took place is isolated but there was one witness able to corroborate that the dog had towed its owner to a convenient landing place and there it dragged him from the water, tearing the shirt in the process.

The reason for giving an account of this episode in such great detail is that it emphasizes two important points. The first is that in trying to reach the one person who could give me an accurate account of what happened, I encountered considerable difficulties. Having spent no small amount of time and effort on this I appreciate that a reporter would not be tempted to spend what he would consider unnecessary time in order to probe the story or to check whether his description of the event was strictly accurate. Indeed, had I not regarded the investigation of this episode as of first-class importance I would not myself have persisted. I would merely have set the story down using the two newspaper reports, as has been necessary with so many of the examples I have included here.

The second point to emerge is that although there are contradictions and deficiencies in the published accounts, and between these and Mr Gibson's later personal account, there remains what appears to be the one solid fact that the man in difficulties in the water was towed by his dog to a spot where the dog was able to pull him out on to a bank. Yet, when one looks further into it, even this is not as straightforward as it appears at first glance.

In order to resolve the many discrepancies between the three reports I had been able to gather, it seemed important to look around for eye-witnesses.

There was at least one, there may have been more, but it has not been possible to find who they were. Moreover, it is a reasonable assumption, since nobody came to Mr Gibson's aid until he was on the bank, that any witnesses, if they could be traced, would have little to contribute. The next line of inquiry seemed to be to start at the hospital and retrace the course of events. The hospital, understandably, were not authorized to disclose details of a patient's condition nor of the treatment given to him. For example, had I been told that on arrival at the hospital he had been unconscious or in a state of collapse, it would have been possible to infer that Mr Gibson's recollection of events would have been necessarily unreliable.

The evidence from the police was that P.C. Ian Bateman was called to the River Kennet and on arrival found Mr Gibson lying on the towpath by the river overflow, wet and in an apparent asthmatic condition. Presumably he was not unconscious although in a distressed condition. The Alsatian would not at first allow the officer near his master, but P.C. Bateman reported that when he spoke sharply to the dog 'it decided to be quiet' and allowed him to give the necessary care and attention to the patient. Although there may have been witnesses present, no record was kept of their identities.

According to Mr Gibson, the dog was swimming in the river with him but made no attempt at rescue until he had reached the bank, failed to negotiate it and started to lose consciousness. If we take the quoted words 'I was out cold' to be meaningful, then Mr Gibson, as he lost consciousness, let go his grip of the metal bar, was carried by the fast-flowing river and grounded in shallow water where the bank was low. By the natural course of events he would have been stranded there, like any other jetsam. Unlike other jetsam he would have been able to drag himself clear of the water, assuming he was not wholly unconscious; and he could well have done this unaided but, because of his physical condition, had no later recollection of having done so.

What needs to be determined is the role played by the dog from the moment Mr Gibson relinquished his hold on the metal bar to the moment when the police officer arrived. The fact that the Alsatian 'stood guard' over his master is a relatively negligible part of the story. There have been very many instances of dogs refusing to let would-be helpers near their dead or injured owners. Among the Canidae there is reason to believe that a sick or injured member of the species may be attacked, even killed, by its fellows and may be defended by an individual of the pack with which it has been a close companion. Assuming this to be true, then we can suppose that a dog is motivated to guard its owner against attack. A dog, commanded by its owner to do so, will guard a jacket thrown on the ground until its owner gives it the order to do otherwise. Certainly, this is a marked feature of some breeds of dogs and it is difficult not to regard it as a form of altruism which cannot logically be dismissed as genetic altruism.

It would be an impertinence to ask Mr Gibson why he should have been swimming in a T-shirt. In any event it is not relevant to the story. Presumably it was a hot day, he was out for a walk with his dog, saw the inviting coolness of

14 Chimpanzee, showing the short thumb set well back on the hand, making only limited contact with the index finger

15 Cow and calf epitomizing the bond between mother and baby

16 A ewe recognizes her own lamb by its odour

17 Father fox forsakes his customary selfishness and brings food home for the cubs

18 Dog-fox brings food for the nursing vixen

19 Wolf spider carries her burden of maternal responsibility

20 Pelicans, poor parents by ordinary standards, were credited in the past with unusual virtues

21 Crowned plover showing concern for her chick

22 Red fox vixen and young cub

23 The black rhinoceros gives no outward sign of emotions that might lead to the beast succouring one of its fellows

24 Red flanked duiker, a small West African antelope

the river, decided on the spur of the moment to enjoy a bathe and plunged in. None of this matters. The only important points remaining are what the dog was doing while the inert Mr Gibson travelled seventy yards downstream to where he became stranded in the shallows, and whether the dog actually pulled him from the water.

On the second of these two points the answer must surely be in the negative. The only information we have is that the T-shirt was torn. If a dog were to pull a ten-stone man from the water, one would expect the thin shirt to be stripped off the man's back, rather than merely being torn, with the effort of hauling the dead-weight out of water. After all, there are several more feasible explanations: Mr Gibson might have come to momentarily or been only semi-conscious, hence able to drag himself from the water, however laboriously, even if he could remember nothing about this. It may even be, and I am sure a barrister cross-examining a witness in the high court would suggest this, that Mr Gibson finding his shirt torn assumed this, or a witness may have assumed this and planted the idea in Mr Gibson's mind. There is the distinct possibility that in the course of those vital seventy yards the shirt may have become torn by catching on to an obstruction in the water, or, most likely of all, the Alsatian may have torn it with its teeth during the journey of seventy yards.

One thing is certain, the man was physically transported seventy yards, aided by the fast-flowing river, and the dog more or less concurrently swam these same seventy yards, also aided by the river. The rest is a blank. What we do know is that some dogs show signs of anxiety when their owners are bathing. Sometimes they express this by standing at the water's edge and barking continuously, or the dog may enter the water and bark or it may swim out towards the owner. If swimming and near the owner, the dog will attempt a 'rescue' by clawing at the owner's chest and shoulders. Such a dog can be a nuisance and may inflict painful scratches (this could account for the torn T-shirt). In the instance under discussion the dog may even have been instrumental in guiding its unconscious or semi-unconscious owner, keeping him near the bank so that his stranding in the shallow water seventy yards downstream became more certain.

This is a speculative area in which the 'dog-lover' sees a dog battling to save its master and a 'dog-hater' sees only one of those savage and unreliable Alsatians (such is the reputation, largely undeserved, of this particular breed) attacking its owner in the water and trying to drown him. Ethological objectivity would favour a middle course between these two extremes, relating the procedure to the known behaviour of dogs taking a companion by the scruff to lift it out of a ravine or on to a railway platform. To speak of heroism or bravery is perhaps no more than rhetorical. Nevertheless, the mere fact that the dog shows anxiety about the welfare of a member of another species connotes true altruism if only of a rudimentary nature. And you never know, Kim may indeed have saved Michael's life and done so knowingly! We don't know all the answers.

We must necessarily be in the dark also about two other incidents that have occurred since then. The first figured in a news item in the Press for 3 January of this year when it was reported that an injured eight-year-old Labrador named Max helped save, so it was said, the life of eighteen-year-old Julia Dolke trapped by her legs for more than six hours in the early hours of New Year's Day. Her car had run off the road and hit a tree and nobody heard her cries for help until a milkman saw the dog which, so it was alleged, led him to the crashed car. Enquiries at source revealed that the accident took place in the New Forest, in Hampshire on a stretch of road where many cars pass and where there are virtually never any foot passengers. The milkman passing that morning in his delivery van, which was travelling at a much slower speed than the other traffic, noticed the dog at the side of the road but gave it no other thought. He returned by the same route five hours later and, seeing the dog at the same spot, and thinking this was unusual, stopped to investigate. He then saw the car in a ditch and was able to render help to Miss Dolke.

Whether the dog led the man to the car or merely followed or accompanied him to the spot must remain uncertain. The important fact is that the dog, itself injured with a gash along the top of the head, stayed in the same spot, so far as we know, for five hours. It may have been trying to attract attention but, as the milkman explained to me, he himself had some difficulty in summoning help. The cars sped by in both directions and it was a long time before each driver responded to the milkman's urgent signals to stop. There was even less chance of a driver, speeding by, noticing the dog, and least of all, stopping to inquire. For a dog to stay patiently, unattended, in one spot for five hours, is so out of character, that one feels bound to credit the dog with a motivation to seek assistance.

A few days later another newspaper report began with the words: 'A spaniel that kept guard on a clifftop 130 feet above the body of his mistress was put down yesterday.' The rest of the story tells so clearly of a distressing tragedy that the details are deliberately obscured here. Through it there emerges, however, an episode of canine fidelity which deserves to be permanently recorded if only as evidence to add to the theme of this chapter.

The dog was discovered standing guard over the dead woman's scarf a short distance from the edge of the cliff. It seems that whenever anyone approached it, the dog retreated to the edge of the cliff but was finally enticed into a car by a friend who pinned the scarf to a rake handle. Once in the car the dog refused to leave it. Was the dog trying to lead people to the cliff edge with a view to rescuing its mistress? It looks very like it. Even if not, its attachment to her belongings is noteworthy.

14.
Beastly
First-Aid

When an animal is sick or injured it normally has to depend on its own resources for relief. We know from domestic mammals that their basic first-aid for sickness is to forgo food, drink water and lie up somewhere where they are least likely to be disturbed. The same inclinations can be seen in human beings if left to themselves, except that the water is usually tinctured with something to make it more palatable, and the lying up takes the form of staying in bed. We also know from dogs and cats that they will seek out herbs, usually grasses, but given a choice they take only certain kinds of grass, namely the coarser types. On one occasion, for example, the owner of a sick dog, seeing it go into the garden, followed it round and noted that it ate certain types of vegetation, and that it was very selective about this.

For actual lacerations mammals rely on the use of the tongue. They are the only animals able to do this. Licking the wounds can, however, be very effective. A dog with a festered paw, for example, will lick the infected spot interminably until it produces a thoroughly clean wound, which eventually heals rapidly.

In general, however, we can take as our starting point that animals have neither the knowledge, the manipulative ability nor the diversified paraphernalia on which humans depend for restoration of full health. It is not surprising therefore that examples of genuine first-aid, given by one animal to another, are few and far between. Indeed, a fair proportion of this chapter will be devoted to instances in which the human observer thought first-aid was being given but careful examination suggests otherwise.

One very interesting example that was brought to my notice in 1976 by S. G. Mercer, of Devon, concerns a blue tit that had flown into a window and was found lying on the ground below, badly stunned, on its back with its feet in the air. Birds commonly crash into windows. The reasons why they do this and the results that follow form an extensive subject on its own. In brief, either the bird is killed or it is stunned, and if it is only stunned it usually recovers after a varying length of time and flies away. In some instances the period of time before recovery may be lengthy and it is always unwise to suppose that the bird is dead and dispose of the body too soon.

Mr and Mrs Mercer had gone out on hearing the bump on the glass, were standing watching the disabled bird and wondering what best to do, when two more tits descended from the bird table and proceeded to render their own brand of first-aid. I was told that one tit hovered above the prostrate one and beat its wings furiously while the other kept prodding the still body as if trying to turn it over. This treatment was said to have lasted for three to four minutes, at the end of which time the patient slowly turned over on to its front, helped by the one that was prodding it. The bird that had been hovering then alighted and the two first-aiders kept the victim company until it had fully recovered, a matter of about three or four minutes. Then all three took wing and flew away.

Mr Mercer went on to say that after this experience he always gave first-aid to a bird casualty by picking the bird up and imitating the hovering action of a bird over it, namely, by blowing in very gentle puffs on the head and face of the victim. He claims that in all cases recovery has taken three to four minutes and the birds have shown no inclination to leave his open hand until they have fully recovered.

Apart from anything else, these things are worth bearing in mind for anyone who finds birds in an inert state after having crashed into a window. Furthermore, the use of the puffs of breath, or their equivalent, the wings of a bird hovering just above the stunned bird, recalls the use of the towel for refreshing a boxer between rounds, or the cry of the first-aid worker in a street accident as the crowd of curious onlookers presses around him: 'Please stand back and give us air.' The only item in this account that invites scepticism is the suggestion that the action of the two blue tits that arrived on the scene was deliberate.

When the sequence of events is submitted to the usual ethological analysis we arrive at the possiblity that the two birds were drawn there by curiosity, possibly morbid curiosity, and that the action of prodding was aggression carried out at a low threshold. Even that is highly speculative, and eventually we are forced to the conclusion that the interpretation of the events detailed here is anybody's guess. Two purposes are achieved by putting this on record. The first is that it indicates the need for careful observation and careful contemplation of events before coming to the conclusion that this was genuine first-aid. The second is to stimulate pragmatic research by observing and treating bird casualties of this kind.

It is worth comparing this with another account that appeared in a Sunday newspaper in 1963. The writer told of a great tit flying into a windowpane and falling to the ground inert and stunned. He described how, as the great tit lay on the ground, a blue tit flew down and bustled around the fallen bird in what appeared to be a state of anxiety. It even hopped on to the prostrate body as if contemplating what to do next. Then two great tits arrived and dismissed the blue tit. The two new arrivals walked around the casualty as if looking at the problem from all angles. Then one of them made a sudden rush and started pecking the injured bird sharply, at the same time pushing and pulling as if in an endeavour to get it on to its feet again. At last this treatment succeeded.

The writer then went on to say that by now the injured tit was beginning to come round, so the other two redoubled their efforts. When finally they had brought it back to a reasonable state of consciousness by continual pecking, they escorted it off the path where it would be exposed to danger and helped it along to the sheltered safety of a bank. Then the two first-aiders flew off and left the bird to recover by itself.

The description itself suggests that the observer of this event had made an anthropomorphic approach which is reflected in the words he uses to describe the event. Subjecting it to ethological analysis once again, we can have little doubt that the two great tits which arrived on the scene were drawn there by curiosity and that their pushing, pulling and prodding were due to aggression rather than compassion. As I have said, this would be the ethological analysis. Yet no ethologist is infallible and I think of a pair of foxes at the beginning of their courtship, when the male is the more playful and can often be seen nudging the vixen as she rests on the ground, to make her get on her feet to play with him. A blue tit pecking a prostrate blue tit may have the effect of causing the other to get on to its feet. That is, the motivation may be non-altruistic but the result is succourant.

We are, however, left very much in doubt because this subject has never been critically studied. Moreover, it could be that the aggression itself is a form of unwitting first-aid, a brutality that causes the victim to recover just as one has to be brutal by slapping hard the face of a hysterical patient or in walking a potential casualty vigorously about to prevent the patient from dying from cold due to exposure. There is of course another possibility, that the action could in certain circumstances result in a mercy killing, sometimes called compassionate killing (See chapter 19).

There is a story of somebody who saw a gull in distress as if it were retching. Several other gulls crowded round and eventually, according to the observer, one of them put its beak in the gaping beak of the afflicted gull and pulled out a large fish bone. This looks on the face of it like a perfect piece of first-aid and, in its practical result, that is what it was. Continuing with the ethological scepticism, however, one could say that the other gulls were drawn by curiosity about the strange behaviour of their congener and the one that apparently administered the first-aid seized the fish bone as a possible object of food. How can we possibly know the motivation? There is at least one instance of a human first-aider who bound up a man's wounds and also stole his pocket wallet! This shows how mercy and mercenariness sometimes flow in closely parallel lines. This incident, however we interpret it, leads us to the same conclusion as did the previous examples, that probably the primary motivation, but one that can lead to a genuine first-aid, is curiosity. Nowhere can this be seen more emphatically than in the crowd of people that will gather around in a street accident.

Inevitably our next first-aid item is to do with dogs. It was provided by Mrs B. L. Whitelaw of Alderney, in the Channel Islands. In a letter written in 1964 she tells of having had a mongrel called Teddy and a black cat, which were not particularly friendly with each other. They never sat close together and their whole attitude to each other was one of polite tolerance only. Then the cat sustained a wound on its face.

There was no vet on the island and the wound went septic, the whole face swelling in an alarming manner. The wound may have been caused by a rat bite. It was on the nose very near the eyes where the cat's tongue could not reach to lick it. Mrs Whitelaw said her own ministrations were completely unsuccessful. One afternoon she noticed that the cat had sat down close to Teddy, facing his head, whereupon the dog started to lick the cat's swollen face. Far from drawing back at the touch, the cat pressed forward, and as the licking continued she gradually turned on her side and then on her back and this licking went on continually for an hour and a half. At the end of this time the wound was open and clean, and all the swelling of the nose had disappeared. Complete healing took no more than twenty-four hours. The altruistic nature of this action can best be assessed by Mrs Whitelaw's final remark: 'The animals were no more friendly afterwards than before!'

Hugh Ingram has currently two Labradors, a dog, Gunner, and a bitch, Suki. Gunner regularly cleans out the ears of Suki and also cleans her eyes whenever these need attention, all by licking. Suki at one time developed a wart on her leg. Gunner licked it, and licked it, until the wart was no more and it never came back. (Whether the lining of Gunner's stomach is now warty is an open question!) There is a sequel: Suki never attempts to reciprocate the kind offices of Gunner.

The remaining items concern monkeys and apes, which are higher mammals with brains comparable to those of the human, so that one would expect to find genuine and purposeful first-aid if it is to be found anywhere in the animal kingdom. Before passing to these, however, it is of interest to recall a report by Mr P. C. Harthoorn and his wife, who had watched two giant anteaters in the grounds of a travelling circus. One of the anteaters had a gash in the top of its head, and its companion was running to and fro between the drinking bowl and the wounded animal, filling its mouth with water each time and dripping it into the wound to the obvious comfort of its companion. Anteaters are not very high in the mammalian scale. Indeed, they seem from their appearance to be the last animals in which one would expect to find deliberate first-aid. It is significant that this method was used because an anteater's tongue is long and slender, about the diameter of a lead pencil, and presumably quite unsuitable for licking. The normal habit of anteaters, as everyone knows, is to use the long sticky tongue for investigating tunnels in ant and termite nests, collecting the insects on the tongue and swallowing them. So the next best thing was hydropathy.

During the winter of 1949–1950 Mr I. Lake lived in Vancouver, British Columbia. On a visit to the zoo in Stanley Park one day he saw in the monkey house in one of the cages half a dozen monkeys playing. The species is not known. There were in addition two monkeys in one corner. One of them clung miserably to a warm pipe. His eyes were red-rimmed, and his nose running, evidently with a heavy cold. His companion sat next to him with one arm round his shoulder and showing all signs of comforting him.

Struck by this apparent solicitude Mr Lake stopped to watch. Suddenly another monkey sprang over to the isolated two and took the place of the sick monkey's friend, who immediately left to join the others in play. This third monkey held the sick one close and went through the motions of comforting it, just as the second one had done, cheek against cheek, and arm around the shoulder. Mr Lake settled down to watch and continued to do so for well over an hour and a quarter. During all that time, despite all the play antics going on around, never once was the sick monkey left alone. Each of the others in turn left its play at intervals and took his or her turn to sit with the sick companion.

Mr Lake concluded his remarks with the following: 'I am not over-sentimental about animals and am wary of crediting them with human qualities, but if what I saw was not kindness and compassion, I doubt if I will ever see these.'

First-aid between animals is by the nature of things unlikely to be photographed. Even when a photographic record is obtained it is not always accepted as evidence, and one case in point is that set on record by Walter R. Miles in the *Proceedings of the National Academy of Sciences of America*. The event took place on 21 February 1954, but Miles did not publish his account of it until 24 April 1963. From this we may deduce that his story met opposition, possibly disbelief, although the event was witnessed also by the late Dr Henry W. Nissen, an outstanding authority on chimpanzees.

On that day in 1954, Miles recounts how, in an outdoor enclosure in Orange Park, there were two chimpanzees, Pan and Wendy. Pan was apt to greet visitors with a noisy display, jumping about, stamping, banging his hands together and shouting. Sometimes he would throw sand at them, with force and accuracy. This time, while Pan was engaged in these tactics, Wendy came up behind him whimpering. Pan turned, looked at her, crouched in front of her as she sat down, and began manipulating her left eyelids with his two forefingers — a chimpanzee's thumb is short and set well back from the index finger. With his left hand he held Wendy's head steady, while he drew down the lower eyelid and removed a foreign body from her eye. When he had finished, Wendy showed appropriate signs of relief and her attitude and posture changed, suggesting that Pan had indeed relieved her of some discomfort, although it was not possible to identify the foreign object — which is not very surprising.

Dr Miles concluded his account with these words: 'Man has become or is becoming wise to the value of succourant behaviour. He did not invent it; there were earlier pioneers.' If we accept this principle, then we are justified in looking for it at a lower level in the scale of life than the human race; and if we were compelled to guess in what form and at what level the beginnings of such behaviour might be found, the stories related in this book could provide an answer. As mentioned earlier, man has not necessarily a complete monopoly of the finer feelings; and if compassion does not enter into these animal acts, there is every appearance that it does.

Walter R. Miles' experience has another value. When chimpanzees meet after having been separated for a while, they greet each other in a very human manner, touching each other, even clasping hands and kissing. Under ordinary circumstances the arrival of a dominant male is an opportunity for the others to hurry over and pay their respects to him. Members of a party spend considerable time grooming each other and grooming themselves. Mothers carefully go through the fur of their babies for any foreign particles, spending more and more time on the tasks as the babies grow older. Dirt, burrs, pieces of dead skin, ticks, all are plucked out and splinters may be removed by pinching them out with the forefingers or with the lips. So in their everyday behaviour chimpanzees are pre-adapted for the kind of actions needed in first-aid. To that extent the photographs by Walter Miles are not remarkable. What is remarkable is the way in which the female chimpanzee seemed so plainly to ask for help, the way in which the male chimpanzee summed up the situation and, most incredible of all, the fact that a chimpanzee should have removed a tiny speck from such a delicate organ as the eye with fingers that look so clumsy, on a hand of which the thumb is short and cannot readily be used for picking up even large objects.

It is not surprising that some of Walter Miles' friends should have shown scepticism of his story, just as there will be sceptics of many of the other stories included in this book and of others that may come to light in the future. What we can say is that if chimpanzees can behave in this way and can show the impulse to help, that impulse is likely to be found, if only in a lesser degree, even lower in the animal kingdom.

15.
Ambulance
Work

A boy aged eleven years wrote to me telling of his small terrier dog. It had been taken to the vet for treatment. Two weeks later there was a telephone call from the vet to say the dog was in his surgery. Apparently the dog had hurt a foot again and had gone direct to the vet, barking outside the door and lifting its injured paw.

On page 100 of the Harmsworth Natural History, published in 1910, is a reproduction of a painting by James Yates Carrington, a copy of which used to hang in King's College Hospital, London. The picture shows a black collie with an injured right paw accompanied by two fox terriers in the act of barking, on the steps of the building. The caption declares this is a picture of two dogs taking another to a hospital.

According to H. Willoughby Lyle, in *King's and some King's Men* (1935), the picture records an incident which occurred one Sunday morning, 31 July 1887, at 9 a.m. The collie was admitted to the front surgery and his damaged forelimb attended to by the accident dresser on duty for the day. All three dogs were later identified and a sitting for the artist procured in each case.

Assuming the two terriers guided the collie to the hospital, the picture raises the question: What is an ambulance? The word came into general use with the Crimean War, in the 1850s, although it is said to have originated in 1819. It meant then a moving hospital (*hôpital ambulant*) which followed an army to attend to the wounded on the battlefield. Later, it was used for a vehicle that took anyone to hospital. Since the word is from the Latin *ambulare* (to walk) it is justifiable to use it here for any casualties that can be classified as 'walking wounded' — or even flying wounded, as in the following incident.

Two men working in a sandpit in Surrey had been taking a day-to-day interest in the nesting activities of a colony of sand martins. These had their nesting holes high in the vertical sand wall bounding the sandpit. Then one of them found a nestling on the ground 'chirruping for dear life'. They tried to get up the face of the sandy wall to replace it in one of the nest holes, but all were out of reach. So they replaced the nestling on the ground where they had found it. During their midday break they sat watching, more or less desultorily, the spot where the nestling lay. In due course they saw two adult martins fly down and bear the nestling up and into one of the nesting holes. So far as they could see, each adult appeared to grasp one of the nestling's wings in its beak and in flying up the right-hand adult seemed to be beating only its right wing and the left-hand adult its left wing.

Even if essential details are missing from the story I find it hard to discredit it, after having interviewed the two observers. At least the story is worth putting on record since accounts of adult birds rescuing young ones are few and far between. Like this one, they always sound incredible, but there are enough of them to lead to the possibility that such rescues do sometimes take place. In this instance the two men assured me that for nearly an hour the baby sand martin had been on the ground calling almost continuously. Then two adults flew down and flew up again and the baby was no longer there. These, the two men assured me, were solid facts. The rest is mainly conjecture, but may be compared with what a neighbour, a zoologist, told me about a baby sparrow.

A fledgling sparrow had fallen from a nest in the eaves down through a cavity wall and was imprisioned behind an air-brick. Attention was drawn to it not only by its calls of distress but also by the behaviour of the parents and a cat. All three were hanging about, so to speak, near the air-brick. Every so often the cat would pounce and a sparrow would fly up just out of reach, but without moving too far away. My neighbour removed a floorboard inside the house and retrieved the fledgling. Then he went outside and gently launched it into the air. As he did so he felt a rush of air past his ear and saw an adult sparrow flying across his own garden and into the next. For the whole of this distance, and until the two sparrows disappeared into the trees, the older bird flew beneath and very slightly in advance of the fledgling but keeping perfect time with it. It needed little more to give an actual air-lift and presumably the fledgling was buoyed up by the cushion of air between itself and the adult beneath it.

I can fully credit my neighbour's story because I witnessed an almost identical situation. I was on a sixty-foot roof looking down when two sparrows flew past a few feet beneath me. One was a paler colour than the other, obviously a young one. The other, a cock sparrow, followed close behind and slightly below it. The flight continued for about sixty feet towards a parapet fifty feet or so above ground level. In the course of this the older bird three times flew forward under the young one, which each time clearly gained height. At the parapet both landed, but the young one missed its footing and fell some twenty feet in a fluttering nose-dive reminiscent of an injured butterfly. Then it recovered and landed thirty feet away on a low roof twenty feet high.

There could be no doubt this was a fledgling that had but recently started to fly. In a few minutes the cock came back and fed it. Then the fledgling again took off to land about twenty feet away. Once more the cock flew just behind it, but this time his assistance was not needed. For the next quarter of an hour the fledgling remained on that perch while the cock joined the hen in feeding two other fledglings on the ground. The young one I had watched must have been the most advanced of the three in its flying, but even it was not sure of itself and might have come to grief completely without the help of the parent.

The importance of the last of these accounts is that I observed it myself, made notes at the time and am clear about what happened. The account preceding it was made by a scientist who told me about it the next day and re-enacted the scene on the spot. Also I was able to interrogate him. The story of the sand martins becomes credible, as an account of adult birds in a transportation rescue, because it is only slightly removed from the other two. Also I was able to interrogate the witnesses.

It may be that the inborn behaviour patterns of sparrows and sand martins lend themselves to this care-giving behaviour. If so, it is surprising there are so few records of it. Both species are very common over a wide range. In any event, the behaviour of the sparrows in the presence of the cat smacks of more than usual persistence in the face of the enemy and suggests higher-order behaviour even if only by a narrow margin.

Another common bird capable of unusual behaviour is the carrion crow, and it figures more in stories of so-called mercy killings than in acts of compassion. Yet a gamekeeper friend told me how a fellow keeper shot at and winged a crow, in a locality where crows were becoming too numerous for his liking. The bird fluttered to the ground and soon two other crows landed, one either side of it, and supported it with their wings. The two men could not stay to see the end of the incident because more and more crows assembled overhead and began to behave in a menacing fashion. Nothing is said in the original account about any vocalizations being used by the wounded crow or by those that first came to its assistance. Presumably calls were used.

Reverting now to the two terriers and the collie, the story behind the painting, even if fictitious, could have a basis of truth assuming that one of the terriers had been taken, or had found its way to the hospital, and had had an injury attended to. Like the terrier in the account that preceded it, it could then have found its way to the hospital for its own benefit. From other accounts given in other chapters, it is conceivable that it could have conveyed its intentions to the other terrier. It is not beyond belief that between them they may have persuaded the collie to make the journey to the hospital. But exactly how they would have done so defies elucidation. It could, of course, be argued that the terriers had merely followed the collie which, for some reason, knew where to go to have its injuries tended.

Mrs N. Clark, of Essex, told me of seeing two dogs fighting, the smaller getting the worst of the fight, so much so that its injuries prevented it from walking. It tried to get up but fell again, whereupon a third dog went to it, and as it tried once more to get on to its feet the third dog pushed it gently with its nose, assisting it to rise. Then slowly and painfully, with short rests between, this third dog assisted the injured dog to another house in the road.

Mrs Clark, who watched these proceedings from her window, commented that she had always regretted not following the dogs to give explanations and make inquiries at the house to which the two dogs went. She claimed she could only stand at the window and stare, overcome by what she regarded as this singular event. She could have said, as I have done: It was a wonderful thing to see.

There are, beyond reasonable doubt, many people who have witnessed similar scenes, but to discover all such people and collate their stories would be virtually impossible. One can only collect such accounts fortuitously as one comes across them in the course of searching the libraries or quizzing one's acquaintances.

Only last year, at the Chester Zoo, a lioness died, suspected of having been given drugged meat. There had been a series of such incidents. Mr William Timmis, the curator, reported that visitors had seen the lioness 'being crowded and pulled around the enclosure by her three female companions, as if attacking her'. (Again we have the appearance of aggression.) Yet when the body was recovered the next day, there was no mark on it. 'What probably happened was that her companions were showing concern and trying to pull her up and keep her on her feet' — a pregnant remark, since Mr Timmis has probably given little thought to concern-showing behaviour or the succourant behaviour of elephants.

This incident involving the lioness nevertheless recalls the observations made of elephants, as well as of otters, wildebeeste and buffaloes, dealt with in chapter 5. It is merely a matter of convenience of arrangement that the two sets of observations should have been dealt with in separate chapters. It is, however, worth recalling the exploits of elephants in the field of ambulance work for comparison with the truly extraordinary story that follows.

A recent press account tells how M. Alphonse Marie, a widower, set out from his house at ten o' clock on a frosty November night taking his three dogs, a Labrador, a retriever and a cocker spaniel, for their usual walk. As usual on such occasions, he left the door open. It seems, see below, that when seventy-five yards from the house he collapsed with a cerebral haemorrhage. M. Marie's bachelor son, Louis, had set off two hours previously for Briqueville-sur-Mer, where he worked as a night-watchman. On his return at six o' clock the following morning Louis found the Labrador and retriever at the front door howling, while the spaniel was lying on the unconscious Alphonse's body, energetically licking the man's face. Alphonse was described as nearly naked, his clothes torn to shreds (journalistic licence, perhaps) although apart from a few bruises and scratches he had suffered no further damage.

It was assumed that had Alphonse lain where he fell he would have died of exposure. Marks in the grass suggested the dogs had dragged him the seventy-five yards to the house and the twelve steps up to the front door were deeply scarred by the dogs' claws where they had presumably dragged the fifteen-stone M. Marie up the steps.

The patient was taken to hospital where the staff were so touched by the story that special permission was obtained from the Health Ministry for the dogs to visit him.

If the story, as told in the newspapers, could be proven correct this would be a most remarkable example of canine devotion, not to say intelligence. It would mean that all three dogs had appreciated the plight of their master and had acted with an unprecedented coordination of effort towards a mutually understood goal. Unfortunately, there is a period of eight hours for which there is a complete blank. The nearest neighbours were three hundred yards from the Marie home. It was night. There were no eye-witnesses. Everything has to be deduced and the vital clues, the tracks through the grass and the pattern of the claw-marks up the steps were not scrutinized by expert trackers, nor is there any record of them for later examinaton.

Three dogs of the sizes represented by the three breeds could have dragged a dead weight of fifteen stone the required distance only if they had acted completely as a team. In the days of horse ploughs a third horse was sometimes harnessed to the plough in addition to the customary pair if the going was likely to be heavy. If this third horse was inexperienced, the trio would make less headway than the pair, who were used to working together as a team, because it would be pulling against them most of the time.

On the other hand several ants will drag an object heavier than their own combined weights to their nest, in an apparently coordinated action. Studies made in recent years have shown that for the most part the ants are pulling against each other but every so often, quite by chance, they happen to pull together and so, because each ant has the impulse to transport the object to the nest, they move it in the right direction. In short bursts of fortuitous coordination they move it slowly to its ultimate goal. And the three dogs had eight hours in which to carry out a similar task.

The actual weight of fifteen stone is no obstacle. Many people have been pulled over and dragged along the ground at a smart pace by a dog on the lead that, because it is untrained to commands, has suddenly taken to rushing headlong away. A dog such as a Labrador could in such circumstances easily drag a 10-stone man on its own.

When a person has a cerebral haemorrhage he may not lose consciousness at once, but when he does recover he has no memory of subsequent events. One man so afflicted drove his car home through winding country lanes yet had to be carried from the car. He could recall stepping into the car and starting the engine. The next moment, it seemed, he was in bed at home. He had no recollection of what had happened in between. Also, even when losing muscle strength down one side, a casualty from a stroke can assist himself along to some extent. M. Marie may have helped himself to the house, then lost all memory of it.

The fact that the clothes were ripped to shreds is suspicious. Men's clothing should stand up to a dragging action even when dogs' teeth are involved. There may be rents in the cloth, buttons ripped off, but 'torn to shreds' suggests something more. Dogs have been known to attack their owners that stumble. When the owner is a woman her skirt may be torn. The three dogs may have panicked and torn M. Marie's clothes from fear, or from frustration at missing their usual walk. They may even have hindered M. Marie's own efforts to reach the haven of his house.

The two dogs howling at the open door may represent calls for help or they may have been the result of frustration at not being taken for their customary walk. More likely they were the result of a recognition that something was amiss. The third dog licking the face of the prostrate man is in character, as we can see in the fox licking its dead mate, and in other examples given in this book.

At best, this could be a wonderful story of devotion; at worst a hideous story of dogs losing their heads and attacking their master, then settling down again. There is room for much argument and more than one opinion. A further interesting point emerges, however: the changed behaviour of a domestic pet towards an owner no longer in the vertical position. A few people, and I am one, sometimes take a midday nap lying on the floor with the head on a low pillow. It is a most refreshing exercise. One man who did this was awakened by his distressed tom cat, who had not before seen him in this position. The cat sniffed his nostrils, breathed into them, sniffed his mouth and his ears, and ran over him mewing pitifully. He reassured the cat, which then settled down beside him.

This discussion contains the important implication that an unusual position may elicit anxiety on the part of another, the mainspring of true altruism. There may have been an element of this in the behaviour of his dogs towards Alphonse Marie, with overtones of less virtuous behaviour.

16.
Fetching Help

Among the many alleged instances of animals succouring other animals, a minority tell of the succouring animal, or succourant, leading or endeavouring to lead a human being to the scene of the casualty. Such examples imply that some species are capable not only of recognizing that human beings can render aid of which they themselves are incapable, but also of guiding those human beings to the scene of the tragedy. This alone is sufficient to arouse scepticism, and the history of our belief in such a possibility does little to allay doubts. And yet there are cases to which some credence can be attached. This means we are on a thorny path along which we must pick our way carefully.

Probably the earliest, and certainly the most strongly established, instance of a bird guiding human beings to a target, though for another reason, is that of the honeyguide of Africa. To begin with, the vernacular name is misleading because the bird does not eat honey but insects and wax, and what it obtains from a bees' nest is the grubs and the wax of the honeycomb.

The story of the honeyguide, as given in the most authoritative works on ornithology, can be stated briefly as follows. The honeyguide, a small bird $4\frac{1}{2}$ to 8 inches long, usually on its own, begins by coming to a person or animal, uttering repeated churring notes, fanning its tail, flashing its wings, and otherwise making itself conspicuous. In this manner it leads the way towards the bees' nest, keeping fifteen to twenty feet ahead. When the bird hears or sees swarming bees, which is usually near a bees' nest, it falls silent and perches patiently until the 'robber' (the man or animal it is supposed to have beguiled into following it) has broken into the nest or hive, taken his loot of honey and departed. Then it feeds on the wax and the bee larvae scattered by the robber on the ground. The animal most frequently figuring in these episodes is the ratel, also called the honey badger, although a baboon and a mongoose have each been recorded as following a honeyguide.

The 'guiding' behaviour of the honeyguide is said to be 'purely instinctive and unplanned' (whatever this may mean), yet it is not dependent on this behaviour for survival, since its main diet is insects. The story, given here in a simplified form, is more commonly encountered in an embellished form in popular natural history books.

The first recorded account of the honeyguide's behaviour was given by João dos Santos, a Portuguese missionary to Ethiopia, in 1569. He found the bird entering his church to feed on the wax from the candles. Thereafter, until

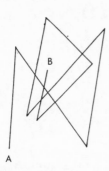
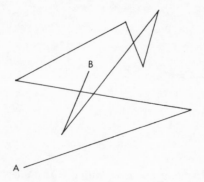

Fig. 15 Diagrams showing the kinds of route taken by a honeyguide supposedly leading a man from A to B (a bees' nest)

1947, follows a long succession of testimony, from missionaries and travellers, whose accounts more often than not were based wholly or mainly on the testimony of Africans.

The first attempt to analyse accurately the honeyguide's behaviour was made in 1946 by C. J. Skead. Then, in 1955, came a monograph on the honeyguides as a whole, by Herbert Friedman, in the *Bulletin of the U.S. National Museum*, No 208, in which fifty-eight pages are devoted to a detailed analysis of the guiding behaviour.

So far as the ratel's association with the story is concerned, the first weakness is that this animal, like other badgers, is mainly nocturnal although, again like other badgers, it may sometimes be seen by day, especially in undisturbed areas. The ratel is said to be able to climb, but it is doubtful whether it is capable of climbing trees to the heights at which wild bees usually have their nests. It is even more doubtful whether having reached that height it could cling sufficiently dextrously to the tree to enable it to free one paw to rake out the nest to get at the honey.

The second obvious weakness is that very few naturalists have investigated the honeyguide's behaviour at firsthand. Those that have done so have invariably found that the bird does not lead them direct to the bees' nest but always by a circuitous route, often going well past it, doubling back and even then not going direct to it. Several ornithologists visiting Africa have sought to investigate the honeyguide's behaviour. As often as not the bird has led the man to a sleeping lion, leopard, large snake or similar hazard.

Other things are clear. In some areas of the range of *Indicator indicator*, the greater honeyguide, the species most commonly associated with the guiding, the habit has never been observed and in whole areas where the habit used to occur it is reported to have been dropped since the local Africans have been able to buy honey and sweet products from shops. Of the dozen or so species of honeyguides distributed over Africa and southern and south-east Asia, guiding has been suggested for three African species only and of these *I. indicator* is the main perpetrator.

It seems very clear, from Friedman's extensive analysis, not only that the guiding behaviour is not instinctive, in the sense of arising from an inherited pattern of behaviour, but that another explanation is more plausible. This is that the Africans, doubtless over a long period of time, have used the bird's excited behaviour as an indicator of the presence nearby of a bees' nest, with its store of honey. It could even be that the bird itself has responded and the habit has spread, as happens with other spreads of habit reliably documented among birds in recent years. This might account for the habit having died out where Africans can now purchase honey in shops. Equally, the chance observation of a ratel taking honey from a nest low down in a tree, or even in the ground, may have set up a slight association between bird and mammal.

A discussion of honeyguide behaviour may seem irrelevant to our general theme. In fact it is of fundamental importance, for if the only accepted example of a supposed purposeful guiding of human beings or animals to a scene of prospective activity is on an unsure basis, then we can assume that generally speaking we should not look for it in other birds.

Walter Hoesch has told of two rollers (*Coracias mozambicus*) leading him with excited calls a distance of three hundred yards to where a genet was caught in a trap. On the face of it this observation can, like the long-accepted story of the honeyguide, only be treated with reserve. The cat-like genet, related to the mongoose, is a natural enemy of birds. It would truly be idealistic altruism if two small birds were to do anything to rescue a genet, and even more remarkable if they purposely guided another of their natural enemies, man, to assist. The greater probability is that the birds were giving their alarm calls, possibly even mobbing the genet. This incident does, however, afford an example of a pattern of behaviour we shall meet later.

It is doubtful whether any of the tens of thousands of people who have kept as pets members of the crow family, acknowledged to be among the most intelligent of birds, could offer a substantial account of being purposefully led by a bird. Cat- and dog-lovers, on the other hand, could and do offer numerous examples of the same thing by mammals. A cat, needing to have a door opened so that it can go out of a room, will if necessary use its claws on a person's trouser leg or skirt to emphasize the urgency of its needs and follow this by walking towards the door. A dog, lacking similar effective claws, uses other means which are no less successful. If we can believe the many stories told, dogs often tug at clothing with their teeth. We can therefore consider with confidence alleged instances of wild mammals, as well as their domesticated relatives, fetching help in an unequivocal sense.

We may start with the domestic cats and dogs because they have the more numerous occasions, as well as the greater opportunities, to carry out this action. A not uncommon example, although it does not necessarily involve fetching help, has to do with the pet cat that has been unaccountably spending long periods away from home. Suddenly, as the owner is standing in his garden contemplating the scene, he feels a gentle tug at the lower part of his trousers. Looking down he sees his cat looking up at him. The cat mews plaintively and starts to walk away. The owner takes little notice. The cat returns, tugs again with its claws in the cloth of his trouser leg, mews and starts again to walk away. Out of curiosity the owner follows. The cat leads him to a shed. Inside the shed the owner sees a nest of newborn kittens. As he gazes down at them the cat rubs purring against his legs, at the same time looking up at him — dare we say? — proudly. At the least, we can say the cat found a way to lead him to her kittens. Instead of using its claws to attract attention the cat may, on other occasions, keep on calling and turning away.

Many years ago, I was told a story, alleged to be true, about a man and his small dog. They lived in Birmingham. The man went to live in Bath, taking his dog with him. Soon after this the dog encountered a big dog, belonging to a neighbour, which set upon the small dog and beat it up. Subsequently, the small dog disappeared and was not seen for several weeks. Then, one day, it re-appeared in company with a large dog which had been its companion in Birmingham. The two sought out the bully dog, set upon him and gave him a severe beating, after which the large dog from Birmingham departed and was seen no more. The large Bath dog thereafter treated the small dog with respect.

Could such a story be true? We know dogs can return home finding their way over a long distance. We know dogs can act in concert, for example in setting an ambush. Could a dog in some way communicate its intention to another? Here we are largely in the dark. The important feature, from the point of view of our present theme, is whether a dog, like the cat with the newborn kittens, is capable of fetching help in this way?

The following are a few selected anecdotes from a variety of sources which seem to indicate that animals, domesticated or wild, are capable of fetching help.

During World War II, a bull terrier and a mongrel developed the habit of daily visiting an army canteen, where they were given biscuits by one of the canteen staff. One day the bull terrier came alone. The canteen worker spoke to it and naturally asked it where its friend was. Equally naturally, the bull terrier made no reply, but when at last the customary biscuit was held out it refused to take it but stood there with an appealing look in its eyes. Then it turned and started to walk away, looking back as it did so. The canteen worker did not follow, so the terrier came back and repeated the action, until at last the woman realized something was wrong. Finally, she followed the dog, which led her to a furze brake. There she found the mongrel well and truly caught up in a gorse bush and unable to free itself.

J.B. was taking a walk one Sunday afternoon. He turned into a side-street which was deserted except for a dog sitting in front of a house. As soon as the dog saw the man it ran towards him, barking softly. Then it started to crawl backwards towards a house and, entering the open door, continued up the stairs to the landing, where J.B. found the dog's owner lying unconscious.

The following appeared in a Dutch newspaper. It tells the story of an Alsatian that saved the life of a bouvier dog which had been knocked down by a motor car near the naval air-base of De Kooy. The bouvier was so badly hurt it was unable to walk, and it seems, from the newspaper account, that the Alsatian must have watched over it for some days. On the day in question the Alsatian's strange behaviour attracted the attention of one of the watchmen. The dog appeared at the gate whining and then ran off into the field again. The watchman thought that perhaps the dog was hunting moles.

In the afternoon the Alsatian appeared again at the gate. This time he howled piteously. He refused all food offered him and at last the watchman, puzzled, told the duty officer. The dog was followed and the injured bouvier was found, the police were notified and the Dutch Society for the Protection of Animals took both dogs, which were apparently strays, into its care. The duty officer was quoted as saying he was deeply touched by this example of animal devotion, especially when the Alsatian, apparently satisfied that help was there, began to lick the bouvier's wounds. And, when suddenly it began to rain, it stood over the bouvier to protect it from the shower.

Now comes the story of dog helping cat. A.F. had some cooked fish left over. She saw a neighbour's dog standing outside the house where it lived. On the impulse she put the food on a piece of cardboard and placed it on the ground outside her own gate, calling the dog to come and eat it. Then she went indoors but went to the window to see if the dog would eat the fish. She saw it sniff the fish and then go home, so she went out, retrieved the fish and brought it indoors. A moment or two later, happening to look out of the window she noticed the dog was back, accompanied by the cat that lived at the same house. The dog was sniffing around where the cardboard and fish had previously lain on the pavement and looking up from time to time at A.F.'s house, so she took the fish out again. She placed it in front of the dog who wagged his tail, nudged the cat towards the fish, then lay down, watching, until the cat had eaten its fill.

J.B.C. wrote, in 1957, of a farmer having trouble with rats in an outhouse. He organized a ratting party and just before they pulled up the floorboards to find the nest they fetched the cat. When the cat saw the number of rats it dashed through the door and out of sight. The men dismissed it as a coward, but were astonished to see it return quickly with two younger cats which caught the smaller rats while the larger cat, a well-grown tom, finished off the larger rats. Many desired details are missing from this story, which seems almost beyond acceptance, but the writer had the reputation of being a reliable observer.

Another unsolicited story is one that properly should be included in Chapter 14, except that it also involves fetching help and is comparable to the story of the Alsatian at the Dutch air base. It concerns two siblings from a litter born to a tabby cat. The tom, which was called George, was later neutered. The female, dubbed Girlie, was smaller, but the two lived together and were close companions. One evening, when both cats were several years old and their owner was seeing a visitor from the front door, George ran into the road, was knocked against a wall by a passing car and fled across the road into a field. A search was mounted for him without success. Then darkness fell. The search was resumed the following morning, again without success.

Later that afternoon, the owner walked down the garden path, Girlie came and rubbed against her leg and mewed piteously. Thinking she was lonely the owner stooped and stroked her, speaking to her comfortingly, then stopped to pick some flowers. Meanwhile, the cat had walked away a few steps but stopped and returned, again rubbing against her owner's leg, mewing piteously. Puzzled, the owner now followed as the cat moved off and was led to an angle between the walls of the house where a roofed-in box was kept in which the cats could shelter if shut out. On a mat outside the box lay George. The puzzle to all concerned was how George, so badly bruised that he could not walk on his own, managed to get back to the box outside the house. That, however, is not the point of the story, which is included here as an example of fetching help.

Similar stories about domestic cats and dogs must be legion. It is of even greater interest that they can be matched for wild animals. An extract from a warden's report for the (then) Royal National Parks of Kenya (*teste African Wild Life* 1960) told of a wildebeest calf making frantic efforts to find its mother, going up to each cow in turn. From another herd, six hundred yards away, a yearling deliberately walked over, bellowing, and edged the calf from the herd it was in to the other herd, where it soon found its mother. Why the mother failed where a yearling succeeded is a question that cannot be answered. Even so, there was every appearance that the yearling appreciated what was wrong and acted accordingly. And although this is not an example of fetching help it has some of the elements of it and helps us comprehend the others.

Then comes a slightly different episode. R.R.S. took to putting out food for the wild foxes and watched them feeding from a window of a darkened room. One night a badger arrived first. R.R.S. saw a fox appear through the hedge as usual, about ten yards from the food. It stood for a moment watching as the badger held down a large bone and tore meat from the other end. Then it turned and disappeared through the hedge. A little while later the fox came back accompanied by a second fox. Both advanced on the badger, one to face it, the other moving to the rear of it. When the first fox was a yard from it the badger dropped the bone and bared its teeth. At the same time the other fox made as if to attack from the rear. The badger turned to snarl at it. The first fox then seized the bone and ran off with it, followed immediately by the other, leaving the badger nonplussed.

There is perhaps nothing surprising in a red fox having sufficient understanding to enlist the help even of its arch-enemy, man. Nor are the stories given here of cats and dogs beyond belief. If we accept these, then there is every reason for the general statement that all but the most primitive mammals may possess the potentiality for similar behaviour, and if mammals, why not birds? Any case in their favour was somewhat peremptorily dismissed in the first half of this chapter. Yet cats pulling at trouser legs recalls the episode in London's St James' Park several years ago.

The ducks living on the lake in the park are regularly fed by visitors. On a particularly cold morning in winter with no visitors about, a man chanced to be hurrying through the park taking little notice of his surroundings. He suddenly felt a tug at the bottom of his trouser leg. He looked down to find a mallard holding the cloth firmly in its bill. A possible interpretation is that the duck was hungry and used this method of drawing attention to itself. That at least is the assumption made in the scientific journal in which it is recorded.

B.C. has set on record an episode that bears some comparison with the action of the mallard and the alleged wiles of the honeyguide. A friend of hers had the habit of scattering food on the ground for the birds outside the back door of her house. One morning, while a group of birds were busy feeding and making little noise, she became aware, as she stood watching, of a pair of starlings on a nearby wall making a great deal of noise and then, while still vociferating, moving away along the top of the wall. At first the friend failed to comprehend, but as the starlings repeated the manoeuvre, retreating and coming back towards her several times, calling all the while, she decided to follow them. They led her all the way to the greenhouse, where a young starling had been inadvertently shut in.

Then there is the episode which involved a pair of blackbirds. A man noticed a pair of blackbirds diving in and out of a hedge in great agitation. As he came nearer, one of them flew towards him and back again to the hedge repeatedly, causing him to go to the hedge to investigate. A large grass snake was climbing up towards a nest full of nestlings. He killed the snake. An alternative explanation could be, of course, that the bird was dividing its time between two supposed predators, snake and man.

In all such instances there is always the possibility that the actions of the birds were misinterpreted, that it merely looked as if they were seeking help. What we need to do is examine the situation for feasibility.

'Fetching help' need not involve guiding human beings. It can be intra-specific as in the Bath-Birmingham dogs, and for another possible example we can turn to a letter received from Edgar J. March, living in the Isle of Wight. He described how during World War II most of the inhabitants of his town were evacuated, which may have been why rooks came and nested in the tall trees around his house. One pair built a nest directly over the entrance to a shed in which the garden tools were kept. One result was that the elderly gardener was often bespattered by rook droppings as he went in and out of the shed, so that one evening, about five o'clock, he borrowed a long ladder, climbed it carrying a long stick and poked the nest to pieces. Satisfied that this was the end of the adventure, the gardener went home.

Shortly after the gardener's departure, Mr March continued, the pair of rooks retuned.

> At once there was tremendous consternation. They flew round and round cawing loudly. Soon dozens of rooks joined them and after much bowing and cawing they settled on the branches of the tree and seemed to be holding a conference. Perhaps it was vital to have a nest because eggs were about due.

Whatever it was we watched enthralled through binoculars. Presently all the rooks flew away to come back each with a stick in its beak and proceeded to build a new nest on the old site. By seven o' clock the hen was settled in the nest with contented caws; obviously a communal effort to assist one in trouble.

Next morning the elderly gardener gazed up in astonishment and decided to leave well alone.

A quite extraordinary story of fetching help has been set forth in the *Journal of the Bombay Natural History Society* for 1951. Frank Nicholls was going down the bed of the Bargung river one evening in April on a male elephant, with his mahout. They crossed the recent tracks of an elephant and her calf, with a tiger following. The tracks were so fresh the water in them was still muddy. All of a sudden there was a loud trumpeting with intermittent screaming coming from about two hundred yards inside the forest. Nicholls immediately made for the direction of the screams but thick cane with three-inch thorns delayed him considerably.

Suddenly a female elephant appeared holding up a bleeding front foot which she placed on the trunk of Nicholls' elephant. Then she turned and started to walk the way she had come. Nicholls followed and found her calf, three and a half feet high, completely scalped and holding up a foreleg from which the foot had been all but severed. He hunted around for the tiger but had to give up since it was growing dark. Finally he departed leaving the mother with her injured calf.

17.
Feeding and Sharing Food

There was a time, some thirty years ago, when those responsible for the wild life in the Kruger Park, in South Africa, decided that there were too many lions in the park. It was decided to thin their ranks, to give their prey species the chance of stabilizing their numbers. The cull was carried out. To everybody's surprise the numbers of lions increased in a year or two, back to the level before the cull. One explanation put forward to account for this was as follows. The lionesses in a pride make the kill and under normal conditions the lion eats first after a kill has been made, the lionesses eat next and the cubs take what is left. This is one reason why there is generally a high mortality, from forty to sixty per cent, among young lions. When the numbers of lions fall below a certain level, especially when the males have been weeded out, the cubs are fed first. This means more than allowing the cubs adequate food. It means also that they have their full share of the entrails of any large herbivore killed and the contents of these are rich in vitamins. As a result the cubs are healthier and more of them survive.

The very fact that the young should, under normal circumstances, not be allowed the first pick of the food comes as a surprise. We are accustomed to the idea that animal parents give top priority to their young in the matter of food. But lions are super-predators, at the top of the food pyramid. When their numbers are excessive there comes a danger that their prey-species may suffer an overkill, when all lions in the area would suffer. So the normal method of feeding, with its consequent high infant mortality, can be seen as a natural population control that benefits the species as well as the surviving individuals.

The story of the Kruger Park is underlined by what has been observed several times in a lioness that has suffered damage, having her teeth kicked out by a zebra or her paws and mouth rendered almost useless by quills of a porcupine embedded in them. Such lionesses appear to be on their own, possibly forsaken by the pride. They are then reduced to killing trivial game such as rodents. These unfortunate lionesses have sometimes been accompanied by cubs. One lioness in this parlous condition, whose claws also were damaged, was seen painfully trying to tear to pieces a lump of dried hide, using her sore mouth and damaged paws, to feed her cubs which appeared well-fed although the mother herself was emaciated.

We can argue that it is instinctive for a lioness to ensure her young ones are nourished. It is almost a rule among animal mothers. Yet there is something pathetically heroic in the behaviour of a lioness, or any other mother, seeking to ensure a supply of food for her offspring against a background of physical suffering.

Every year in many species the world over, animal mothers nurture and care for their offspring. This is the norm and instinctive patterns of behaviour control the norm. In the care of offspring, as in everything else, it is the period of crisis which calls forth the acts of heroism, in humans and animals alike. The patient heroism may go beyond care of infants, as in the elderly couple reduced to poverty. The husband was half-blind. There was a limited, meagre ration of butter on the table at mealtimes. The slightly less handicapped wife went through the motions of spreading butter and ate her bread dry so that the husband should not go without.

On rare occasions one can see this kind of magnanimity extended to the young of another species, as in the gander which fostered a brood of ducklings. Near the lake where they lived was a house the occupants of which put out food for the birds. The gander would shepherd the ducklings up the path to the house to where the fragments of bread lay scattered on the lawn. There the gander would stand back while the ducklings ate their fill, then he would take what was left. After that the party could be seen returning to the lake, the ducklings in front, the gander waddling behind. No doubt it is instinctive for geese to let their goslings feed first and to this extent the actions of the gander merit no praise. At least the story suggests the potentiality within every goose for unselfish behaviour.

Another remarkable scene which I observed concerned a tame jackdaw. Like all the several tame jackdaws we have had in our care, this one was human-fixated and consequently sought human companionship. It was evidently someone's pet, hand-reared from the fledgling stage, that had regained its freedom. Such birds become a nuisance to people who are not pet-inclined, tapping on their windows, entering houses and generally getting in the way. This one was brought to us one evening as night was falling. We put it in a large, portable aviary placed just outside the kitchen door, where it could enjoy human company, had room to fly but was prevented from regaining full liberty. It repaid us by daily going through its extensive repertoire of mimicked sounds and words. That bird could chatter!

Came the spring, and a pair of blackbirds brought their fledglings to feed around the aviary. The jackdaw's food was placed each morning in a shallow dish inside the aviary. The bird was soon seen taking food from the dish, putting its beak through the meshes of the wire-netting that formed the walls of the aviary, to feed the blackbird fledglings. Then, one morning, after its food had been placed in the dish as usual, the jackdaw pushed it out of the aviary for the fledgling blackbirds to help themselves.

We never caught it in the act of doing this but the facts speak for themselves. The aviary consisted of a framework of wood covered with wire-netting on four sides and the ceiling. It stood on flagstones and there was only one point at which a slight depression in the flagstones allowed the dish to be pushed under the wooden frame forming the base of the aviary. The dish, on being replenished each morning, was left on the ground in the centre of the aviary. The jackdaw had to push it two feet along the ground and under the base of the aviary at this one point in order to share its rations with the fledglings outside.

Here again we can argue that the action is instinctive. I have seen, in a seaside town, household scraps thrown out for the birds with gulls descending on them. A solitary jackdaw flies in, quickly fills its throat pouch with food and flies out again as the greedy gulls start to harass it. The jackdaw flies to the nearest roof-top where other jackdaws are waiting, empties its pouch and shares the food with its fellows. This I have seen often enough to suppose that food-sharing is part of the social behaviour of this markedly social species.

Then came a sequel to the story of our tame jackdaw. The feeding stopped when the fledglings became able to look for their own food and departed. Several weeks later the mother blackbird appeared with two fledglings from a second brood. We again saw the jackdaw feeding the young birds in the same way as before.

Long before the hen blackbird had her first brood she had been coming into the house to forage. She continued to do so even when feeding her first brood. Now, however, she brought her second lot of fledglings with her. She seemed to have established her own welfare state with the jackdaw entering into the spirit of it. With the second lot of fledglings he was more selective. His daily rations consisted of brown bread soaked in milk to which were added grapes, banana, raisins, sultanas or hard-boiled egg. Each day, beginning with this new session, he picked out the fruit and fed these to the blackbirds, giving them bread only when the delicacies were finished. This selectivity seems to take the jackdaw's beneficence even more certainly out of the realm of a fixed behaviour pattern and into the realm of real generosity.

Blind Jack was a sightless jackdaw made famous by Mrs Ryder in her book of that name (See chapter 9). On one occasion Blind Jack fed two orphaned jackdaws that had been brought into the garden where he lived. He filled his beak and tried to find his way to them by hearing their 'hunger' call. He himself made the 'I have food for you' call normal to jackdaws as they approach the nest. He heard only their calls. He could not see their bright red throats or fluttering wings to draw attention to their needs. It was, Mrs Ryder said, a touching sight to watch him fumbling his way to his food dish, filling his pouch, then turning towards the fledgling jackdaws, uttering his own parental cry. It was more than this: it shed light on the mechanism involved in feeding young birds. It is always said with confidence that the stimulus which causes a bird to thrust food into the throat of a nestling or fledgling is the sight of the brightly coloured throat. Blind Jack taught us otherwise.

Altruism, heroism and other such qualities are difficult to define precisely, but if they can be taken to mean carrying out an action beneficial to another at unusual sacrifice to oneself, even if that action is basically a fixed and inherited pattern of behaviour, then both Blind Jack and our loquacious jackdaw were behaving altruistically, in the true sense of the word.

The same can be said of a South African crow, a member of the same family as the jackdaw. The *Cape Times* of 30 April 1966 carried the story of a crow found injured that was rescued by a man and wife at Wankie, on the Bulawayo-Victoria Falls road. It soon became the companion of their ridgeback puppy. Then the puppy disappeared and could not be found in spite of a wide search for it. The couple noticed the crow was not eating as usual. It would take some food, fly off, return again and fly off with more food. In the end they followed the crow, which in this way led them to their puppy which was trapped in a snare and for six days had been fed by the crow. The puppy was in perfect condition. A simple story, relatively, yet the crow had succeeded to the limit of its ability to help.

A farmer was puzzled by the way his store of carrots was disappearing. He kept watch and saw his dog, as soon as the horses were bedded down, take carrots to one particular horse. It is not easy to explain this on the basis of a dog following an inherited pattern of behaviour! The same can be said of the dog that was observed to take bread daily to feed the swans on a nearby lake. It would go to the house for bread, go down to the lake and drop the bread into the water when the swans approached.

Some domestic animals have been recorded as bringing strange animals into the garden to be fed, like the neighbour's dog that normally kept to its own garden. One day it came through the hedge followed by a bedraggled mongrel, its coat sodden and mud-splashed, its head drooping, and altogether looking a picture of misery. The neighbour's dog led it to a bowl on the lawn containing food put out for the birds. The mongrel ate the food, the other dog standing by, and when it had finished the other dog led it back through the hedge.

If we can accept this story as an accurate description of what happened we can count this as an example of true altruism. A dog will eat until it is satiated, but if another dog comes near the excess food it has left it will gobble up all the food. This dog apparently not only guided the mongrel to the food but resisted what must have been a natural tendency at least to share it.

Gwendoline Adkins, living in the south of England, recorded in 1970 that her tom cat showed clearly it wanted its food dish put down by the French window. Cat-owners will find no difficulty in accepting that much. More remarkable, it then stepped outside, called softly, whereupon an emaciated she-cat came out from among the shrubs and walked towards the house. She hesitated on the threshold of the French window but the tom made encouraging noises until she came inside and cleared the dish while he sat purring. Then the strange cat scuttled away.

In the same year came another similar report, of a house cat which, having eaten most of its food, went outside and returned with a thin black stray that ate the rest.

If there is any scepticism towards these last three stories it can only be slight, for cats and dogs are carnivores and domesticated. Being carnivores they have well-developed brains and it can be readily accepted that carnivores stand third in the non-human part of the animal kingdom, after apes and monkeys and porpoises, for mental capacity. It is profitable therefore to turn to a story about wild birds, the best of which are inferior to carnivores in the development of the brain. In this instance the bird species concerned does not stand high in intellectual achievement.

M. J. Dawson reported in *British Birds*, in 1959, that when he approached an ivy-covered tree in Sussex a wood-pigeon flew out. He then saw another sitting very still with neck stretched out, in the 'frozen' attitude. The bird made no attempt to fly. Mr Dawson shot it. On examination the wood-pigeon was found to have no primary feathers at all except the outer one in each wing. The rest were newly growing but were only one and a half to two and half inches long, little better than stubs. The body of the dead pigeon was warm and fat, the crop was half-filled with barley grain — and there was no barley field within half a mile of the tree on which it had been perched. It was estimated that the bird had been unable to fly for the last ten days, perhaps more, and the only conclusion seemed to be that the other pigeon had been feeding it, although the flightless bird was fully adult. This should be compared with the story of supposed grief in a pigeon in chapter 7.

There was a report many years ago of a consignment of adult jays having been sent across the Atlantic. On arrival at their destination one, although fat and healthy, was found to have lost the whole of its beak. It was assumed to have been fed by its companions, a first-class example of compassion if ever there was one. Unfortunately, some doubt must be cast on this because fully wild birds, lacking the whole of the beak, have on rare occasions been seen feeding themselves. They put the head on one side and manage to shovel food into the throat, using the tongue.

Even if it could have been shown that the beakless jay had been fed by its companions, this would have been because a bird instinctively reacts to a gaping brightly coloured throat. As Blind Jack has taught us, there are other stimuli that can achieve the same end. Perhaps even more remarkable was the case of the North American bird, a cardinal, that took to feeding the goldfish in an artificial pond. The brightly coloured gaping throat of the goldfish would have been a suitable substitute for the gape of a nestling cardinal. More astonishing perhaps was the fact that the goldfish cooperated.

Such events at least remind us that strange things often happen and the liaison between the cardinal and the goldfishes would be almost unbelievable, except that it was supported by photographs.

Some animals, certainly some mammals, possibly some birds, recognize juvenility in human beings. Our pet foxes, tame as they were with us, would bolt for cover at sight of an adult stranger advancing towards their pen, even when that person was twenty feet away. For a child of twelve or less not only would they not retreat, they would positively come forward to meet it.

This may explain why, in one household, when the first grandchild was brought to the house as a baby, the resident cat went out, caught a bird, brought it in, plucked out many of its feathers, pummelled the carcase with its forepaws and laid it beside the infant. There was also an eight-month-old half-Persian cat that made friends with a seven-month-old Scottie pup. It would bring dead mice to the puppy and lie near it purring while the puppy played, as a kitten would, with the mouse before finally eating it.

There are, of course, many known instances of cats bringing dead birds or dead mice and laying them at their owner's feet. This tendency was put to practical use as described in a letter from Dr E. Donald Asselin of Falmouth, Mass., who in 1959 sent me the following account:

'. . . the yellow cat had tackled an auto and come out the loser. He limped for several weeks and was unable to hunt. The grey cat would catch two mice each morning and bring them to our patio. He played with them for a few minutes then would walk across the patio and bring the smallest mouse to the yellow cat, dropping it between his paws. Some days he would catch only one mouse. Then he ate the head and gave the yellow cat the body. Many times the grey will eat only the mouse head and leave the body, depending how full he is — he seems to think the heads are a gourmet item. When these cats catch mice, the mice can rest all day and each cat will respect the other's catch . . .'

In 1949, a year of drought in South Africa, I. M. Lloyd noticed that when he put out bread soaked in milk for the birds, numerous pied starlings came to feed on it. The bolder of these, having eaten some of it, would then pick up pieces of the bread and go over to their more timid companions and thrust it into their beaks. If any refused the offering it was taken to another one. Surprisingly, two pairs of hoopoes also came to the bread and they too fed each other.

Adult birds feeding each other! Perhaps they were doing it for fun, which is what one might suspect when the elephant gave the camel a drink. This was in the zoo at Sacramento, California, when Bill Morley from Pennsylvania was visiting it. He describes seeing an elephant and a camel in adjacent corners of their neighbouring pens. The elephant's water trough was close by, the camel's some way away. The camel started tossing its head, we are told, and making throaty noises. Suddenly the elephant, who had been busy doing nothing, flapped its ears and stepped briskly to its own water trough. It took a deep draught, raised its trunk over the high fence and dropped the end of it into the camel's waiting mouth.

'With a mighty swoosh', Mr Morley continues, 'the elephant filled the camel with a torrent of water. The camel ambled contentedly away.'

The critical reader might point out that a camel would have difficulty in coping with 'a torrent of water' squirted into its mouth. While the precise details of the manner of its swallowing are not known, what is known is that a thirsty camel has been recorded as drinking thirty gallons in five minutes.

The only animals that have been scientifically recorded as sharing food, in the sense of breaking pieces off and handing them to a congener, are chimpanzees, gorillas and gibbons, and at least one species of monkey, the douc langur.

This had been seen in both captive and free-ranging primates, during the 1960s and 1970s. These observations were, however, pre-empted in 1912 when a Barbary ape jumped on a schoolgirl's back in Gibraltar and pulled her hair. An artillery sergeant of the garrison, who had made friends with the monkeys, suggested that this one should be punished. The monkey, brought before the Governor, was said to have hung its head in shame and was duly sentenced, with all judicial gravity, to ten days' exposure on the hillside in a portable cage. His fellow monkeys, free to roam, visited him on the hillside and fed him through the prison bars.

The action of the Barbary apes can be compared with that of the farmer's dog in Gwent. The farmer had two dogs. Then came the time when one was missing. A few days later the farmer noticed that the other dog was absent for a while each day and eventually he followed it, to find the missing dog lying injured, unable to walk. Nearby were half-chewed bones and other remains of food that could only have been transported there by the second dog.

18.
Protecting
the
Young

The selfish (*sic*) act of heroism referred to in chapter 1, in which a father loses his own life in saving his two sons from drowning, is one of many that can be grouped together under the title of parental care. We are more familiar with it under the name maternal care, the maternal instinct being stronger and more pronounced in most species than the paternal instinct in the care and protection of the offspring.

Until less than fifty years ago the sacrifices made by the female on behalf of the welfare of her offspring were regarded as little short of heroic. In the lay mind even today maternal care is accepted as synonymous with such terms as devotion, self-sacrifice and gallantry. Such ideas are now outmoded. Now, in the most modern thinking, the parent, mother or father, that risks its life to protect its offspring is automatically credited with no more than responding to an inherited behaviour pattern having only one end, the protection and perpetuation of its own genes.

If we examine closely all the species in the animal kingdom living today, variously estimated at anything from a million to ten million, the vast majority show no parental care. The precise proportion in which it is manifest is probably well below one per cent. Yet some form of parental care exists in some species of every major group of animals, from the lowest to the highest, becoming increasingly more common as we ascend the scale.

So, in over ninety-nine per cent of animals, the female lays her eggs or gives birth to young and takes no further part in their survival. It is in fact only in the warm-blooded animals, the birds and mammals, that parental care is the rule, and it may be not without significance that it is in these that the brain reaches its highest development. Moreover, it is in the more highly developed of the birds and mammals that brain development reaches its zenith and with it the capacity for higher-order behaviour and parental care.

The behaviour of the cat that hid all her kittens except one (see chapter 1) clearly supports the genetic altruism theory but it also shows remarkable resource (higher-order behaviour) and persistence on the part of the cat, as if it knew that a greater effort than usual were demanded of it. The same is true for many other anecdotes told. Thus, I have myself watched for some five minutes a cock blackbird at nightfall chivvying a tawny owl round and round the trees surrounding the site of its nest. Only because the two birds were silhouetted against the dimly lit sky, aided by the continuous alarm calls, was it possible to follow the progress of the battle, in which the blackbird drove its far larger opponent, armed with cruel talons, hooked beak, and the advantage of night vision, from branch to branch by sheer persistence.

There have been accounts from elephant country, both in southern Asia and Africa, where a railway has been newly-built, of bull elephants charging railway locomotives, presumably protecting their territories from intruders. In all these instances, the elephant has been described as charging the moving engine head-on, battering the 'iron horse' with its forehead, sustaining grievous injuries as a consequence, yet persisting and giving up the fight only when physical exhaustion compelled it to do so.

Even more truly a modern edition of the David and Goliath story is that of a swan ushering its cygnets across a railway track when a train bore down on them. In its desperate anxiety to protect the young ones, the swan flew straight at the engine and attacked. It died in the process but the cygnets got across safely, which they probably would have done anyway. Similar episodes, of animal parents taking on opponents of large size in defence of their young, must be legion, as with the warthog that routed a leopard, and the one that forced an elephant to retreat.

Stoats are small mammals, considerably smaller than the average domestic cat. They have been known to attack a full-grown man bodily, not just biting the fingers of an outstetched hand, when they have their kits nearby. More than one instance has been recorded of a cow elephant, with a calf at foot, having been observed doing battle with one or even two lionesses, even lionesses with cubs, and winning, merely by trampling their antagonists. In one case the elephant continued the battle after its calf had been killed and the mother had covered its corpse with branches torn from the trees around.

One needs to go no farther than the garden, during the breeding season, to see one after another instance of defiance and persistence. Cock blackbirds, so consistently aggressive between themselves, will show the same or greater aggression and persistence in seeking to drive the household cat from their nestlings. One pair of blackbirds built their nest near the kitchen door of a house where the occupants fed them. At first there was peace, then, when the nestlings were nearly fledged, pandemonium broke out. The birds were screaming their alarm calls while the cat crouched low, scared, on the rockery beneath the nest, as the blackbirds dived repeatedly at its head.

The lady of the house went out, picked up the cat and carried it down the garden. This was not enough for the birds who joined the procession still screaming their alarm notes, flying from bush to bush. The cat was placed on the ground. It cowered in the long grass, the blackbirds still calling vociferously. It escaped into a hedge. The hen blackbird took up position a foot from it, the cock perched on a twig over its head, both still vocalizing loudly. The cat made a dash for safety across the lawn, with a blackbird on each side, flapping their wings, bounding along, still screaming. The cat struck at the cock blackbird, missing it by a fraction of an inch. Finally, the owner rescued the cat.

The situation was put more succinctly in a letter to *Animals*: 'I noticed a thrush swooping between some trees and then saw a cat leaping into the air trying to catch it. At first I thought the bird was teasing the cat for fun. Then I saw feathers on the ground and a thrush's nest with one nearly fledged chick in it; this must have been the reason for the display. Is the female such a good mother that she risks her life?'

There was an editorial comment beneath the letter: 'Birds will often swoop repeatedly at cats and other carnivorous animals, especially if they have a nest nearby, and they sometimes get caught. It is probably not correct to say that the thrush is "such a good mother that she risks her life"; she swoops at the cat because in the circumstances she has an irresistible impulse to do so.'

Years ago, when motor buses had just replaced horse-drawn buses in London, a child who had been left outside a shop by its mother, while she went inside to purchase something, stepped into the road. A bus bore down on the child. A woman, a complete stranger, leapt forward, threw the child to safety and was herself killed. She had an irresistible impulse to do so — but the newspapers, in reporting this, praised her great courage!

The cat in the story above, chivvied by the blackbirds, merely wanted to pursue its everyday living. Another black cat in Tanzania had kittens. She and her kittens were in the drawing room of a house with the French windows open. A leopardess walked in from the verandah. The cat leapt at the intruder, clung to its face, biting and clawing. The leopardess hurriedly retreated to the verandah. There was a tremendous noise of verandah furniture being knocked about. When this had ceased the black cat returned quietly to her kittens.

If these stories are set down here in the dramatic terms used by their tellers, it is done deliberately to emphasize yet another paradox. Careful censuses taken of the mortality among young birds has shown an annual death rate of around seventy-five per cent during the first three to six months of life. Figures for mammals must be comparable. Such losses are necessary to keep the population numbers stable. Perhaps this is less of a paradox than an anomaly, that so much effort should be expended by the parents when a high proportion of their offspring are doomed to die in their early days anyway.

These losses among young animals are due to weather, parental negligence, accident, shortage of food and other such factors. The second of these highlights the wide differences between parents. There are, in any species, very poor parents and exemplary parents, with all gradations between. The differences between them may be genetic, although experience is important, but they are none the less real, and the behaviour of the best parents suggests true altruism, or else words have lost their meaning.

Mchilagule Kachari, a game scout in Zambia, was on patrol when he encountered three cow elephants with four calves. When they scented him the elephants quickly made off, up a small hill. The scout noticed the leading cow pushing her calf forward to increase its speed. Then the group reached a place where there were many fallen trees. The calf could jump some of these, but others were too high for it. The mother lifted each such tree to let her calf pass underneath. This, too, is higher-order behaviour and is an index of the level that can be reached in parental care.

A female elephant that endeavoured to protect her calf from two lionesses and eventually drove them off, although they had already killed her calf, was watched by a party of rangers and twenty-four hours later they returned to investigate. They found the mother still there, mounting guard over the corpse of the calf. The mother drove the rangers away.

There are not lacking records of mammalian mothers showing similar devotion to a dead infant. Dolphins will, as we have seen, persist for long periods in the fruitless endeavour to resuscitate a stillborn calf. Mother monkeys have been seen to carry a dead infant until it putrefied. A cow elephant in Queen Elizabeth Park, Uganda, was observed carrying a dead calf held under her lower jaw and shoulder 'as a violinist holds his violin'. She dropped it to feed or drink, then picked it up again. This slowed her up, but the herd waited for her 'with every sign of anxiety' (or was it impatience?). At all events they waited for her. The action of the mother and the herd transcend the limits of purely genetic behaviour— unless we are to describe all behaviour as purely genetic and so lose all sense of values.

An unquestioned example of genetic altruism can often be seen on a poultry farm, when a bird of prey flies over it. A hen with chicks gives a particular call on seeing the outline of the hawk or falcon, or even its shadow on the ground. On hearing this the chicks instantly run to the hen and shelter beneath her feathers. There they stay, hidden from sight until the bird of prey is out of sight. The hen's call and the chicks' response, as well as everything else, is automatic and requires no learning. It arises from a fixed action pattern. To make a kill a bird of prey must use surprise, as the kestrel did on a farm in the north of England.

The poultry farmer saw the kestrel swoop down and then fly off with one of the chicks. Later that day he heard the hen's alarm call and turned in time to see the hen savagely pecking the kestrel, on the ground. He went to pick up the dead bird to verify its identification and the hen struck his hand with her beak. Like the swan with the railway locomotive, the hen was probably prepared to take on any Goliath at that moment.

The weather, as we have seen, is one of the main factors, perhaps the main factor, in the heavy mortality among young birds. The long drought in Britain during the summer of 1976 resulted in a low rate of survival of small songbirds. Rain is normally less of a problem because the parents in some species seem to anticipate its arrival and will sit tight on eggs or nestlings even when the sky is clear and they continue to do so during the rain that follows. This can lead to tragedy.

A hen song thrush was on a nest, containing nestlings, situated between the wall of a house and a large rainwater tank. A night of torrential rain caused the tank to overflow for a long time during the night. In the morning the thrush was found dead with her wings spread over her still living brood, seemingly the victim of a hopeless but heroic act. This time we can invoke an irresistible impulse, reinforced by the fact that it was night, when diurnal birds do not move about. Pathetic to see, but only the result of genetic altruism?

When one considers the millions of birds that nest each year and the widespread human interest focused on birds annually, the crop of stories suggesting any form of true altruism is remarkably small. That the potentiality for it is there can best be judged by reference to the house sparrow. Here, as in the tree wasp (chapter 2) and in pet cats and dogs, the artificial conditions provide an outlet for these potentialities.

The house sparrow is an especially good species for study, for it has given ample evidence of higher-order behaviour, as shown repeatedly in these pages. It is also the bird species most closely associated with buildings that provide an artificial environment. Regarding the parent–young relationship, observation in a large aviary giving semi-natural conditions, using marked birds, has shown that house sparrows, instead of deserting a brood when the nest is disturbed, will carry the nestlings one by one to a new nest. In one instance, the nestlings were transferred to another nest already containing the young of another pair, the foster-parents then rearing the newcomers as well as their own young.

The house sparrow is exceptional also in continuing to show attention to its young after fledging is complete. This must increase the survival rate and represent an important factor in the rapid spread of sparrows in countries where they have been introduced. Together with their care-giving behaviour towards the young, sparrows show a greater problem-solving capacity than most other birds. Some of the examples of a combination of these two qualities are quite striking. Further close observation of the species could be highly rewarding.

In his book *The House Sparrow* (1963), J. D. Summers-Smith tells of an observation made by Major A. C. Booth. A pair of sparrows were noticed flying regularly to the ventilation grilles in the walls of a house, for a period of three days. Investigation showed they were feeding, through the holes in the grille, one of their fledged young that had fallen through the cavity wall. The imprisoned bird was released by Major Booth and it then flew away with the parents. Had this not been done, the parents would probably have continued to feed it until such time as it found its way out.

William Yarrell, the nineteenth-century ornithologist, has left us a record of sparrows taking food into a hole in the thatched roof of a house throughout the summer and well into the winter. Investigation revealed a nest in the thatch with a young sparrow held prisoner by a piece of worsted, used in constructing the nest, twisted around its leg and holding it fast. The behaviour of the parents went so far beyond the normal sequence that it seems to qualify as altruistic.

J. D. Summers-Smith has described also the remarkable action seen in a pair of house sparrow parents nesting in a ventilator in a cavity wall of an office occupied by his colleague. The ventilator grilles, both inside and out, were rusted so there were holes through which the sparrows could pass to build their characteristically large untidy nest. This completely filled the space between the grilles, the entrance to the nest being through a hole in a grille leading to the outside. A few days after the eggs had hatched, the noise created by the young birds as they clamoured for food from the parents that flew backwards and forwards became intolerable to the owner of the office and he tried to dislodge the nest. All he managed to do was to block up completely the access to the nest from the outside of the building. Almost immediately, the parents entered the office through an open window, made a new entrance through the wall of the nest exposed to the hole of the inside grille and began to feed the young from the inside of the room.

So far as was known the sparrows had never entered the office before, had not used the inside ventilator as a route to the nest, and indeed had apparently sized up the problem of keeping their young ones alive and found a solution to it almost instantaneously. This is insight behaviour of a high order verging on intelligence.

Smellie, in his *Philosophy of Natural History* (1790), relates how, as a boy, he found a nest containing baby sparrows, and this he transported to his home, a mile away. Both parents followed him all the way, and the thought struck him that they might feed the youngsters, so, on arriving home, he put the nest in the corner of a wire cage, outside the window.

The subsequent events are best given in his own words:

> The young animals soon cried for food. In a short time both parents, having their bills filled with small caterpillars, came to the cage; and after chatting a little, as we would do with a friend through the lattice of a prison, gave a small worm to each. This parental intercourse continued regularly for some time; till the young were completely fledged, and had acquired a considerable degree of strength. I then took one of the strongest of them, and placed him on the outside of the cage, in order to observe the conduct of the parents after one of their offspring had been emancipated. In a few minutes both parents arrived, loaded as usual, with food. They no sooner perceived that one of their children had escaped from prison, than they fluttered about, and made a thousand noisy demonstrations of joy both with their wings and their voices. These tumultuous expressions of unexpected happiness at last gave place to a more calm and soothing conversation. By their voices and their movements it was evident that they earnestly entreated him to follow them, and to fly from his present dangerous state.

To cut the story short, they at last encouraged him to fly with them, as they did also each in turn of the remainder of their brood placed out the next day. We may not use this same poetic language today, but we can still see sparrows behaving in the way Smellie described.

One observer who was not afraid to use household language was Major W. E. Poles, M.C., senior game ranger. Writing in *Oryx* he describes how he was driving through the Luangwa Valley Game Reserve, when he disturbed a group of baboons, which dashed away at top speed. An infant and a subadult female were left behind. The two stood hesitating, the female resting one hand on the infant. Suddenly, a large female raced towards the pair and, without faltering or changing her stride, passed over the baby. Then as she ran on to overtake the troop, with the young female running by her side, the baby could just be seen clinging to her belly. Major Poles commented: 'Such a feat required perfect timing.' He also praised the young female, 'for it takes real courage to stand still and face danger when everyone else is fleeing to safety'.

Why should a mother kill or otherwise neglect a weakly member of her litter or brood, as so often happens, yet go to such lengths to succour, at a later stage of life, one that is injured? This is especially true of birds. The answer probably is that the illness or other handicap of a nestling is communicated to the parent merely by the refusal to feed properly, or to be fed properly. At a later stage the mother not only recognizes that an otherwise normal offspring is now hurt but she has had time to learn to recognize it as one of her own. This means in effect that by this time it is to her a personality rather than a cipher.

19.
Mercy
Killings

In 1966, the National Parks Newsletter, in South Africa, carried the story of an alleged mercy killing of an aged cow elephant by the leader of the herd. It was said to have been carried out in the Addo Elephant Park. Nature Conservator Sep le Roux had seen a huge festering sore, two feet square on the side of Ouma, one of the oldest cows in the Park. He was keeping watch, intending to anaesthetize her and treat the sore. Three or four days after first sighting her, he saw her come down to drink, alone. Shortly afterwards, a full-grown bull was seen following her trail. He brought her back to the herd, pushing her from behind or propping her up on the side.

A day or two later, eight elephants came down to drink, among them Ouma, who was assisted by the others. Le Roux fired the anaesthetizing dart into her and after twenty-nine minutes she collapsed, but immediately got on to her feet again. Then Hapoor, the bull elephant, the alleged leader, approached her and supported her along, helped by another cow. The three went into the bush, where Ouma again collapsed and was later found dead, stabbed four times, once between eye and ear, the site of the traditional brain-shot of the hunter, and three times behind the eye. Blood seen on one of Hapoor's tusks immediately after the affair left little doubt he had killed her, stabbing with his tusk.

At all events, Hapoor returned to the other cows, led them to the carcase and, while the cows stood in a ring around them, he stood beside the carcase trumpeting. After this he departed, followed by the cows, each touching the body with her trunk before leaving.

Reports of this incident varied. One suggested that the rest of the herd, which was said to have totalled forty-five individuals, also gathered round and broke into a loud trumpeting, staying there throughout the night. Another, that the herd returned three days later and gathered round the spot where the death had occurred, ignoring food in bins which they passed on their way.

This episode received considerable attention in the press and on radio, as a mercy killing. There was, however, one dissenting voice, that of Allan Wright. He claimed that it was most unlikely that the bull which killed Ouma was motivated by mercy, and he argued that the effect of the drug was to make Ouma behave unusually and appear abnormal. He claimed that anyone with experience of animals, whether dogs, goats, cattle or elephants, knows that strange behaviour on the part of one individual, especially when it results in the animal falling down or making unnatural noises, almost invariably results in a vicious attack by other individuals of a species. In short, Allan Wright maintained that there was no question of mercy as such being shown.

There is much truth in this and Wright could also have added birds to his list, in which these killings were first observed and for which the names 'mercy killings' and 'compassionate killings' were used. It was unfortunate perhaps that such terms should have been used, since although zoologists know how to equate them, the non-zoologist is likely to take them literally.

Sentiment is apt to get the upper hand on such occasions because we tend to interpret such scenes against the background of our own feelings. There is a good example of this in a story told in *African Wild Life* for 1953 by W. J. Wessels. He was out with his gun when he saw a bush cat, the African wild cat, regarded as vermin for its attacks on poultry. He encountered the cat in a sloot, or dry watercourse, with steep sides. He fired, wounding the cat and later saw she had struggled up the steep side to a rocky ledge. He was about to fire again when the heads of two kittens appeared from a cavity in the bank above the ledge. The mother cat failed to reach the ledge and slithered painfully down the wall of the sloot. Finally she found another way round and Wessels was able to watch the drama that took place within the cavity.

There proved to be three kittens inside. The mother was gathering them to her and when she saw her persecutor she lifted her head and spat at him. From her open mouth came a rush of frothy blood. She had been shot in the lungs. He saw her lick each kitten in turn, washing it, and as she finished this she bit each in the neck, fatally, finally gathering the three to her body protectively. Then came the final spasm, as her body stiffened, the mouth opened again, there was a gurgle of blood through mouth and nostrils, and mother and kittens lay dead.

Wessel was deeply touched. He put his hand on the cat's body and remained there for a long time saying to himself repeatedly: 'Poor, poor kitty. I am sorry, kitty, terribly sorry.'

Anyone who has, as I have done many times, tried to hospitalize an injured animal — and this is true especially when trying to hand-rear abandoned fledglings — will understand Mr Wessel's feelings and sympathize. You spend several days trying to cheat death and finally the patient dies. The memory and remorse linger on for days. Yet if we are to be rational and objective, our own feelings must be set aside. 'Poor, poor kitty' was not, we can assume, aware of her own impending death (or was she?). In washing each kitten she was reacting to the touch of its body, as normal. In killing each, she was showing that complete reversal of behaviour so frequently seen when an animal is sick or distressed.

The terms 'mercy killings' and 'compassionate killings' have most often been used about birds, in which actions are so often ritualized, as in their courtship. This has led to the use of yet another term, 'ceremonial killing'. It is best exemplified by what has been observed in turkeys.

When a turkey is sick the rest of the flock gather round and then, almost as if by pre-arrangement, the hens form a circle around the ailing bird, all facing inwards. The cock turkey approaches the circle with his feathers spread, his wattles distended, and uttering the characteristic gobbling call. As he does so the hens lower their heads, as if bowing, more or less in unison. The cock retires and again comes forward, the hens again bowing their heads. He retires again, then comes forward for the third time. Now, instead of halting outside the ring of hens, he walks through the circle to the sick hen and strikes her with each of his spurs, leaving her prostrate. This is apparently the signal for the hens to attack, each hen advancing in turn to peck at the stricken bird's head, leaving her in the end stretched out on the ground, dead.

This has not often been observed, although turkeys are reared in large numbers commercially, because on a large turkey farm a sick bird is quickly removed from the flock. It has, however, been twice observed in wild turkeys and is sometimes seen in small flocks kept by farmers for their private use.

Although the appearance is as of a set-piece ceremonial the sequence can be broken down into its components. The flock recognizes a difference from normal in the behaviour and appearance of its sick member. All draw near actuated by curiosity. The advance of the cock, the dominant individual in the flock, in full aggressive display causes the hens to adopt an attitude of inferiority as he advances towards them, and the attitude is relaxed as he retires. Hence the apparent ceremonial bowing by the hens. The movements back and forth by the cock are probably due to nothing more than hesitation. Finally, as the hens move to the centre to contribute their blows to the prostrate hen, they probably do so in the peck order of precedence. Dominating the whole proceedings is the fact that a sick bird automatically drops to the bottom of the peck-order scale, and so can be pecked by every other member of the flock.

The apparent ceremonial, spectacular to the human eye and accordingly labelled a mercy killing, can be seen as little more than the operation of a sense of curiosity followed by the well-known rules of the peck order. Of the other two examples so far given, one resembles euthanasia, the other a merciful infanticide, all emotive words against which we need to be on our guard. When Alan Wright spoke of such killings being commonplace to anyone versed in the ways of animals, he spoke truly. Nestling birds are sometimes thrown out of the nest or are otherwise abandoned by their parents. When a well-meaning person attempts to rescue them there is a high percentage of failure. If they are put back in the nest the parents throw them out again, leaving them to starve. When the person rescuing them takes them home to feed and hospitalize them he finds, in a majority of instances, his ministrations come to nothing and final death has merely been delayed.

Parent birds are sometimes seen to kill a nestling or even a fledgling. Wolves have been seen to set upon an aged or sick wolf and kill it. Domestic cows will attack an injured cow or one suffering from milk fever. A household bitch may be seen to bite and kill one of her newborn litter, which on examination is found to be a deformed puppy. A sow badger caught and put into a zoo cage is delivered of a litter soon after her incarceration, and she kills the whole litter. All these things are well known to naturalists and breeders. People less well versed in natural history see them, but as single and isolated events, and tend to credit those doing the killing with humane or compassionate intentions.

Let us take a specific instance. It concerns a young moorhen. Moorhens are unusual in that the half-grown members of the first brood of the year help the parents repair the nest, if necessary, and habitually help feed and care for the young of the next brood. In the instance to be discussed a member of the first brood, which we can call 'auntie' for convenience, was seen to be concerned with a younger chick, about half its size or less and newly hatched. The smaller chick was evidently sick. Auntie looked it over, with curiosity, it seemed, then swam away. Soon auntie returned with an adult bird, presumably one of the parents, which after contemplating the sick chick, pecked it to death.

Fig. 16 Half-grown moorhen leading parent to the nest where there is a sick chick of the second brood

Humanly speaking, auntie was perplexed and disturbed, but would not take further responsibility. Instead, it went away and sought parental advice, which resulted in the parent coming to investigate. She (or he) decided it was necessary to put the chick out of its misery, and that she (or he) was the proper executioner.

There is, however, another way of interpreting the sequence of events, as a series of reactions to the environment, accompanied by a consciousness of events but with no power of mentally grasping the situation.

A moorhen chick is merely aware of its brothers and sisters and reacts to their presence by keeping near them. The brood is also aware of the parents and reacts to an uncomfortable environment by moving towards one or both parents. The parent reacts to their seeking it by becoming alerted to anything unusual in the environment in the direction of the movement, and if there is nothing of a repellant nature, moves towards it.

25 Female Tullberg's rat carrying one baby in her mouth, with others hanging on to her teats

26 Female greater Egyptian gerbil about to carry her baby

27 Serval, African spotted cat, grooming

28 Burchell's zebra in East Africa necking
in what could be a display of affection

29 Zebras' mutual grooming is at least a
gesture of friendliness

30 Friendship between species: small boy and his guinea pig

31 Vivacious expression of a young goat

32 A kid makes friends with a pet rabbit

33 Ewe that showed its gratitude by licking the hand of the young man who dressed her injuries

34 Kissing gouramis with mouths apposed, but whether in aggression or courtship is not certain

35 Eurasian common jay in the preliminary anting posture

36 Eurasian common jay in full anting posture

In the moorhen, the half-grown young still react to an uncomfortable environment by going to one or other of the parents. When, in this instance, the parent in turn reacted to the auntie's approach by moving in the direction it came from the auntie kept close to it and so accompanied the parent to the spot. Although it may be difficult to account for the 'instinct', which occurs in so many mammals and birds, to kill a sick, deformed or dying member of the family, flock or herd, this does happen. The reaction of the parent to the sight of the sick chick was to kill it, and this called for no sizing up of the situation or decisive choice on the parent's part. Since the older chick took no part in the killing, it would seem that, in moorhens at least, the sight of a sick relative produces no murderous intent in a young individual, only the realization that something is amiss.

It is easy to understand why people's descriptions of what they see animals do should be personalized or humanized. In the account of the moorhens just given, the scientific description takes more than twice the words necessary for the humanized description. The words chosen are less familiar and so are the concepts involved. Since, for most people, nothing important hinges on the way they recount their observations the easier path is chosen. Unfortunately, as we shall see in dealing with the next subject, this is a slippery slope and allows of comparisons and similes that take us even farther from the truth.

In Britain there has long been talk of rooks' parliaments and crows' courts. The two are in essence the same and a rook and a crow are similar birds, often confused in identification. The accounts of rooks' parliaments are many and varied. Basically, the parliament is an assemblage of rooks on the ground, numbering a dozen to a hundred or more, forming roughly a circle around a small clear area in which stands a single rook. Beside this single rook are two, sometimes three, others and the single rook itself looks dejected. There is a great deal of cawing by the assembled company, followed at times by a silence that is broken by one or other of the rooks that is standing near the central figure. In the end, one of the three near it attacks the solitary bird. This seems to be the signal for all to attack. In the end, all fly off leaving the dead body of the dejected one or even only a few feathers and fragments of flesh.

From early times it has been assumed that the solitary rook has been guilty of a misdemeanour, of having broken the rooks' code of laws. Some people have written of a judge, of counsel for the defence and counsel for the prosecution arguing the case, the rest of the rooks venting in chorus their approval or disapproval of what the two 'lawyers' are saying. Finally the judge gives his verdict and the sentence of death is carried out.

Where a corpse has been left behind, after the rest of the rooks have flown, it has been found on examination to be that of a diseased, elderly or heavily parasitized bird. Occasionally it proves to be the corpse of a healthy bird or even a pair of birds. One explanation offered is that the victim is attacked because, being unwell or aged, it is incapable of giving the appropriate responses denoting to another member of the flock its rank in the peck order. In more human terms, the others 'know' it is sick unto death and the killing not only 'puts it out of its misery' but also prevents it being a source of disease to other members of the flock. Rooks being social, the killing is shared by all; and because they are birds, the killing is ritualized.

If these attempts at explanation are mildly unconvincing it can only be pleaded that the accounts we have are varied and couched in imprecise terms. There is support for them from another quarter, however. Rooks nest in colonies, in one large tree or in a clump of tall trees or in a wood. In any case, the nests are relatively close together. Several people have described seeing one or two pairs of rooks start building nests a short way from the main colony. What then happens can be best appreciated from a letter received from Mrs B. S. Blundell, of Surrey.

> There was a good-sized rookery in the trees along the drive of the house, but a pair of young rooks decided to build *their* nest about thirty yards away from the main rookery. The older rooks destroyed it three times. Finally the recalcitrant pair were arraigned before their elders, standing in the meadow below in the centre of a triple ring of all the rest of the colony. There was a long session of hoarse cawing from the black circle of rooks, at the end of which the whole lot rose up in the air, descended on the luckless pair — and pecked them to death. Then, apparently satisfied with their execution as a warning to any other disobedient rooks, they returned to the rookery and their normal activities of food gathering, nest repairing, and brooding.

In the autumn of 1952 I was walking along a country road in southern England when I heard, just ahead, a tremendous chorus of rooks. As I rounded a bend in the road, there came into view a field black with rooks. It was a spectacular sight. The ground was covered with the birds and each bare branch of the score or so trees that grew up from the hedgerows bounding the field bore its row of rooks perched almost shoulder to shoulder. The field was not less than five acres in extent and there could not have been fewer than ten thousand rooks assembled there, calling and chattering continuously.

Circumstances made it necessary that I should not linger long to watch, but had I known as much then as I do now about the so-called rooks' parliaments, I would have thrown everything to the wind to concentrate on watching to the bitter end. As it was I returned to the spot as soon as it was possible, but there was not a rook in sight. So the question still remains whether this was merely a gathering of rooks prior to setting off for their communal roost, whether it was one of the famous rooks' parliaments, or whether some other cause had brought the birds together.

Unusual gatherings of birds of many species are sometimes encountered although their significance is not always clear. When several hundred magpies come together temporarily it is known as a ceremonial assembly and is vaguely supposed to be connected with the formation of pairs. That abnormal gatherings of rooks and crows do occur very occasionally may be taken as a fact. The motivation is, however, in doubt. It may be fairly safely assumed that what brings them together is some kind of vocalization (See chapter 3), possibly a distress call or in other instances a call or calls of which we have little knowledge. Farmers shooting a crow marauding poultry chicks and gamekeepers doing the same to a bird molesting pheasants tell of seeing the air above, a few minutes later, crowded with a mass of crows wheeling around in a menacing manner leading to ignominious retreat on the part of the man with the gun. As with the so-called ceremonial assemblies of magpies, we can only guess, and somewhat wildly, at the possible causes that bring the crows together.

An especially interesting observation was given by G. A. Mariette in *The Countryman* in 1956. He told of being awakened one day in June, in the early hours, by the loud cawing of rooks, so insistent and so close that he went to the open window. On the driveway below, a number of rooks was grouped in a circle at a respectful distance round two others, which were quarrelling over an outsize worm, each trying to wrest it from the other. The clamour increased as rook after rook arrived quickly on the scene and joined the circle, adding its caws to the rest. Only the two disputants in the centre were silent. As the struggle continued the encircling crowd gradually grew quieter, giving only occasional caws. Then the chorus began to rise again until a grey-headed old rook, which had stood quietly on one side of the ring, took a couple of steps forward and uttered a loud resonant 'caw'. There was instant silence and the two in the centre both dropped the worm. The old rook cawed twice again. Then one of the two in the centre picked up its end of the worm and flew off with it unmolested by the other. Thereupon the gathering, which cannot have lasted more than ten minutes, dispersed. The episode seems to have had the appearance of an internal quarrel being settled by one in authority. This is a far cry from the more customary suggestions of a crude measure of hygiene or a brutal euthanasia.

Those who advocate euthanasia for human beings are idealists. The few, isolated individuals who practise it out of compassion for a friend or relative suffering from an incurable disease, wracked by agony for which there is no hope of relief, usually end up in court for having transgressed the laws of the land. There is therefore an aura of altruism attached to the idea of mercy killings, as they have been called. Applying the term to animals is probably totally misleading, with little basis for any altruism. Nevertheless, because the term has been used for animals and because the idea that mercy killings may occur among them, it has been deemed necessary to present some of the evidence which led to the use of the term, if only for the sake of completeness.

The opinion expressed by Allan Wright is probably the only one worth considering.

20.
Midwives
and
Nursemaids

Walking alone at sunset one evening on his farm at Klaserie, in the Transvaal, Gael Cooper came upon a duiker doe in distress. Thinking this small antelope had been trapped, he investigated. There was no trap. He removed the duiker to a clean patch of grass and as she was greatly distended he massaged her body. The flies told him the antelope must have been there two days. As he massaged he noticed a pair of tiny hoofs protruding from the birth canal, so he continued the gentle massage, the duiker jerking her body and whimpering. As the jerking continued he stopped massaging, but confessed he did not know what else to do. Then the duiker's eyes slowly glazed, the small body jerked twice and she was dead.

Mr Cooper remarked that he was surprised, after many years in the bush, that a wild animal should have difficulty in giving birth. Most people would doubtless express the same surprise. We are apt to suppose that difficult births are found only in peoples of advanced civilizations and in domestic animals. That this is not so is suggested by the story of the duiker and also by a report of the Royal National Parks of Kenya, for 1960. In this a warden described being in a glade and seeing four female rhinoceroses coming out of the forest and crossing the plain, moving in a strange manner. Three were in front, shoulder to shoulder. The fourth was following behind.

The cow rhinoceros in the centre was heavy with calf and it appeared she was being helped along by her companions. When they realized they were being watched, all stopped and were clearly on the alert except the fourth one, which was rubbing the flank of the mother-to-be with the side of her head and her horn. Eventually all retired to cover. Three days later, the rangers reported the birth of a calf in that area.

The action of supporting a companion in distress is more characteristic of that typically herd animal, the elephant, yet there appears to be no comparable record of a cow elephant being so escorted. Even so, when a cow elephant is about to give birth she retires into the bush, accompanied as a rule by one or two females. After a while these two midwives leave the hide-out followed by the formerly expectant mother who is now accompanied by her newborn baby that is able to walk shortly after birth.

This has been seen many times by explorers, hunters and naturalists. For example, J. R. Vincent has described, in the *Journal of the Bombay Natural History Society*, how he came out one morning about 9 a.m. with G. A. Marsh to inspect a small banana plantation that had been damaged by elephants.

Hearing a herd a considerable distance away making a tremendous amount of
noise, much more than usual, they moved towards the herd, which could not
be seen because of the dense jungle. The two men found a wild fig tree and
climbed into it to about twenty feet from the ground. Soon three female
elephants came to the tree and one entered a cane break (*Eeta*) directly under
the branch on which they were sitting. The other two remained outside the
clump of Eeta apparently keeping guard, for when other members of the herd
approached them they were definitely warded off.

Half-an-hour later the two guards went away and a full hour later the third
elephant came out from the bamboo, put her trunk to the ground and made a
peculiar drumming noise so frequently heard from elephants. At once a very
small calf came out from the bamboo and walked slowly to its mother. It was
wet and shiny and not very dark skinned. It was suckled for a short while, after
which both moved off in the direction of the herd about half a mile away.
Vincent and his companion now came down from the tree and inspected the

Fig. 17 Female elephant emerging from the cover of the bush with her newborn calf

bamboo break. They found a pale pink placenta about ten pounds in weight. Although they were unable to witness the actual birth, they judged from the marks in the ground that the mother may have had the calf while kneeling.

Twenty years ago Commander Lefevre was in charge of an elephant training station in Zaire (then the Belgian Congo). He not only saw the parturient elephant go into the bush but was able to watch for two hours what took place. The birth was difficult and Lefevre saw one of the accompanying midwives use her trunk to deliver the baby.

Sometimes the cow elephant is thrown entirely on her own resources, as the report of a game guard in Northern Rhodesia (now Zambia) in 1960 shows. While on patrol he saw a female elephant leaning against a large tree and in a state of parturition. The head of the baby appeared at the vulva and after continuous heaving on the part of the mother the baby dropped to the ground. The cow turned, stood over the newly born calf, sniffed it with her trunk, then remained standing over it for twenty to thirty minutes, at the end of which time the baby rose to its feet and sought the mother's teat. No mention is made of the mother licking her baby or severing the umbilical cord.

Perhaps the most unusual observation is that made by S. T. Godfrey, published in *African Wild Life* for 1949. It concerns an adventure during World War I when, with a friend, Mr Godfrey was travelling by car through Nyasaland (now Tanzania). After rounding a bend in the road, they saw a group of elephants forty yards away: a cow lying on the ground giving birth and four young bulls standing round her, as if forming a protective shield. The friend sounded the hooter, for no good reason, whereupon one of the bulls walked over to the car with all the signs of aggression, the occupants hastily vacating it and running to the top of a small hillock. He placed his trunk under the car, lifted it about five feet in the air and then let it drop with a sickening thud. After this, he walked round the car and pushed his head against the bonnet leaving a huge dent. Then he rejoined the other bulls. The calf was born soon after this and eventually the mother walked away with the calf following and the young bulls bringing up the rear.

On 21 December 1956, Captain F. Poppleton, warden in the Queen Elizabeth National Park, Uganda, observed over a period of four hours the events following the birth of an elephant calf. When he came upon the scene there was a packed mass of six adult cows and five young calves, standing apart from the main herd, which was spread out. Some of the attendant cows were nudging and pushing a small, slimy black object on the ground, a calf newly born. They used trunks and feet in what seemed to be an endeavour to get it on to its feet. Others took the birth membrane and threw it into the air. Any vultures coming near were chased away by the cows. For about ten minutes there was much trumpeting and screaming. Then, after half an hour all departed, leaving the mother, her newborn calf and a young bull, which was almost certainly her offspring, as well as another adult cow. For about fifteen minutes the two females continued to coax the newborn calf to its feet, then the other cow left.

Two hours after the birth the newborn took its first stumbling steps but fell forward on to its head, rolled on to its back and stayed there. Its mother and brother forced it to rise, the brother being especially attentive, passing his trunk round the newborn's belly or between its front legs. The mother meanwhile had dropped the placenta, which she had toyed with, even chewed at, but finally abandoned it complete. Then the brother lost interest, emitted 'fearful sounds' not normal trumpeting, and left to join the herd. (The fearful sounds may have been because the young bull realized he was being observed.) During the next two hours the baby elephant and its mother had travelled only a hundred yards towards the herd.

The latest contribution is by Walter and Barbara Leuthold who, in *Wildlife*, for November 1977, describe with photographs, the birth of a baby elephant. A group of elephants were going to drink when one of them started to back away. Suddenly there was a tremendous commotion, and a newborn calf was seen lying in the short grass, still enveloped in its foetal membranes. The mother started to strip the membranes using her trunk, tusks and a forefoot. The largest cow in the group stood beside the mother and, once the baby was free of the membranes, joined the mother in nudging it on to its feet. Gradually the other elephants, including the large elephant, lost interest and moved away, exept for a female smaller than the mother and a young bull, who remained with her. When, about an hour later, the mother went to drink, the smaller female remained with the calf, fussing about it as much as the mother did, and fondling it all the time with her trunk.

No systematic study has been made of elephant births and we have to rely for information on scattered reports, such as those given here. These reports differ in details but generally suggest a concern on the part of other cows in the herd for the protection of the mother, and later the infant, and for the welfare of the newborn calf. The fact that, in one instance, a young bull played this role is a little surprising. Usually only the females are involved, not only among elephants but in other species too.

Domestic cows may gather around one of their number when she is giving birth, drawn it is always assumed out of curiosity, just as they may form a circle around a dying cow, possibly for the same reason. Curiosity may represent the primary motivation but it seems to lead to something more positive. Thus, when the calf is born, one or more of the cows may examine it, even lick it. The mother will then get to her feet and drive them away. The licking can, however, lead to a form of midwifery, for should the mother be too weak or shocked to clean and revive the calf, the others will do it for her. Moreover, their attentions are useful in another way, by causing her to make the effort to get on to her feet more quickly. This reduces the chances of the infant suffering from neglect. It may also serve to protect both mother and baby from predators, for in the wild prowling carnivores are often near the scene of a birth and vultures are drawn by the sight of the afterbirth and could later turn their attention to an inert and neglected baby.

From curiosity, therefore, spring several beneficial effects. First, it brings together a defensive screen. As we have seen, in one instance female elephants drove away vultures from the afterbirth. Secondly, it may lead to a female licking the newborn baby which stimulates the mother into appropriate action. Thirdly, with other females in the near vicinity of the parturient female, there is always the possibility of some assistance being given to her in the case of a difficult birth, for example the massaging of her abdomen by the rhinoceros and the elephant assisting the actual delivery of the baby. In other words, curiosity can lead to midwifery.

Scattered throughout the popular literature are several reports of hoofed animals forming circles. Sometimes, it would appear, these are definitely defensive measures against predators but no more. Others are inexplicable. Some are probably of the same kind as has been seen in domestic cattle. Thus, two visitors to the Kruger National Park, in 1965, saw nine giraffes in a circle. After about ten minutes the gathering began to break up to reveal a female in the centre that had just calved. Apparently all in the circle were females, and when after twenty-five minutes the calf was on its feet and running strongly, each female in turn nuzzled it. There were three male giraffes about fifty yards away and also two hyaenas who were probably waiting for the opportunity to kill the calf. Had the mother been alone with her calf this might have happened.

Surprisingly, the best examples of animal midwifery are found in mice, rats and marmosets. The first two of these, more especially, are not usually regarded as highly evolved mammals and in most species of the Rodentia, to which they belong, the females keep the males away from the nest at all times. Yet in 1969, F. Dieterlen, of Freiburg, West Germany, was able to report that he had watched the birth of 40 litters, totalling 86 babies, of the Egyptian spiny mouse, and found definite midwifery practised in 66 per cent of births. The young of this species are relatively large at birth and are precocious, leaving the nest soon after they are born. Their size alone probably makes birth difficult, which may be why females that have once had litters tend to assist those giving birth. They bite the umbilical cord, assist the delivery and lick and clean the baby while the mother is occupied with extruding the rest of the litter.

In the southern bush-rat, of eastern Australia, in a pair observed in captivity, the male attended the female during parturition. He acted as midwife. He ate the placentas, licked the babies to clean them and 'brooded' the young in the nest. In fact, he seemed a model 'mother' for he pulled nesting material over the babies whenever he left the nest. Similar behaviour has been seen in the deer mice and grasshopper mice of North America.

Post-natal clinics, if one may use the term, are most strongly developed among the marmosets and tamarins of South America. Males as well as females within the group assist the mother. Shortly after birth the male takes over the care of the young. He carries them around, twins or triplets being the rule, usually handing them to the mother only at the appropriate times for suckling. Older females, known as aunties, take as much interest in the babies as the males. Even an older brother or sister may participate, acting as a kind of babysitter. In the silvery marmoset the male has been seen to assist at a birth, receiving the newborn and cleaning it with his tongue.

Because the habits of marmosets were not then generally known, there was tragedy when the first birth occurred in captivity. Those looking after the pair of marmosets decided to remove the male from the cage in case his presence was detrimental to mother and young. The babies starved to death. The marmoset not carrying the babies had been removed under the mistaken impression it was the male.

Looking at the history of our knowledge of the natal and post-natal care among mammals, it seems likely that eventually both will be found to be far more common than is at the moment supposed. Until now, there have been only scattered observations in the wild with occasional more systematic study in captivity in research centres. Thus, it was not until 1960 that Ishwar Prakash, of the Department of Zoology, Maharaja's College, Jaipur, was able to report an example of 'nursemaid' care in the Entellus langur or hanuman, one of the best-known of the leaf-monkeys. He was watching a small troop of them consisting of a male, five females and five babies. He was surprised to see one female carrying two babies. The troop came to halt on a roof of a house and immediately one of the two babies was passed to the female that was carrying none. She suckled it. As soon as the troop started to move off, it was handed back. Then Ishwar Prakash saw that the real mother had an injured left forelimb, which she kept pressed against her breast, using only three limbs for locomotion. He watched the troop for two and half hours and saw the handing over and taking back several times at feeding time.

There are other stories suggesting that while midwife and nursemaid care may be more frequent and pronounced in some kinds of animals than in others, both may emerge from time to time in species in which they are not normally encountered.

Beatrice H. Tracey, of South Africa, was in her car in the Kruger Park. She stopped to watch a female giraffe browsing. Its calf was thirty yards away. The adult moved to the edge of the road, then stopped and looked back at the calf. A large shaggy wildebeest had been grazing near the calf. It almost butted the calf causing it to move towards its mother, who stalked to the centre of the road and again looked back. The calf ignored her until the wildebeest again shepherded it to the middle of the road. Meanwhile the mother had completed crossing the road. The wildebeest shepherded the calf to the other side. Then all three moved through the bush, the mother with her calf being shepherded by the wildebeest. Unfortunately, the sex of the wildebeest was not recorded.

Whether the behaviour of the wildebeest has any significance and if so what this significance may be, are questions quite impossible to answer. The wildebeest's behaviour may belong to that ill-defined area which one author has called misfiring behaviour, as when a domestic cat or a bitch brings home a baby rabbit and mothers it. Stories of this kind are legion. What they may do is to underline what seems to be a general principle that animals seem to recognize juvenility in members of other species, as well as their own species.

This is a line of inquiry that has occupied my attention in a desultory way for the twenty-five years that we have kept a private zoo in my garden. It initially came to my notice when we had our first foxes, shy animals that bolt for cover whenever an adult stranger appears yet will come out of cover and show the greatest excitement when the stranger is a child. It is not an invariable rule but happens sufficiently often to impress. It is seen in other species as well.

This is not the same as the theory postulated by Lorenz, which gained currency in the late 1940s and 1950s, that the parental instinct is aroused by the short face (or short muzzle, in the case of animals) in relation to the large forehead, protruding cheeks and maladjusted limb movements of the infant. His theory related especially to human beings and Lorenz pointed out that dolls had to have 'baby faces' to be attractive to children, that the film industry cashed in on juvenile leads of the Shirley Temple type and that childless women tended to choose as pets animals with short muzzles, such as the Pekingese and other lap-dogs. There are weaknesses to the theory, which need not detain us here.

What interested me was that the behaviour of our foxes, and of other animals I observed, went beyond this stage to the teenager. I came to the conclusion the friendliness of the observed animals towards subadult humans was the result of an absence of aggressiveness in the movements, poise, pose and posture of subadults, the absence of aggressive expressions in the face, possibly, and also the softness in the voice. All these act as signals, visual and auditory, to which the animals respond, as indeed so do we.

There was, for example, a cat and a male dachshund brought up together that, among other things, hunted rats together. When the cat had her first kittens she often left the dachshund in charge of them. If one of the kittens strayed too far he would nudge it back to where it should be. He was, indeed, a model nursemaid.

In another instance, a domestic cat and her daughter lived together in a house. When the daughter had her first litter, of six kittens, it nearly cost her her life. Almost as soon as they were born, her mother took on the responsibility for keeping them clean and she licked their mother (her own now adult daughter) all over as well. This, however, is not surprising. The story is included here as an example of unusual midwifery.

For the most part, examples of supposed midwifery, and post-natal care in general, merely add up to the conclusion that both may be observed on occasion. Their occurrence seems, however, to be sporadic, except in species like the spiny mouse and the marmosets. Whether they occur more often than has been observed to date is due, in part at least, to the difficulty of planning experiments to extend our knowledge of these sporadic events. An outstanding example of a serious attempt to do so is contained in experiments aimed at a different objective, although the results have some bearing here. They have already been mentioned in chapter 4 in connection with dolphins. It is useful to turn again to them for other implications that can be drawn from them.

Since succourant behaviour is most frequently evidenced at the birth of dolphins, this must rank as the nearest thing to midwifery that can be expected in these animals. Melba and David Caldwell carried out a series of tests with several species of captive dolphins, to study the basis of their succourant behaviour. They used five artificial stimuli: a wooden log twenty inches long by six inches diameter; a crude, inflatable red plastic model of an infant dolphin; a dead infant that floated at the surface, probably being buoyed up by the gases of decomposition; and a fine nylon string which was dragged towards the experimental subjects.

As was almost to be expected, the results were negative. The dolphins were living in captivity, were more or less strangers to each other, and the objects used in the test were unnatural. It is not surprising therefore that the dolphins were either frightened by them or ignored them, sometimes showed slight curiosity about them or merely became excited on perceiving them. They were strangers in a strange environment confronted with strange objects. In other words, succourant behaviour or any form of altruistic behaviour cannot be imposed. It must come about naturally, and the animal must be in the appropriate mood. For instance, a dolphin living free and in a playful mood may push along a beach ball or a waterlogged mattress (See chapter 4), but the same dolphin transferred to an aquarium and not in a playful mood may ignore these same objects, or even be frightened of them, especially if it is with an unwanted or unfamiliar companion.

Nevertheless, there are valuable lessons to be learnt from these experiments in relation to dolphin midwifery. As we have seen (chapter 4), a female dolphin about to give birth is accompanied by another female, usually referred to as 'auntie' but more appropriately to be designated 'midwife'. So far as we can tell, mother-to-be and auntie are normally companions within the school; they are familiar with each other. Therefore they will be the quicker to react to each other's moods and needs. The midwife will respond to the distress calls of the mother (no distress calls were emitted by the five experimental objects). The calf as it emerges may be a stranger in the sense that it has not been seen before, but to the midwife it is effectively part of the mother, her companion, and therefore not unfamiliar. Finally, even without any emission of distress calls by the parturient female, her bodily movements will indicate more or less distress. This will put the midwife in a reciprocal mood so that she is ready to come to the mother's aid.

To date, observations on fewer than two dozen births of young cetaceans have been set on record in a published form. All were normal births except for two stillbirths. In some of these the midwife has been seen to help, by lifting the newborn to the surface to take its first breath. In the majority, those that occurred in captivity, a human attendant has been standing by to help, if necessary, in the delivery, so the midwife has not been called upon to show her paces. What we do not know, as a consequence, is whether a midwife, in the case of difficult births, would or would not seek to assist delivery or sever the umbilical cord if the mother failed to do so.

It is usually assumed the dolphin midwife is an auntie standing by to repel aggressive males or sharks, for which her presence is an obvious help, but it may be she would also act appropriately in other ways in easing the burdens of her companion's labour. Having regard to what we know of other of the higher mammals, it would be surprising if it were not so.

This is where the natural history tittle-tattle, of which this book is largely composed, can be shown to be so valuable. Scientific experiments on animals are more frequently inconclusive than is commonly supposed, precisely because it is impossible to govern the likes and dislikes and the moods of the subjects. Without the anecdotal evidence to aid us in this particular field, the results would be sparse indeed, because anecdotal evidence results from actions dependent on the idiosyncracies of mood and temperament of the subjects. The next story underlines this.

Mrs Margaret Palamountain bought an English setter puppy named Cindy. She was determined the puppy must spend the night in the kitchen, in a sleeping box. From the very first night Cindy determined otherwise. All night, she barked, howled, whined and scratched. The family upstairs lost their sleep, and the same happened several nights running. The vet prescribed sleeping pills — for the dog — but to no avail. Finally, Cindy had her way and spent each night asleep beside Mrs Palamountain's bed. Young animals, more particularly, have idiosyncracies, whims and fads which they insist on indulging. A polar bear cub, bottle-fed by the superintendent of the Prague Zoo, insisted for a time on standing on one hindleg and swinging the other while drinking from its feeding bottle.

Cindy's idiosyncrasy about where she wanted to sleep had an interesting sequel when she had a litter. The household cat watched the delivery of the puppies. At night, Cindy slept upstairs as usual and left the cat in charge of the puppies. Cindy suckled the puppies, but the cat looked after them in every other respect, taking on the burden of midwife, then nursemaid and foster-parent combined.

Adoption is common among birds and mammals but this enforced role of nursemaid and foster-parent by the cat must surely qualify as unusual. It serves to show the lengths to which altruistic adoption can be taken, as does that of the piglet and the bitch. A wild piglet had been brought into the house and was left overnight in the same room as a bitch bull mastiff. The next morning the piglet was seen trying to suck milk from the bitch, which by the following morning had come into milk. The two animals thereafter became inseparable.

The use of the word 'auntie' to describe a female that assists another female with young was started by zoologists. They also applied the word 'crêche' to penguins, because in some species the young gather together at a certain stage of development, leaving the parents free to go on feeding expeditions. Adoption and fostering have long been recognized as essential features in the behaviour of birds, more especially, and of mammals. Even 'baby-sitters' has been blessed by use among zoologists. Young hippopotamuses within a colony spend much time in the care of one female while their mothers are away feeding. Such a female has been called 'auntie' or 'baby-sitter' and the group of youngsters in her charge has been called a 'crêche'. If, therefore, I have introduced the terms 'midwife' and 'nursemaid' it is consistent with orthodox zoological practice.

The impact of bringing together these terms serves to emphasize that there is a common bond between animals and humans in matters of birth and infancy. If this is true for the physical aspects, the chances are it is to a large extent true for the emotional processes. To a large extent, in animal and human being alike any altruism will be largely genetic. This is very obvious in the Egyptian spiny mouse and marmosets. Nevertheless, where midwifery, or acting as nursemaid or as baby-sitter, and other such acts of assistance, occur only infrequently in a species, there must be the suspicion that true altruism is sometimes involved, especially where the assistance is given by a member of a totally different species, as with the wildebeest and the giraffe (p. 177).

21.
Recognition

The ability to recognize members of one's own species as well as those of other species must play a large part in altruistic behaviour, whether of the genetic type or in true altruism. Although it may not act directly, it is closely linked with the threshold of such behaviour. Certainly the factors that make for such recognition are operative in matters of affection, love, loyalty and all such intangible features of daily life without which altruism could not mature and fructify. Memory also counts, but the fields of recognition and memory are both vast and can only be surveyed in the briefest manner in the space here available.

I have studied in a desultory way over the years how animals recognize either their human friends or members of their own species. Thus, a cat presented to a mirror sees its own reflection and then, as a rule, looks behind the mirror to see where this other animal is. Birds display to their mirror images, as do reptiles and fishes; their reactions depend on their sex, nearness of the breeding season and other such factors. By contrast dogs usually just sniff the surface of the mirror and then quickly lose interest. There is a similar reaction when they are presented with a life-like and life-size painting of a dog: there is no sign of recognition. I believe there are dogs that have recognized their mirror images or have shown interest in pictures of dogs on television screens, but I have not myself witnessed this.

The difference in the reactions of cats, birds, reptiles and fishes and those of dogs to mirror images is simply the difference between those animals in which sight is the most important sense and those that are 'smell animals'. It is a trivial point but one that needs to be kept in mind in assessing the behaviour of animals. Two contrasting events make this clearer.

Some years ago I received a letter. The writer told of a thrush tame enough to come to the kitchen door to take food from his hand, and it did this at 8 a.m. regularly each day. My correspondent said that one morning he had overslept and was in the bathroom at 8 a.m., having forgotten about his daily visitor until he heard a commotion downstairs, in the region of the kitchen door. Remembering his thrush he hurried downstairs to feed it. The bird was there and was endeavouring to attract attention, but instead of taking the food as usual it flew away. My correspondent added that he tried in vain to coax the bird to him. Then he remembered that he had left his dentures in the bathroom. He hurried upstairs, replaced his dentures and came down again. This time, all was well. The thrush now saw a familiar face. The letter emphasized that the only change in the man's appearance was due to his not wearing his dentures.

A lady staying at a house where I was a guest had, over a period of a fortnight, made a great pet of the dog belonging to the house. The moment the dog saw her it would run towards her with every sign of affection. At the end of this time, the lady went away to call on some friends, returning the same evening. For this occasion she wore clothes which she had previously not worn while at that house, and having changed into them she left without the dog seeing her. On her return, the dog barked furiously at her, its hackles up, as it rushed at her. Then it suddenly stopped, realized its mistake, started to wag its tail and to show its usual affection towards her. It was a striking confirmation that one dog recognizes another first by sight (see chapter 10).

Over two thousand years ago, Alexander the Great carried out what must have been the first experiment to test how animals recognize their own kind. It was unintentional. Alexander had had his portrait painted seated on his beloved horse Bucephalus, by Apelles the celebrated painter of those times. The portrait was life-size and when it was finished Alexander was dissatisfied with the way Apelles had painted the horse. Seeking to defend himself against criticism Apelles had Bucephalus brought before his painting. Bucephalus neighed — and all was well.

The next test was made in the mid-twentieth century, this time deliberately by the distinguished and indefatigable Dr Bernard Grzimek. He brought together pairs of horses that were strangers one to the other and he found that in almost all the many dozens of pairs the meeting ritual was the same. The horses pricked up their ears and each sniffed at the other's nostrils, neck, flank, withers and tail. So he had his behavioural standard for comparison. Then he introduced horses in turn to a stuffed horse the hide of which was faded and tanned and could not have carried even a vestige of the odour of horse, yet the live horses behaved towards it as they would have done to the living animal.

Now Grzimek painted a life-size horse on some sheets of packing paper and leaned the product of his artistic skill against the wall of a riding school. He then filmed and took still photographs of horses greeting each other and single horses being introduced to his painting. Horses have capacious noses lined with mucous membrane, which includes an extensive olfactory membrane. Yet recognition seems to be almost wholly by sight, since Grzimek's painting could not have smelt of horse.

Other tests included presenting horses, one by one, to stylized drawings of horses, in which the legs were no more than straight lines. So long as a body, neck and head were represented approximately, most of the experimental horses treated these cruder pictures as real horses.

An amusing side-effect of Grzimek's experiments, and one not wholly divorced from the present discussion, involved the behaviour of a gelding. Its feed of oats was interrupted when it was taken into the riding hall to meet the stuffed horse. It was clearly annoyed at having its meal interrupted but apparently dared not vent its anger on the stablehand, who was carrying a whip. Instead, it galloped the length of the riding hall, bit the back of the stuffed horse, turned round and kicked it in the belly, knocking it over.

Although amusing, this episode provides a valuable point. The gelding's reaction was one shared by the human species and the higher animals, certainly by mammals and birds, possibly by reptiles and fishes. In man the classic example is known as 'taking it out on the office boy', or the office cat. A good example among birds came when I offered a burnet moth, experimentally, to a tame rook. This is a moth with warning coloration that is highly unpalatable. My aim was to see for myself whether an aviary rook, which I could be certain had never before encountered a burnet moth, would react instinctively to the warning colours or would need to learn by experience.

The rook readily accepted the moth but immediately dropped it. For the next few minutes it was occupied with trying desperately to remove from its beak the minute traces of prussic acid given out by the moth. It opened and closed its beak, salivated heavily, wiped its beak repeatedly on any stick or stone on the ground, and finally turned on a magpie, which occupied the same aviary and was normally its close companion, and beat it up, chasing it around the aviary floor unmercifully.

I take no credit for having played a dirty trick on a beloved pet, in the supposed cause of acquiring direct knowledge. At least the spectacle that ensued as a result of it left me in no doubt that this one bird reacted in exactly the same way as Grzimek's disgruntled horse or any human, who has not learned self-control sufficiently, reacts when aggrieved. Such reactions are far removed from altruism but they do indeed indicate one area in which man and animals share an identical emotional behaviour. Their inclusion here may represent a straying from the strict path of the discussion. They provide, however, yet another instance of the way human reactions and behaviour are shared with animals.

Finally, the persistent and painstaking Grzimek tested wild horses, in the form of zebras, on the East African savannah. He took a zebra skin, stuffed it with cushions and blankets, and set it up near a waterhole. The zebras ignored it until Grzimek noticed that the coats of the living zebras were soiled with dust and earth, from rolling. He sullied his decoy zebra with earth. Some of the zebras seemed still to be afraid of it, but others approached it and touched it with their noses, on withers and flank. Two stallions became particularly excited!

Thirty years ago, Cecil Sims, of Nashville, Tennessee, had this to say:

> A jack is the sire of a mule colt. A partial jack is one who has formed such an abiding affectation for a jennet to whom he has been bred that he declines to be unfaithful to her. It is inadvisable to stable a jack so that he can see mares grazing, even in a distant field. He may take a liking to one mare and no amount of persuasion will make him change his mind. In Marshall County a jack was owned by a widow who always bred him when she was wearing a poke bonnet. After she died, he refused to breed until the old man handling him put on a dress and poke bonnet. Last year we had a jack who would not perform unless our man had on a light-coloured felt hat which we kept hanging in the barn for that reason.

This illuminating passage is quoted here for the statement that a jack may take an irreversible liking to a mare seen in a distant field. In view of Grzimek's experiments one wonders what he could see in her, to use a phrase so often muttered about married couples of our own species. Thus, if a horse will accept a crude painting as a comrade, what does a stallion look for in choosing a partner when he does so at a distance?

The first time I tried to make precise observation of an animal's ability to recognize its owner after a period of separation was twenty-five years ago, when Diana Ross, the novelist, had to find a home for her tame rook, Corbie. When I went to fetch him, from his then home in southern England, I found a situation that was novel to me. The rook had been hand-reared as an abandoned fledgling and had been free to wander in most parts of the house, and also free to fly out over the fields to spend the day with the wild rooks. Yet although completely unfettered, he always returned at night to roost in a parrot cage in the kitchen. Corbie understood a limited number of words of command or persuasion, but the most striking spectacle was to see Diana Ross with Corbie perched on her shoulder talking to him in what seemed to me an almost perfect imitation of rook language. While this conversation went on the two indulged in a sustained show of mutual affection. The least that can be said is that there appeared to be a very strong bond between the woman and the rook.

My parting with Diana Ross, as I walked away with her pet in a closed basket, was abrupt. I could see her eyes filled with tears at the loss of her pet so I did not linger. As to Corbie, during his first three days with us he sat on a perch in his aviary, his shoulders hunched, silent, and looking the picture of misery. At the end of his third day he suddenly rose to his full height on the perch, mimicked the voice of a barnyard hen (he had chosen a hen as a companion in his former home), brightened up completely and from then on behaved normally.

After Corbie had been with us for a year, Diana Ross found herself making the journey from her home in southern England to London, and she took the occasion to visit us to see Corbie. We were all anxious, in anticipation of this visit, to see how readily Corbie would recognize her. So far as we could tell, there was not even a flicker of recognition, even when she tried the magic of talking to him in his own language.

Four years after this encounter, Mr Stanley Cook returned from Canada. Before he went there he had visited us on a number of occasions and a strong friendship had grown up between him and our boxer-cross, Jason, even though their opportunities for meeting were casual and at best no more than weekly. Mr Cook returned a year later, and this time also I was anxious to see what would happen, and deliberately kept the dog in the house so that he could not see Mr Cook come through the gate, which was some twenty-five yards away. I did not hear Mr Cook, but Jason did before he came into view. Immediately, the dog recognized either his voice or his step, and went almost crazy with excitement. He barked and cried, wagged his tail furiously, bounded and jumped about, and, finally, he leaped upon the returned traveller with every appearance of utmost joy.

The dog wagged his tail so vigorously that his whole body joined in — dog owners will recognize the symptoms — as he leaped up repeatedly to lick Mr Cook's face. He cried, he howled, he whimpered and barked. He seemed beside himself with unadulterated pleasure. This was in striking contrast to Corbie's reaction to Diana Ross.

In 1953 I had been presented with a genet, an African animal related to mongooses but looking more like a slender, delicately built tabby cat. After the genet had been with us only eight months, her previous owner returned once more, from West Africa, and came to see her. The relationship between the genet and her former owner has a close parallel in the relationshp I have described between Corbie and his previous owner. While with her in Africa the genet had had its freedom to wander, but chose always to return to the house daily. It took food from its owner's hand, allowed itself to be fondled and petted, and at times would push its way under the bedclothes to curl up and sleep beside its owner.

The response of the genet to its name being spoken by what must at one time have been a very familiar voice was disappointing indeed. All genets have characteristically poker-faces and one has to rely on other criteria than facial expression. They are also relatively silent animals. They do not wag their tails or indulge in other manifestations of emotion we look for in our pets. Yet, even allowing for these things, there seemed to be not the slightest spark of recognition to be detected.

One is tempted to speculate whether an animal's recognition of a person who has returned after an absence, in cases where there has existed a strong bond between the two, might possibly be linked with the level of intelligence in the animal. The marked contrast between the behaviour of Corbie the rook and our boxer-cross dog, under what were closely similar circumstances, could represent the marked difference in their mental attainments. So I was particularly interested to see what might happen when a vixen, Vicky, which we looked after, was reunited with its owners, since a fox is so much nearer a dog in mental capacity.

For the sake of completeness, it is necessary to say why the vixen was in my care. I had offered to take her while Mr and Mrs Malcolm, and their son James, whose pet Vicky was, were absent for a month on holiday. The vixen had an aversion to Mr Malcolm's gardener, which she apparently transferred to me, and we should have been more perturbed about her well-being but for the fact that our friend, Mrs Seymour, volunteered to come along and try to make friends with her. This, in fact, was successful, for while Vicky showed little interest in any other visitor, and positively kept out of my sight whenever I went near her, despite my taking food to her regularly, she showed the greatest animation and excitement during each of Mrs Seymour's visits.

When the Malcolm family arrived to reclaim their pet, at four o'clock one afternoon, at a time when Vicky would normally be asleep in her kennel, I asked them if they would carry out a test; to talk for half a minute out of sight of the vixen, to give me time to go into the house and observe from a window the fox's reaction. Nothing happened. Vicky was fast asleep. I could see her face framed in the opening of the kennel. Her eyes were shut, her ears pricked as usual. But there was not the slightest movement to indicate that she had heard familiar voices. Then James went in, followed by his mother. James went to the kennel and spoke to the vixen, holding out his hand to her nostrils to let her scent him. Still there was little animation on the part of the vixen that I could see from my observation, but Mrs Malcolm turned to where I was watching from a window, set her mouth in a broad grin, mimed with her forefinger, passing it from ear to ear, and nodded approvingly. In other words, she was signalling to me that Vicky had opened her mouth wide and all was well. There was no mistaking this dumb-show. A fox when pleased, or in a contented mood, when playing or courting, opens wide its mouth, sets its ears back and wags its tail. So the signal meant that Vicky, although she had not yet emerged from her kennel, was pleased to see James.

After a few seconds she came out of her kennel and began to show more animation, and it was clear that the old relationship between James and his pet, which had existed before he went on holiday, had been fully resumed. The vixen had recognized her friends, not as I had imagined she would, by leaping and frisking even at the sound of the familiar voices — because I am quite sure from my knowledge of foxes that they sleep with ears cocked — but by almost a nonchalance. Indeed, Vicky showed less excitement than at Mrs Seymour's daily visits.

What did interest me was the comparison to be drawn with Jason's behaviour. I have already described his transports of joy at the return of Mr Cook, one of his friends but only a casual friend of ours. And now it is necessary to compare this with what happened the first time my daughter Jane went abroad for a long period.

Jason was very much her dog. The bond between them was stronger than with any other person. When she went to West Africa for three months, Jason obviously missed her, and I had anticipated that the moment he heard her voice, on her return, we would have a repetition of the scene we had when Mr Cook came back from Canada, only more so. I had imagined Jason even more beside himself with pleasure, barking and crying and leaping up at Jane. Instead, he showed pleasure, but if anthing there was less than he had shown on previous occasions when she had been absent merely for half a day. Vicky seemed to be following the same pattern.

During these past twenty-five years I have taken special note not only of these moments of reunion between a person and an animal, but also the reunions between persons. The period has included the years when my own children have gone abroad for the first time, apart from holidays, and it has struck me that one makes more outward display in welcoming once again a casual friend after an absence than one's own kith and kin. This may be the result of several factors. With your own close relations you are more sure that they will return. It is something you can count on, barring accidents, and to that extent you can take it for granted. In addition, and perhaps this is more important, your feelings are so strong that you are bound to curb them. So not only must these factors be taken into account when assessing the reactions of animals, but there is the sobering thought that the emotional reactions of the higher animals may be more nearly like our own than we sometimes admit.

The first written record of the reactions of a dog to its owner's return is in Homer's Odyssey. Odysseus returned after an absence of nineteen years and nobody recognized him apart from Argus, his dog, now neglected and senile. The dog 'wagged his tail and dropped his ears' but lacked the strength to approach his master. And he died, overcome we may suppose by extreme old age and the upwelling of joy which his physical condition could not contend with. (The elderly rector of Albury, England, is said to have died of joy on hearing the news that Charles II had been restored to the throne!)

During the two thousand years that have elapsed between the return of Odysseus and Mr Stanley Cook, there must have been innumerable reunions between animals and their human friends. Those I have accumulated are relatively few in number by comparison, but they constitute that requisite for scientific research known as the random sample. From them, it can be seen that animals, like humans, vary in the length of time over which memory is preserved and the degree of demonstrativeness shown at the meeting. One writer has claimed that 'hedgehogs, toads, even slow worms recognize their owners and show some sign of recognition at their approach'. People have sent me examples of wild birds they have encouraged to come to hand for food, that have done the same without hesitation after an absence of months. Others have done the same for mammals, usually the domesticated kind. Typical of these is the description received from Irene H. Bagwell of the donkey Bobs, the companion of her childhood which detested men and hated being caught by one of them.

> Bobs would always come to my call and would let me do what I liked with him. I rode him and drove him. We played games together, such as hide-and-seek, in the garden. My nannie would hold him until I disappeared and then release him with the order 'Go and find her', which he never failed to do. Bobs used to express his pleasure and affection by making a curious noise we called 'wuffling', which might be described as braying in a whisper. For years we thought he could not give a real bray, but this was not so, although he used the full-throated bray very seldom.
>
> By the time I had outgrown a donkey Bobs was elderly. He was retired and given a home by one of my uncles. We met from time to time until war broke out in 1914. It was not until 1919 that I arrived to stay again and went to see my old friend at once. As my uncle opened the gate of a long field, where Bobs was grazing intently at the far end, he remarked: 'He still hates men and he will not come near me. Call him, to see if he remembers you.' I called. Bobs stopped eating, raised his head and listened. I called again and he came galloping across the field as fast as his donkey's angular gallop would cover the ground and pulled up beside me, wuffling joyfully in his old affectionate way.

I had two donkeys for several years and can fully flavour these events. It must have been the asinine equivalent of Jason and Stanley Cook, one of those trivial but unforgettable scenes.

A wren, one of the smallest of European birds, had managed to squeeze through the half-inch wire mesh of a cage in which a pair of red squirrels were kept. It could not find its way out. On the outside of the cage a second wren, presumably its mate, followed its wanderings inside. When the captive settled on a perch for a breather, the companion would settle on the outside of the wire, as near it as possible. When the bird inside flew to the other side of the cage, the one outside flew up and over to come down and settle near it.

It is possible, and this is the prevailing fashion, to put a low estimate on the motives and emotions of birds. So what happened was worth watching. To release the captive a small feeding hatch in the wall of the cage was propped open. The companion bird took its stand on a branch near this, flirting its tail in obvious excitement. In due course the captive wren found this exit and joined the one outside, the two flying off, spiralling around each other, in what appeared to be a joyful reunion.

It is at such rare moments, trivial in themselves, that we seem to catch a glimpse in the behaviour of animals, of qualities akin to loyalty, anxiety and joy. One cannot resist comparing this with our stories of Jason and Stanley Cook, Bobs and Irene Bagwell, and hosts of similar examples that could be mentioned. We wonder how often, in the wild, birds and mammals are reunited after an absence, or after some contretemps, and show the same appearance of joy, fidelity and affection.

We can, moreover, extrapolate from such examples into a field of speculation which is as interesting as it is unsubstantial. For example, starting with the lavish display of affection Jason bestowed on Stanley Cook, are we to suppose that, if Cook had fallen into a river and been in need of help to enable him to reach the bank, his cries would not have brought Jason to the water's edge? Are we to suppose also that the dog would have been unaware of the urgency in Mr Cook's cries for help, and have we no grounds for supposing that the dog would not have entered the water, at the very least, if only out of curiosity? After that there can only be the wildest speculation; and yet it would be speculation not wholly without basis (compare chapter 12).

Dogs, domesticated, feral and wild, as we have seen in the foregoing chapters, have shown themselves capable of dragging a congener to safety. Incidentally, they must, in these instances, have recognized it was one of their own kind that needed help.

There is the story, honoured by antiquity if nothing else, of a farmer in the nineteenth century who, returning home drunk late at night, wandered off his path into a quagmire. As he sank he cried for help. At his isolated home his dog set up a furious barking. Other occupants of the house, thinking robbers were lurking around, came downstairs and opened the door to let the dog out. The farmer later reached home, covered in mud, and related how the dog had suddenly appeared in the darkness and dragged him to safety. The dog must have heard his master's voice, inaudible to other occupants of the farmhouse, recognized it, tracked him by the sound of his voice and recognized the man even in his submerged state. It is also reported that the farmer's coat was pulled from him in this rescue attempt, which gives an air of verisimilitude to the story of M. Marie (chapter 15).

It is difficult to believe that, had Mr Cook been in a similar predicament, Jason would have been wholly unconcerned about it. Whether he would have had sufficient nous to do something more than that is problematic. Had he done so it would have been truly altruistic, by motivation if not by execution.

22.
Kissing, Gratitude, Friendliness

Several times I have received a letter from someone quite unknown to me, asking if I thought one is justified in supposing that animals are capable of showing affection. An answer was given by an erudite, reverend gentleman who was being quizzed on a British radio programme. He was emphatic that no animal is capable of affection.

How does one answer such a question, short of writing a long exposition? I mentally scratch my head and ponder the question afresh with each successive letter. My next action is to consult a good dictionary where I learn that affection is the act of affecting (most unhelpful!), an emotion of the mind (does any animal have a mind?), especially passion and lust, as opposed to reason (lust is the last thing one associates with affection!). Then, the dictionary continues: 'a mental tendency, disposition or inclination towards, love'. And I suppose, for the ordinary person, the last is the only one that matters, for out of the tangle of subtleties presented by the dictionary definition most people would settle for love as the concomitant of affection.

The zoological savants are hardly more helpful. Of those who make a study of animal psychology, some cut the Gordian knot by speaking of affectional behaviour, although a few are bold enough to use the word 'love' — even in an otherwise coldly objective scientific dissertation! But they use it only in dealing with the reactions between parent and baby chimpanzees, and to go further would presumably be unacceptably anthropomorphic. For animals of inferior status to the chimpanzee, it seems we must confine ourselves to the use of such terms as the 'parental bond' and others equally non-committal.

But if a chimpanzee can show affection, in the same way as human beings do, why not gorillas, orang utans, baboons, monkeys or even lemurs? After all, these are all classified as primates. And why not cats, dogs, donkeys, horses and the rest? In my perplexity I seek refuge in an appeal to first principles. Out of the many actions, and the hidden motivations that direct them, there is one which, above all, can be taken to epitomize affection. That is the kiss.

To love is to wish to give, to share and therefore it is truly altruistic; and it may be genetically altruistic or idealistically altruistic. That is to say, we should be able to trace its evolution in the animal kingdom from its first inception as a fixed inherited pattern, the formation of a bond having basically no more than a survival value, to a higher form of behaviour that engenders satisfaction, contentment or pleasure, and is associated with the higher feelings of generosity, loyalty and devotion.

In seeking to trace the evolution of affection, as exemplified, for the sake of simplicity, by the kiss, the path to be trodden is thorny and largely speculative. It will be necessary at times to use almost the *reductio ad absurdum*. Thus, one should not look for affection in sedentary animals. Sea anemones spend their lives fixed to a solid support, and only rarely move about; they are self-sufficient, needing no contact with each other. Even their reproduction is by shedding their genital products — their ova and sperms — into the water, where they meet and effect fertilization.

Animals capable of locomotion and habitually moving about are divisible into solitary and social types, with the usual gradation from one to the other. The individual members of some species live such solitary lives that they never meet, except by accident, until mating time and their only contact then is brief and confined to the act of coition, after which they go their separate ways. Should they meet at any other time, the meeting is brief, usually slightly aggressive and entirely fortuitous.

At the other extreme are the social animals. Among the invertebrates, the backboneless animals, are the social insects, which include some of the bees and wasps, the ants and the termites. These live in well-organized, closely-knit societies while others may live in loose aggregations.

We are familiar with the way two ants, on meeting, touch antennae. This may serve a number of purposes. Primarily, it is a means by which each ant determines that the other belongs to the same colony; but that is not all. The antennae contain the main sensory organs and all manner of messages may be passed as the antennae of two ants come into contact. The main point that concerns us here is that when two worker ants meet they do so face to face and make contact with their most sensitive parts. It is not wildly unreasonable to see this as the equivalent of kissing.

It is, however, in the vertebrates that the apposition of the lips or the tip of the snout and, more especially, the use of the tongue come most into evidence. One or other of these two processes can be seen in some fishes, amphibians, birds, in many mammals and possibly in some reptiles, although it is hard to find anything comparable in them. A few examples must suffice.

If there is any single act which, above all others, symbolizes human emotional behaviour it is the kiss. It is closely associated with the finer feelings — of affection, generosity, loyalty, fidelity, sympathy and compassion. It may also epitomize the depths of degradation, as in the Kiss of Judas, and it is inextricably linked with procreation and with motherhood. We must not suppose, however, that kissing is the monopoly of the human race.

In fishes there are a number of species which in courtship, as well as at other times, come snout to snout, the best-known being the kissing gourami. In that species, two individuals meet with open mouths and fleshy lips pressed close together and maintain this position for a perceptible period of time. The function of this is in some doubt. It is assumed to be aggressive but may also be part of courtship, and is taken to be akin to the mouth-holding of cichlid fishes generally, in which one individual grabs the jaw of another. This too is presumed to be aggressive but may also be part of courtship.

In their reproduction the male of lungless salamanders emits a spermatophore then rubs noses with the female who is thereby stimulated to pick up the spermatophore with her cloaca, for fertilization of her eggs.

The truth is, of course, that no systematic study has been made of the use of the mouth in aggression or in courtship. Consequently, one can only mention examples that spring at random to the mind. Moreover, where this is known to occur it may be frequent and therefore obvious, as in the kissing gourami, or rare, as in the European robin, in which only very rarely do a pair of birds bring the tips of their bills together. The position is also complicated by the fact that a common feature of courtship, especially in birds, consists of what is known as courtship feeding. In this the two bills are brought together, the male at the same time placing food in the female's bill. In addition, as in lizards, among reptiles, and polecats, among mammals, the male often seizes the female by the neck with his jaws as part of his courtship. In doing this, the male polecat draws blood and then licks the wounds.

The billing of birds, occasional only in the European robin, is recognized by ornithologists as a regular feature of courtship. It reaches a peak in the billing and cooing of pigeons and doves. In their billing, according to some authorities, there is an exchange of saliva which brings the pair into breeding condition simultaneously. It also determines by hormonal action the timetable for nest-building, egg-laying and the production of pigeon's milk, the secretion in the crop with which the young are fed.

In mammals the resemblance to true kissing, as seen in human beings, becomes more regularly canalized. The list is far from complete but includes many rodents, especially those that live in clans or communities, touching noses when they meet, and dogs that touch or sniff noses. The tip of the tongue is often slightly protruded, so that the action is more a 'wet kiss' than a mere apposition of the tip of the snout, and this takes us to licking as a form of kissing. The mouth of rodents is underslung: the snout protrudes beyond the lips, so this alone would preclude bringing the lips together.

A good example of licking being used to express sympathy was seen in a dog and a cat that were fast companions and were often seen lying together, the cat nestling into the dog's neck. One day the dog was given a reproving pat for a misdemeanour. The cat walked over and licked the dog's nose, after giving the woman who administered the pat what can only be described as a look of disapproval (and anyone who claims a cat cannot give a dirty look either has never kept a cat or is singularly unobservant!). This licking of the dog recalls that cats which normally live together and meet again after a short absence can be seen to indulge in mutual licking of the head, the feline expression at a low threshold of the Jason-Cook meeting.

Elephants, like rodents, are handicapped by the position of the mouth, which is overhung by the trunk. Indeed, the trunk, which is an elongated nose, is chiefly used for displays of affection. An elephant will caress the back of another with its trunk, and the two will probably end by bringing the tips of the trunks together.

Grzimek has shown that a chimpanzee when presented with a portrait of itself, took a close look at it and then planted a kiss firmly on the face.

If what has been listed here as possible equivalents of kissing for animals is varied so is the kissing as used by human beings. This varies from the passionate kiss which is sexually motivated, to the kiss of affection without sexual overtones, the greeting kiss, and what has been called the 'morning peck' — the purely conventional touch of the lips on the other's forehead or cheek to start the day.

It may well be that extensive study would reveal in animals a similar subdivision. This assertion is based on my personal experience of Jason, the dog we had for thirteen years. He was large and heavy, and not particularly graceful in his movements. I began to notice that when I left the house in the morning to walk along the garden path, having paid no especial attention to Jason, he would come bounding after me and nearly knock me over as he rushed past. At first, I merely thought what a clumsy brute he was. Then, as this was repeated morning after morning, I became aware that his wet nose always came in contact with my hand hanging at my side. Subsequent, more careful, observation led me to believe that the dampness on the back of my hand, after he had blundered past, could have been from the tip of his tongue slightly protruding from the mouth. I was never able to be wholly certain because it happened too quickly. If my deductions are correct this was the canine equivalent of the morning peck. It never occurred except on our first meeting of the day. I have little doubt that this is very commonplace since I have experienced something similar with a number of other dogs with which I have struck up a more casual acquaintance.

The usual greeting by a dog which is showing great affection is expressed in licking, and putting this with the damp 'kiss' on the back of my hand suggests that licking and kissing cannot be far removed from each other. Thus, the mammalian mother typically licks her offspring from the moment it leaves her birth canal. This at first is severely functional. It results in the removal of the birth membranes. Also, licking the infant's nose stimulates breathing, licking of the skin stimulates the circulation of the blood, and licking of the body helps to clear the skin of the birth fluids and so keeps the infant warm. Another essential function is that licking of the anogenital area induces defaecation and micturition. Above all, continued licking forms a bond between parent and infant that keeps the two together for the period during which the parent is responsible for the growing infant's safety. It also has an important subsidiary function, as described on pages 14–15 and mentioned again here for emphasis.

Experiments with young rats, carried out years ago, showed that those that were regularly stroked daily were more intelligent, healthier and more capable of enduring adverse conditions, such as low temperature, lack of food or physical strain, than their litter-mates, which were denied such petting, even though both were otherwise kept under the same environmental conditions. So licking and petting, in which must be included kissing, have a greater functional value than merely meeting the needs of early infancy. In so far as the physical and psychological needs of an organism are interwoven, their effects are more far-reaching and of more subtle benefit than is usually imagined.

These affectional processes are also reciprocal. The infant mammal soon learns to lick its mother in a rudimentary and not very extensive manner, and by doing so it is beginning to return the affection received. Later, and especially in social mammals, mutual grooming preserves social cohesion and the love of being stroked with the human hand forges a bond between the pet mammal (dog or cat) and its owner. Both mutual grooming and being stroked are most appreciated when they are applied to certain pleasure spots. These are more especially located in places the animal cannot conveniently reach, or cannot reach with the tongue, such as behind the ears or under the chin in cats and dogs, at the base of the neck or the root of the tail in horses.

Mutual grooming, petting and stroking by owners and self-licking (toilet) seem not to be confined to stimuli in the skin but are triggered by something inside the animal. When a baby mammal is born this 'something inside' the parent is primed ready to come into effect, as shown by a particular cat about to give birth. It had previously driven away an older kitten, but later, as the birth pains began to be felt, this older kitten happened to go near the mother. This time, instead of driving it away, she licked it. The same process is probably at work when a bitch steals another bitch's puppy and licks it as the moment for parturition approaches.

This 'something inside the animal' is also exemplified by every dog that licks its owner's hand, or, for that matter, any other animal that does so. For example, a ewe being injured, had its wounds dressed each morning. The young man who did so carried out his work conscientiously, and with sympathy for the patient. The ewe seemed to appreciate his ministrations for on the third day she turned her head, with some difficulty, and licked his hand as he was putting the final touches on dressing her injuries.

So much of animal behaviour is in response to signals from the environment that the tendency is to overlook the importance of actions engendered from within. The stability of any group of social animals depends partly on successful aggression against outsiders, and partly on limiting aggression within the group. The second of these is dependent on what has been called socially positive or amicable behaviour; friendly behaviour is an equally acceptable description. It is recognized as existing between parent and offspring, between members of a mated pair, and even between adults that are firm companions.

That amicable or friendly behaviour is independent of sexual relations is shown by the many instances in which a bitch chooses a dog for constant companion but accepts another dog for reproduction. Similarly, a tom-cat may choose one female as companion while continuing to mate with another female.

Fig. 18 Dog-fox nibbling the fur of a vixen in a display of friendliness (or affection?)

More importantly, friendly behaviour can be quite independent of the other necessities of life and all the evidence suggests that it takes the form of an upwelling within the organism that must be satisfied. It is not that an animal is friendly because an entity is present to call forth the feeling, but that the animal needs a companion upon which to bestow its friendliness. The same is true of humans and no better story can illustrate this than the behaviour of the only child. Thus, a woman related how, when her small son was in the bath, she had occasion to go downstairs. As she returned she could hear her son talking to an imaginary companion, addressing him by name and discussing with him what they could do the following day. The longer friendly behaviour is denied an outlet the stronger is the need for it to be performed.

On the first meeting between two animals, or two humans, there may be feelings of hostility or, at best, neutrality which soon gives way to amicable behaviour. The two later become friendly. Continued friendship leads to affection, and affection often to love between two individuals of different sexes or two of the same sex. This can be described as a 'natural' sequence, so natural indeed that no scientific deduction or research is needed to prove its existence, at least in humans, so why not in animals, especially the higher mammals.

23.
Summing
Up

In the preceding chapters the attempt has been made to bring together some of the stories of animal behaviour that smack of devotion, loyalty, compassion and other qualities recognized in human beings but commonly denied in animals. The attempt has also been made to analyse these within the framework of accepted principles of animal behaviour, to see how far we are justified in supposing that some animals may show at times something of these qualities. In making this attempt the author lays himself open to the criticism of having gone beyond what is scientifically acceptable. His reply would be that these stories come to the notice of large numbers of people who would like to know more about their significance. As to their being scientifically unacceptable, that is merely to say they cannot be tested by precise means because they cannot be precisely repeated.

Perhaps the first thing to be said is that throughout the months during which the text of this book was being prepared the author has suffered the trials and tribulations of ambivalence. At one moment the depressing thought would occur that the conclusions being drawn could not make sense: how can we suppose that animals, even the highest of them, could experience motivations that would lead to the higher actions implied? Then would come the feeling that to suppose otherwise would be to fly in the face of the accumulated evidence. The vacillation between these two occurred almost daily and this recurrence of alternating doubt and confidence led at times to the verge of abandoning the project altogether.

The determination to press on to the end was sustained by several substantial considerations. These are worth setting forth, especially as they represent the background evidence against which the subject has been discussed.

The first impressive consideration is the tremendous accumulation of stories of 'good deeds' performed by the higher mammals, beginning some two thousand years ago. Some of these derive from the written records of ancient Greece. Many more were doubtless retailed orally and have been lost. With the coming of commercial printing, with its newspapers, books and magazines, untold thousands have been set on record. These indicate what the ordinary person, as well as people of high intellect, have thought about the actions some animals have been observed to carry out. Some of this may have been extravagant, even misguided, yet there is no smoke without fire, and one is sustained by the thought that if only one individual non-human animal can be shown convincingly to have performed a deed that can be truly called altruistic, this alone would point to the potentiality for other such deeds being present in the higher animals as a whole.

The second important consideration is that in the course of several decades of close study of the living animal, I have been impressed by witnessing at first-hand unusual feats by animals that have transcended significantly the bounds of usual behaviour for the species. Most have been outside the area now under discussion, but they suggest that animals, like ourselves, are capable of otherwise incredible feats in moments of crisis or emergency.

A third important consideration is that every now and then one happens upon an account of an episode which, so far as we can see, leaves no room for doubt that a particular animal has performed a deed that by any standards can be equated with those of which we ourselves are capable. Among these, I would list the sheep leading a blind sheep to safety, the chimpanzee removing a foreign body from the eye of another chimpanzee, the several well-attested observations of dolphins and whales risking their safety for a wounded companion and the springbok guiding the wildebeest to water. It was these that gave me my moments of hope.

Other stories recounted in the foregoing chapters are arguable. The observations were no doubt accurately recorded but the interpretation offered by the witness may have been faulty. It was these that caused my moments of doubt and depression.

Against these considerations, and contributing mightily to the doubt and depression, was a very weighty consideration. This is, that during the last half century especially, there has been a massive and widespread study of animal behaviour. Its results are embodied in numerous scientific papers and also in books on the subject. These cover every aspect of usual behaviour, in detail and comprehensively. They are written by fair-minded and erudite scientists, yet the kind of anecdote used extensively in this book finds little place in their pages. To that extent, it is fair to describe the materials being analysed here as outside the concern of systematized science. In other words they are beyond the fringe — into the lunatic fringe, to use a current idiom. Does this mean therefore that they should be wholly ignored?

Clearly, one is on the defensive in seeking to answer this question. The first thing to be said is that a significant proportion of the rules of animal conduct, as put forward in these scientific journals and books, is based on hypothesis which tends, in the course of time, to be stated as fact. I have already questioned the accepted explanation of the submissive posture. Also, the accepted view about the honeyguide's behaviour has been shown to be tenuous, to say the least. There are others that could be quoted. In addition, it is noteworthy that for many points on which some authors are categorical, other authors are doubtful. This applies in matters large as well as small. Clearly therefore finality is a long way away, which leaves room for other possibilities.

Another point to be kept in mind is that it is not unknown for a view or a hypothesis to be rejected at first by the experts, only to be fully adopted some years later. An outstanding example is to be found in the Theory of Drifting

Continents. Although this has nothing to do with animal behaviour, it is closely linked with some of the broader aspects of biology. This was first propounded in the early 1920s by the Austrian, Alfred Wegener, and although it received some support, what has been described as its poetic simplicity caused it to be heavily criticized. It is now generally accepted. Unfortunately, Wegener did not live to see this.

Above all, I have taken strength from the steadily growing list of subjects which are now familiar, even commonplace, matters of zoology which escaped observation until the last decade or two. For example, there has been for a long time a special interest in animals that use tools. Before 1940 the number of species known to do this could be numbered on the fingers of one hand. Within more recent years that number has been suddenly increased to nearer a score, and it is a fair forecast that this is by no means the total yet to be discovered.

One of these tool-users is the Egyptian vulture, which uses a stone, held in the beak, to smash ostrich eggs to eat the contents. This is a common enough species of vulture which must have been familiar to thousands of people over the centuries, yet this particular habit was not observed until a few years ago. It has been authenticated by photographs as well as by the description of the habit by an accepted scientist. Had it been reported first by a layman, writing to a magazine or newspaper, without supporting photographs, it would have been disbelieved, just as the first record of a sea otter using a stone as an anvil to crack shellfish was not at first given credence. It has now been filmed.

Anting by birds was well known to laymen but was regarded by the pundits as 'an old wives' tale' (these words I have myself used about it). Once attention was focused on it, the truth emerged that this is a relatively common phenomenon but one which evaded the notice of ornithologists everywhere, until they were forced by laymen's observations to look for it. Described by Sir Julian Huxley as the most puzzling ornithological problem, it consists of a bird taking an ant in the bill and rubbing it on the underside of its wing, then repeating the process, first under one wing, then under the other. Several theories were proposed as the function of anting. It is now accepted as a method of feather maintenance, the formic acid from the ants helping to tone the feathers.

There are several objections to this current view, but the most remarkable of all is the one that eluded those several experienced ornithologists who have studied the phenomenon intensively over a period of years. The objection is that a bird anting always starts with the left wing, which suggests that it is a form of ritualized behaviour. On average it anoints the left wing three times for every once under the right wing. This I have established by scores of observations that I tabulated. If anting were a method of feather maintenance an anting bird should be more glossy, and have stronger feathers, on its left side than on its right. One might facetiously suggest that birds anting habitually, as some do, would tend to fly in circles!

For centuries, dairy farmers in Britain have averred that hedgehogs take milk from cows. Cogent arguments have been marshalled by savants to show that this is impossible. Theoretically, however, it is possible and within the last few years a veterinary surgeon has shown that certain lacerations on the teats of cows were consistent with the toothmarks of hedgehogs, thus upholding the assertions by farmers that cows 'gone dry' (allegedly because hedgehogs have drunk their milk) occur only in the spring and summer, when hedgehogs are not in hibernation.

The habit of hedgehogs known as self-anointing, in which they lick favoured substances, then anoint their spines with a copious saliva, was unknown before 1913. It was recorded first in Germany and there was no mention of it in the English literature before the 1950s. Yet this habit was well-known to gipsies and others, although they failed to interpret correctly what they saw. Unknown to scientists for so long, this behaviour is now known to be commonplace.

Although, as has been already suggested, the detailing of these items is partly defensive, there are firmer reasons for doing so. First, they represent the thoughts at the back of my mind which acted as a corrective to the persistent ambivalence. More importantly, they emphasize the need for an open mind in assessing contributions by untutored witnesses to the general records of unusual animal behaviour. Perhaps my attitude to these is more than usually sympathetic because my own researches and discoveries in the field of animal behaviour have been made in a manner that puts them midway between professional research and intelligent but untutored observation. One particular line of research is especially relevant here.

For twenty years an African grey parrot named Bassie lived in our house. It developed an unusually wide range of vocal mimicry, as well as mimicry of other sorts, such as mimicking movements and tapping selectively the metal parts of her cage to imitate mechanical sounds. It is generally agreed by those who write about talking birds that a parrot, or any other talking bird, copies human speech without the slightest regard to the meaning of the words. The same principle is embodied in the much-used phrase, 'To repeat words parrot-fashion', to describe somebody who uses words and phrases while ignorant of their meaning.

It may well be that this is true for talking birds as a whole. At least one parrot, in my experience, has proved to be an exception. Over the twenty years that Bassie was with us I noted numerous occasions when the bird used words it had learned and applied them appropriately to objects, situations and persons. A simple example will be sufficient to illustrate this.

When the telephone bell rang Bassie would immediately say 'Hello'. This was no more than a simple conditioned reflex. Taking careful note, however, I found that the parrot would say 'Hello' in the recognizable voice of whoever went across the room to lift the receiver. It is not unusual for a parrot, when addressed by a person saying 'Hello' to it in the form of a greeting, to reply using the same word but in the voice of the person addressing it. To do the same as somebody approaches the telephone, and before that person has had time to speak, takes it a step further in the association of ideas.

A child learning to speak uses a similar association in learning to name objects appropriately. By observation of Bassie and of infant humans, and comparing the results, I have confidence in asserting that the parrot had, to a large extent, the ability of an average child of two years in associating words with objects and to a lesser extent with events. I tried numerous experiments to test this.

The significance of this for our present discussion is that probably only one talking bird in a hundred or more would show this capacity. It may be that only one in a hundred or more, whether dogs, cats, sheep, elephants or springboks, has the ability to rise above itself and perform deeds of altruism. Moreover, such deeds will be of a simple character, those that lie within the scope of inexperienced, immature humans, just as Bassie's vocal associations did not rise above the accomplishments of a child of two.

If what has been said about Bassie's associating words with people and events is received with scepticism by my fellow scientists it will be following a familiar pattern. It was the same with anting, the milking of hedgehogs and other such phenomena, now accepted or acceptable as fact. The scepticism is understandable and to a large extent justifiable. If nothing else, the manner in which the story of Winston became distorted, from that of a rogue dog that had run away and taken up its home at the crossroads to that of a dog showing grief, contains a strong warning about accepting too readily colourful stories printed in the newspapers or given out over television and radio. We are prone to read more into an event than is justified and to want a garnished story instead of the plain truth. Moreover, when we consider the stories sent in as letters or written up by reporters that appear in newspapers and magazines we have to remember that the writer, without malice aforethought and with complete sincerity, merely sets down the story as he sees it without being particularly careful of the precision of the words he uses. The story of Michael Gibson's rescue is another example.

Putting this on a broader canvas we have the example of the honeyguide, where something very similar has happened in the scientific world and the pages of scientific journals. In the end one therefore tends to grow sceptical of anything that is said or published. That has been my greatest problem, in writing this book, to endeavour to maintain an impartial approach while treating each incident with a tinge of scepticism. To allow such scepticism to go unbridled would be to believe in nothing. This would be as fallacious as too ready a belief, for in studying this matter one gets the general impression that some animals are capable of something more than the ordinary instinctive behaviour and that this excess is shown, as in humans, by exceptional individuals.

We come therefore to the question of what we can believe. We can place fair reliance on accounts of episodes of animal behaviour that are supported either by photographs or films. Even these are not a hundred per cent reliable, but photographic evidence of this sort does at least give an air of verisimilitude. I place even greater reliance on accounts I have been able to check by talking to the eyewitnesses concerned. In such conversations one has to assess not only the reliability of what the eyewitness says and the answers to one's own questions, but the knowledge of the people themselves. For example, if in talking to an eyewitness it emerges that he or she is very short-sighted, one must make suitable allowance for this. Finally there are those instances which I myself have personally witnessed and— which is highly important— recorded in the form of notes immediately afterwards. Memory can be so misleading even when the event is only a few hours distant.

Perhaps the most important single factor that has been exposed in the course of writing this book is that an animal's behaviour can be completely reversed by circumstances. A sick animal, for instance, may be completely docile and inoffensive, but when it is well again it may become aggressive and unmanageable. Such complete reversal of behaviour also occurs in other circumstances, as in the dog-fox that changes completely from being utterly selfish to being completely unselfish the moment the cubs are born. If this can happen as a result of sickness in an individual it is reasonable to argue that something of this change may be transmitted to its associates, with the result that their behaviour also changes and they show sympathy or actual help where at any other time they would show selfishness or even aggression.

It may well be that some of the examples given in this book are misleading, even false. It could be also that I have given undue importance to some of the observations people have recorded and that unjustified deductions have been made from others. Even so, if only a half or a quarter of what has been said here is acceptable, then it is inescapable that some of the higher animals are capable of a higher order of behaviour than that with which we normally credit them. It follows therefore that the finer feelings, such as compassion, pity, sympathy, affection and grief, are not wholly the prerogative of the human species. Had I not believed this the book would not have been written, and my own belief in it stems initially from those incidents I have myself witnessed and pondered over the years.

Perhaps I tend to take a more unorthodox view than most scientists as a result of listening to some of my fellow scientists. Some years ago there was a top-level discussion in London between scientists from both sides of the Atlantic on the effects of drugs on animal behaviour. Most of the speakers were primarily chemists working on behalf of commercial producers of drugs for medical use. As one listened there came the uneasy feeling that these learned gentlemen were not always too well versed in the normal behaviour of the species with which they were experimenting. It became hard to see how they could, with any great accuracy, tell the effect of drugs on their animal subjects when they were largely ignorant of how the animal behaved normally.

It is worth keeping in mind that a similar pitfall may be awaiting the student of altruistic behaviour. One reason for this cautionary note is that as more and more people study animals in the wild by going and living with them, as Jane Goodall and George Schaller have done with chimpanzees and gorillas, the more examples come to light of behaviour that has been over-looked for centuries. Even animals nearer home, living almost on our door-steps, can spring surprises, as in hedgehogs, with their self-anointing.

Even more telling for our present purpose, perhaps, is the history of our knowledge of the breeding behaviour of crocodiles. A century ago it was customary to say that the female crocodile laid her eggs in the ground and left them to be hatched by the sun. Bit by bit this has been extended: that the female builds a nest, that she guards the nest and helps the young to leave it when they hatch, even leads the young crocodiles to the water. Then came the revelation that she actually carries the hatching crocodiles to the water, a few at a time, in her mouth, enters the water and, with jaws slightly parted, swills the inside of her mouth washing the sand from the skin of the hatchlings inside. More surprising still, it has now been found that sometimes the male participates even to the point of taking some of the hatchlings to water and washing them.

If an observer, a century ago, had seen a male crocodile solicitously caring for the young, the probability is that no one would have believed his story. Or if he had been believed there is the likelihood that the male crocodile's behaviour would have been classed as altruistic. This it may be, even now, but we have to await further investigation to see how far his behaviour is normal, instinctive, gene-controlled or only occasional. And if it is occasional, how far the word 'altruistic' or any other such word can be applied.

The history of self-anointing by hedgehogs illustrates almost what could be the main purpose of this book. From being a type of behaviour completely overlooked, it was thought, when it first came to be discussed, to be excep-tional. Within a few years, self-anointing was being reported in one hedgehog after another until now it is accepted almost as commonplace, except that no adequate explanation for it is yet forthcoming. Some day, no doubt, it will be elucidated, now that this form of behaviour has been brought to general notice. The same may happen with any of the many items examined in this book. Some will be shown to be due to faulty observation, others to faulty recording and yet others to incorrect interpretation. There will be some, however, that will stand up to further examination, to be joined no doubt by others not yet observed, and all these may be shown to be higher-order behaviour, altruism or compassion, as the case may be.

Already, even while this book was being compiled, an apparently trivial event seems to be now invested with a greater significance by the results of a new piece of research. This is the behaviour of dwarf mongooses (See chapter 7). Another instance of a piece of recent research contributing at a late stage to the structure of this book concerns the nanny goat and her two kids (chapter 10). If we may revert to this for a moment it could be to say that perhaps the researchers had missed an essential point. Perhaps they were expecting to find that the mother goat's reactions to her babies would be as automatic as that of a machine that delivers chocolate or hamburgers when a coin is inserted. What they did find was that the goat did not always behave as expected, just as a slot-machine sometimes goes wrong. Moreover, at risk of being ridiculed, we could say that perhaps the nanny goat was using a certain amount of judgement, in her behaviour towards her drugged kids, which was not apparent to the researchers because they could not think like a goat!

Fundamentally, part of the everyday pattern of behaviour of all social animals is aimed at keeping away strangers or diverting attack. The more animals associate in social groups the more the stability of the group depends on aggression being minimized within the group. In other words, if they are to live together they have got to be 'friendly'. Social animals use postures, facial expressions or vocalizations to indicate a friendly approach. They also use what has been called amicable behaviour. This has its roots in the behaviour between parent and offspring. It re-emerges in courtship and especially between parents that do not separate immediately after mating. It is not without significance that ethologists should have been prepared to speak of both amicable and friendly behaviour in animals, as if there could be no doubt about it, at least in social animals.

Social behaviour has evolved in a number of animals, notably in the social insects, the bees, wasps, ants and termites. In these, the welfare of the individual is subordinated to the good of the society. The behaviour of the individual is to that extent selfless or, to use another word, unselfish. Other animals live either in almost complete isolation or in communities often referred to as societies, though even these are less closely knit than insect societies. The behaviour of the individuals composing them is more obviously directed to individual survival, and therefore more clearly aimed at the safety of their genes, and finds particular expression in the protection of offspring or, less markedly, in the defence of a mate. Such protection and defence frequently result in acts of apparent courage and heroism. These acts, however, are intraspecific (within the species) and must qualify for inclusion within the concept of genetical altruism. Occasionally they are interspecific (between different species), at times between two markedly dissimilar species, and these are more genuinely altruistic.

The simplest forms of interspecific associations have long been known under the title of 'strange companionships', as when a dog and a goat, a barnyard hen and a tame crow, become firm friends and spend most of their time in each other's company. Some are even more diverse. Nor are interspecific associations limited to tame and domesticated animals. Ostriches and zebras often associate, the defence of both species against predators being enhanced by the zebras' keen sense of smell and the ostriches' keen eyes held aloft on a long neck. At a less obvious level, a wild rabbit will respond to the alarm calls of a bird, such as a blackbird, by bolting for cover.

Normally an animal species responds only to certain appropriate stimuli out of a potentially wide variety. This has survival value in that the animal wastes no energy responding to non-relevant stimuli. A dog and a goat in company need in a sense to learn each other's language. The dog expresses pleasure, anxiety or distress in a different form from that of a goat; each uses different signals. If their companionship is to be of value, both must become habituated to these. This may be relatively easy, but it is a different matter when the association is between a cat and a mouse, not only because of the disparity in size but because the one is the natural predator of the other. Yet such a bizarre association has been reported from time to time. A woman was bothered by the knowledge that there was a mouse in her kitchen which evaded all her efforts to find or catch it. Then one day she saw the cat rise from its basket, yawn, stretch and step out. She saw then that the mouse had been curled up asleep beside the sleeping cat. A real-life Tom and Jerry. Unfortunately the sequel is not recorded.

Even more remarkable is the story set forth by Syd Radinovsky, Professor of Zoology and Entomology at Millerville State College, Pennsylvania. One afternoon he placed a saucer of milk beside his cat which was asleep with her litter of week-old kittens. He was surprised to find that of one of these only the head remained. His surprise was the greater on seeing a meadow vole, in size and ecology not unlike a house mouse, nestling against the cat.

It is unknown how the vole came to be there, whether of its own volition or whether the cat had caught it, brought it in and then became possessed of an excess of maternalism. Professor Radinovsky saw cat and vole drink milk together after which the vole groomed the cat's tail and hindquarters while the cat licked the vole along with her kittens. He filmed the scene and took still photographs but decided to leave everything as it was, including the deceased kitten's head and the vole. After this, he went off to his college class. Later that afternoon his wife, who was ignorant of what had happened, telephoned to say she had found the kitten's head and removed it and had put the vole in a jar. So the professor's idea of watching what would transpire in this unusual situation was rudely shattered; the vole was dead by the time he returned home.

Radinovsky explained the situation as one in which the animals were 'misled' and spoke of behaviour misfiring, perhaps because with hormonal changes and the accompanying maternalistic behaviour of the cat to her kittens she had extended the role of mother to embrace a member of her natural prey. It probably could not have happened except to a beast of prey that had no need at that time to hunt for food.

Presumably there is no difference in principle between the actions of Radinovsky's cat and the universal behaviour of human beings the world over who, as far back in history as we have adequate records, have kept pets. It would have been something similar to this 'misfiring behaviour' that laid the foundations for the massive domestication of animals that seems to have been initiated in different ways at different times in places far removed geographically.

If this sounds too far-fetched, let us consider the relationship between ants and aphids, two very dissimilar species of insects. Aphids or plantlice, variously known as greenfly and blackfly, parasitize plants, including horticultural crops. The aphid plunges its sucking proboscis into the delicate skin of leaves and tender stems to suck the sap. It does this in such quantities that the sap is passed through the gut and out by the anus little changed, in the form of a sweet liquid or honeydew. Ants visit the aphids to lap up the honeydew, in effect milking them.

Comparison has often been made between this and man's husbandry of cattle. The comparison is apt. Man, also a social animal, maintains pastures, moves the cattle to fresh pastures, protects the cattle from enemies and provides shelter for them during periods of adverse weather. Ants, by drinking the honeydew, prevent the aphids' food plant from becoming covered by the liquid that would otherwise clog the breathing pores and give an ideal base for the growth of mildews on the leaves. So the ants maintain the aphids' pastures, as certainly as man maintains pastures for his cattle. They also move aphids bodily to fresh food plants (fresh pastures) when those they are on wilt. They protect them from enemies and some species of ants may remove the aphids to prepared cavities underground, the counterpart of cattle stables, for the winter.

Just as we could compare, in chapter 2, the quite unemotional good manners of wasps with the more emotional good manners of higher animals and man, so we can see a similar comparison between the ants' 'domesticated animals' and our own, the difference being that a degree of friendliness enters into the human relationship with cattle (or pets). This gives rise to the idea of an evolution in behaviour in which the ground is prepared in the lower animals for the emergence in the higher animals, as the brain capacity increases, of emotional behaviour.

We can see something of this in the behaviour of the bird known as the oxpecker. This is an African bird, nine inches long, related to starlings and it spends most of its time in association with large mammals, such as zebras, giraffes, rhinoceroses, hippopotamuses, eland and other antelopes. The association is mutual. The birds ride on the mammals' backs and feed on ticks on the mammals' skin. The mammals are cleaned of their parasites and are warned of danger by the alarm calls of the birds. The birds have very curved and sharp claws so that they can cling to their hosts, and so close is the relationship in every way between bird and mammal that there is little in their respective lives that is not linked. When the mammal lowers its head to drink, for example, the oxpeckers on its back scuttle down its neck to its head and, clinging with their claws, dip their beaks into the water.

Research has shown that the oxpeckers do not choose their hosts at random nor do they merely settle on those with the most ticks. Having settled on a particular mammal, the oxpeckers stay with it — the beginnings, as it were, of loyalty. Should the mammal die, its oxpeckers will stay with its carcase, usually for two days, the usual grief-period for birds (see p. 74).

Oxpeckers are unpopular with hunters because their alarm calls alert their hosts. This apparently is not just a matter of the host learning to associate the calls with possible danger. There have been instances of oxpeckers, to all appearances, deliberately trying to alert their host. One group of oxpeckers was seen flying low around the head of an exhausted rhinoceros, which failed to respond to their earlier calls, as if urging it to greater effort, until it eventually rose to its feet and summoned the further energy to continue its flight from the hunter (rescue: see chapter 11).

The linking of the oxpeckers' behaviour with loyalty, grief and attempted rescue is based on the long-recognized biological principle of pre-adaptation. An animal is said to be pre-adapted in its behaviour when it uses an action seen in less highly evolved species as a specialized activity of another kind. Thus, a honeybee returning to the hive with nectar from a newly-discovered source of food conveys to other worker bees the location of the plants from which it has gathered the nectar. It does this partly by its so-called tail-wagging dance. The other workers crowd round it, jostle it and, from the frequency with which it waggles its abdomen (or tail), gain information on the length of its flight from the food source. Solitary insects also wag their 'tails' at the end of a long flight.

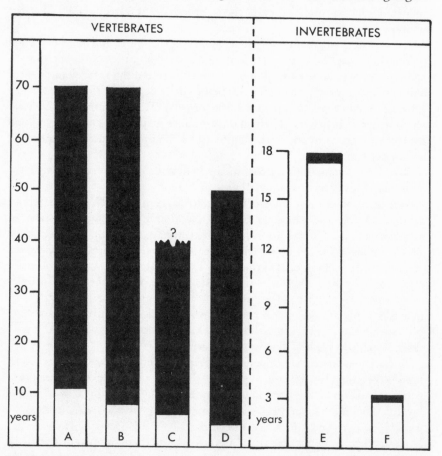

Fig. 19 Infancy and adult life compared; this shows that vertebrates, quite apart from brain capacity, have a far greater span of adult life in which to develop emotional qualities: A. man; B. elephant; C. dolphin; D. parrot; E. seventeen-year locust; F. stag beetle; adult life is represented in black.

It is a form of panting and no more, but bees have come to use the information it conveys purposively. The tail-wagging is therefore a pre-adaptation.

By anology we can call the apparent loyalty, grief and rescue of the oxpeckers a pre-adaptation to the more emotional behaviour seen in animals with a greater brain capacity than the oxpeckers.

A dog, or any other animal, cannot give out friendliness unless it has a companion on which to bestow this friendliness. This is axiomatic and the same is true for human beings. This much is admitted in the textbooks as being the basis for social behaviour. Therefore in the matter of friendliness alone there is a definite link between human and animal behaviour. If we can say that much, then there is no reason why, in a situation where human beings can show courage and heroism, we should not assume an animal cannot show the same things. Perhaps the big difference between a display of courage and heroism by an animal and by a human being is that the animal expects no reward for what it does and doesn't brag about it. As in the cat and leopard story (chapter 18), the cat went quietly back after driving away the leopard. If a person had driven away a leopard he would have been so excited and proud of himself that he would have wanted to phone up his friends and tell them all about it and it would have been in the daily newspapers the next day.

People reading this book will believe or disbelieve, or question, and probably the majority will choose merely to question. To that extent this book has a value in drawing attention to particular problems and causing thought to be focused on them. And in the end it may be proven beyond doubt that one of the many qualities shared by the higher animals with mankind is the potentiality for true altruism which even in human beings is, relatively speaking, only rarely evidenced.

Index